ISES
International
Solar Energy
Society

The
Fifty-Year History
of the
International
Solar Energy
Society
and its National Sections

Volume 1

The
Fifty-Year History
of the
International
Solar Energy
Society
and its National Sections

Edited by
Karl W. Böer
University of Delaware

Published by
American Solar Energy Society, Inc.
Boulder, Colorado

Volume 1

Notice

Copyright © 2005 by the American Solar Energy Society, Inc.

All rights reserved.
Printed in China through Synergy Press Ltd.

Printed on recycled paper.

LIBRARY OF CONGRESS CATALOGING IN PUBLICATION DATA
Main entry under title: The Fifty Year History of the International Solar Energy Society, 2005
1. Solar Energy History
ISBN – 0-89553-325-1

Publisher

American Solar Energy Society

The American Solar Energy Society (ASES) is the national individual membership organization dedicated solely to promoting solar energy technologies. ASES has over 8,000 members and 25 state, regional and student chapter affiliates serving 34 states. ASES members are engineers, architects, scientists, researchers, educators, builders, planners and interested individuals who support the development and utilization of solar energy technologies. Founded in 1954, ASES is also the United States Section of the International Solar Energy Society (ISES) and works closely with ISES to promote the use of solar energy technologies worldwide.

The ASES mission is to advance the use of solar energy for the benefit of U.S. citizens and the global environment. The ASES strategic goals are:
- Ensure that federal, state and local policies support the development and use of renewable energy;
- Advance research, development, demonstration and use of renewable energy technologies;
- Educate consumers about renewable energy technologies;
- Prepare the future workforce for the transition to renewables and support continued development of professionals currently in the field. To support these goals, ASES operates the following programs:
- ASES publishes SOLAR TODAY, the award-winning magazine providing engaging articles on practical solar technologies. In addition to distribution to members, SOLAR TODAY is available by subscription and on over 300 newsstands nationwide.
- ASES sponsors the National Solar Energy Conference. This annual conference showcases the state-of-the-art in solar technologies.
- ASES sponsors the National Solar Tour in October each year. Over 75,000 people visit solar houses across the country at this event.
- ASES publishes briefing papers on the development of solar energy technologies. Written for non-technical audiences, these papers provide excellent background information for people unfamiliar with the field.
- The ASES bookstore is one of the most complete sources of solar and renewables related publications.
- ASES uses the media to educate the public on renewable energy technologies.
- The ASES Solar Action Network alerts members when to write their legislators in support of good federal solar policy.

American Solar Energy Society • 2400 Central Avenue, Suite A • Boulder, CO 80301 • USA
303-443-3130 • ases@ases.org • www.ases.org

Foreword

It takes a significant event to make us want to review what has happened in the past. It is the fiftieth anniversary of the International Solar Energy Society, an important reason to celebrate and to take account of the historical development of the Society and its many international Divisions, to review the progress of solar energy development.

But this anniversary has much more importance to it than looking back to the forming of a society. It is based on the recognition of a few visionaries that it was time to elevate solar energy, the most important source of life on earth to become the focal point for energy in modern history; a focal point for human ingenuity, technical creativity, societal acceptance of the necessity to have our future's wealth determined by solar energy; the focal point of more developed means to use this resource, the sun's energy as a dominant source of energy in all of our future life.

The leader of this group of visionaries, no doubt, was Farrington Daniels, who, fifty years ago, assembled a group of world experts in solar technology and movers in economy, finances and politics to view in Arizona an unprecedented exhibition of solar conversion equipment, and to probe their assessment of the evolving field. This group wanted to assure us that modern means for solar energy conversion are feasible, and that the field needed an initial momentum to enter the future of universal acceptance for modern solar energy conversion, replacing conventional conversion of energy.

To give lasting credence to this initial step, a professional society, the Association for Applied Solar Energy (AFASE) was formed in 1954, among the initiators of these first events being a meeting in Tucson and a Symposium and Exhibition in Phoenix in 1955. This Association became the forerunner of today's International Solar Energy Society (ISES).

But again, there is more significance to those first events: Farrington Daniels and his co-founders already recognized that the resources for conventional energy conversion—fossil fuels—were limited and began to advocate the development of solar energy. This fact has come today into new focus. We have now been confronted with the data that the much accelerated use of these resources by all of us, including the rapidly developing countries, has shown that the time of maximum recovery of oil and gas (the Hubbard peak) has passed and depletion will approach in our life span. The price increase of oil and gas is real and determined by the interplay between supply and demand; and supply is no longer only in the hands of a capricious cartel. Also demand can no longer be switched around at liberty without major consequences for world economies and must be orchestrated carefully, requiring substantial lead time when alternatives are to help.

And again, there is still more significance to the event that inspires this celebration of the fiftieth anniversary. As never before, we must recognize that with the increasing use of fossil fuels, we are filling up the formerly seemingly unlimited reservoir for our waste, the earth atmosphere, which reacts measurably, macroscopically with significant increases of this waste contaminant, most importantly with the increase in carbon dioxide, a powerful greenhouse gas. We can no longer ignore its effect in catastrophically increased weather patterns, with effects that cannot easily be returned to normal, even if we come to accept the need to become reasonable again and reduce pollution. It will take time to normalize, the more so the longer we wait.

This monumental task requires the help of professionals who have learned to investigate complex problems carefully, to assess the dynamics of events, and who are capable of extrapolating and producing unquestionable conclusions. Who else can amass such evidence to convince all of us to react within a time frame that is carefully evaluated, and who can come up with solutions that are realistic and achievable? And here again, it needs an international society to peer-check the evolving results, to provide credibility.

Finally, fifty years ago, when Farrington Daniels and the other solar pioneers put into motion the process that resulted in the creation of ISES, they began to replace uncoordinated research, often done as a hobby, with an urgent, large scale and coordinated development. This was a prophetic recognition that solar development can no longer be an activity of a few enthusiasts, but was to become an absolute necessity to meet the energy needs of the future.

Here, the International Solar Energy Society has become a most important visible forum for scientists and engineers in the world to communicate amongst each other, to check their results with each other, to critically analyze all ideas and findings, and to arrive at a constantly increasing wealth of facts that can be followed by armies of entrepreneurs and factories to provide the means for changing over from old technology to the benign and profitable technology of the future.

It is in recognition of the achievements of these fifty years that challenges us to assemble this documentary of the solar energy developments of the sections of ISES; to produce material that illuminates the many steps that have been taken during the last fifty years in so many countries of the world, showing the enthusiastic response of a few who have crystallized the work of so many to create a worldwide force that cannot be shaken by adversaries. It may be that this document can encourage and invigorate many to prevail in the effort to further solar energy conversion, to strengthen the international communication among professionals as well as to provide more of the foundation that is urgently needed for the necessary progress in global solar energy utilization.

All of this would not have been possible without the untiring help of the many authors of the chapters of this book, following up through many revisions and providing their final manuscripts in time for publication; and for the excellent help received from the editorial office of the American Solar Energy Society (ASES), mainly from Dona McClain, Richard Haight and Patty McIntyre; and from the International Solar Energy Society (ISES) Headquarters, Christine Hornstein. To all of them, I would like to take this opportunity to extend my expression of deep gratitude.

My special thank you goes to Cesare Silvi and my wife Renate who have both encouraged me to solicit contributions, organize and edit this publication. I am very thankful for the patience and love Renate has given to me during the two years of working on this history book.

Karl W. Böer

International Solar Energy Society

The International Solar Energy Society (ISES) is the world's largest and most established membership organization dedicated to promoting renewable energy technologies. ISES consists of 54 National Sections and 30,000 members in more than 110 countries organised on a national, regional and international basis, representing a large international infrastructure in support of renewable energy.

ISES has been serving the needs of the renewable energy community since its founding in 1954. As UN-accredited NGO the Society supports its members in the advancement of renewable energy technology, implementation and education all over the world. Most importantly, it provides the platform through its international conferences for direct communication between professionals. Its goals include:

Towards a Sustainable World: Encouraging the use of Renewable Energy everywhere, through appropriate technology, scientific excellence, social responsibility, and global communication.

Realising a Global Community: Bringing together industries, individuals and institutions in support of Renewable Energy technologies - through communication, co-operation, support and exchange.

Supporting Development: Applying practical projects, technology transfer, education, training and support to the issue of global energy development. Supporting the Science of Solar Energy: Stimulating and encouraging both fundamental and applied research in solar energy.

Contributing to Growth: Ensuring individual and community growth through support of private enterprise and empowerment in the area of Renewable Energy.

Information and Communication: Rapid access to information through tailor-made communication and exchange platforms utilising modern technology.

With a long history and extensive technical and scientific expertise provided by its members, the Society is a modern, future-oriented non-governmental organisation (NGO). Clearly defined goals, extensive communication networks and practical, real-world projects are the hallmarks of ISES.

International Solar Energy Society (ISES)
International Headquarters
Villa Tannheim
Wiesentalstr. 50
79115 Freiburg, Germany

Tel. +49 761 45906 0
Fax. +49 761 45906 99
Web: http://www.ises.org/
E-mail: hq@ises.org

Table of Contents

Adolf Goetzberger
Retired, Professor, former Director of the Fraunhofer Institute
for Solar Energy Systems
and Sigrid Jannsen
Professor, President, Deutsche Gesellschaft fur Sonnenenergie, e.V

Bernard McNelis
Managing Director
IT Power
The Manor House, Lutyens Close
Chineham, Hampshire
RG24 8AG UK

Gershon Grossman
Faculty of Mechanical Engineering
Technion – Israel Institute of Technology
Haifa 32000, Israel

Cesare Silvi
GSES (Gruppo per la Storia dell' Energia Solare)
Via Nemorense, 18
00199 Roma, Italy
Email: csilvi@gses.com

Tetsuo Noguchi
Chief, Solar Research Laboratory
Government Industrial Research Institute, Nagoya
Agency of Industrial Science and Technology
Ministry of International Trade and Industry
Hirate-machi, Kita-ku, Nagoya 462
Japan

Eng. Mhamad Bakhour
Assisted by
Dr. Fateh Sakkal
Eng.Walid baba
LSES, Lebanese Solar Energy Society
Beirut-Lebanon

Eduardo A. Rincón Mejía
School of Engineering
Autonomous University of the State of Mexico
Cerro de Coatepec, C.U., 50130 Toluca, Mexico

Rolf Jarle Aaberg
Statkraft SF, PB 200 Lilleaker
NO - 0216 Oslo, Norway

Dr. Nasim A. Khan
Member Technical / Secretary,
Alternative Energy Development Board
344-B, Prime Minister's Secretariat, Islamabad
Director, Solar Systems Laboratory, Rawalpindi Pakistan

J. Farinha Mendes and M. João Carvalho
INETI—Department of Renewable Energies
Estrada do Paço do Lumiar, 1649-038 Lisboa, Portugal

D. S. Strebkov and I. I. Tyukhov
All-Russian Research Institute for Electrification of Agriculture
2, 1-st Veshnyakovsky proezd
Moscow 109456, Russia

M. N. A. Hawlader and K. A. Jahangeer
Department of Mechanical Engineering,
National University of Singapore
9 Engineering Drive 1
Singapore 117576

Brian Schaller
with contributions by Dieter Holm
and Charles Eduard Barnard
Private Bag X010
Howick, 3290, KwaZulu-Natal,
South Africa

Jan-Olof Dalenbäck
Building Services Engineering
Department of Building Technology
Chalmers University of Technology, Sweden
SE – 412 96 Göteborg, Sweden

Necdet Altuntop, Ph.D.
Associate Professor
Department of Mechanical Engineering
Erciyes University, Kayseri 38039, Turkey

Barbara J. Graham and D. Yogi Goswami
Department of Mechanical & Aerospace Engineering
PO Box 116300 University of Florida
Gainesville, FL 32611-6300 USA

Dr. Jayarao Gururaja
Now
Senior Interregional Advisor
Energy and Transport Branch
Division for Sustainable Development
Development of Economic and Social Affairs
United Nations
2 UN Plaza New York, NY 10017

Chapter 1

The International Solar Energy Society: The First 25 Years, 1955 to 1980

by
John A. Duffie[1] and Harry Z. Tabor[2]

Abstract

The International Solar Energy Society had its origins in late 1954 when it was incorporated in Arizona as the Association for Applied Solar Energy, AFASE. The nature of the organization, its activities, and the challenges it faced changed with time; and it became the Solar Energy Society, SES, in 1964 and the International Solar Energy Society, ISES, in 1970.

In this story of the years to 1980, Part I briefly reviews the state of solar energy development and applications in the early 1950s—when the Society was first conceived by its founders. Part II sets the stage for solar energy at the time of the start of the Society and highlights a few of the advances in solar research, development, and applications of the past fifty years, to emphasize the growing need for a society concerned with the many disciplines and nations involved in solar energy.

In Part III, the evolution of the society is traced. Its founders and directors for the first decade were Arizona businessmen who saw an opportunity to contribute to the solution of growing energy problems and at the same time promote the Arizona economy. They were succeeded by scientists and engineers who turned the society into a more professional interdisciplinary and international organization devoted largely to exchange of information. Data on membership, officers, meetings, and sections are shown in an Appendix.

---

[1] Retired Director of the Solar Energy Laboratory, University of Wisconsin-Madison; President of ISES, 1971-73. Address: 6225 Mineral Point Road, #D-75, Madison, WI 53705, USA; e-mail: jaduffie@aol.com

[2] Retired Director, NPL of Israel, Director, Scientific Research Foundation, Jerusalem, President of ISES, 1981-83. Address: POB 3745, Jerusalem, Israel, 91036

1.1   Introduction

The term solar energy has many diverse implications. All have one under-lying, common motif, i.e., a concern with radiant energy from the sun—which can be converted by many different processes to meet many kinds of energy needs. The diversity of applications means that people of many backgrounds and disciplines are concerned with solar energy. Hence the multidisciplinary nature of a solar energy society.

1.1.1   Solar Energy Processes and Disciplines

Photosynthetic conversion is the process driven by solar energy absorbed in leaves, resulting in the formation of biomass. In the broadest sense, all agri-culture is solar, with the objective of producing foods. It includes synthetic processes that convert solar to plant mass and store it for future harvesting as fuel for power production.

Photochemical or *photochromic conversion* are processes through which the absorption of solar radiation on a substance causes a chemical change in the substance. The change may later be reversed, resulting in the freeing of the solar energy absorbed.

Photovoltaic (PV) conversion, is achieved when solar radiation incidence on a semiconductor structure generates electricity (direct current). Electricity being the most versatile form of energy, PV has attracted an enormous amount of R&D.

In *thermal conversion*, solar energy is converted into heat by absorption by black surfaces This heat can be used for a myriad of purposes, such as heating of buildings, heating in general, for driving engines to produce mechanical or electrical energy, operating cooling systems, cooking, etc.

Evaporative processes include evaporation of brines to produce salt (a huge industrial operation) and distillation to produce purified water. These are special cases of thermal processes.

Architectural design can maximize or minimize the effect of solar radia-tion in our homes and buildings. The radiation, as light, can reduce the amount of artificial lighting needed during daylight hours. As heat it can save fuel or electricity in cold weather. Since the total amount of energy used to heat and cool buildings in the developed world is a sizable fraction of all the energy used, it is clear that intelligent architectural design is a vital factor in saving energy, apart from making the buildings pleasant to be in. The ancient Greeks and Romans understood this—and we still have a lot to learn.

Affecting all these processes is *meteorology*, which provides the basis of understanding, measuring, and predicting the solar energy supply. Additional relevant sciences include cosmology and space science.

These various kinds of processes are the concerns of a wide variety of scientists and engineers, botanists, plant pathologists, chemists and photochemists, physicists, and mechanical and chemical engineers—and of manufacturers.

On the applications side, there are other kinds of people involved. Evaluations of processes are considerably affected by economics. Acceptability of solar equipment and applications, particularly in developing economies, is a concern for sociologists. Political decisions that relate to energy economics and availability of fuels have far-reaching effects on the success or failure of solar energy applications.

Thus there is a wide range of disciplines that is concerned with solar energy and its exploitation. The International Solar Energy Society has provided a vital forum for interaction of those involved in these many disciplines and has itself been shaped by the diverse people involved in solar energy.

1.2   Solar Energy in the Early 1950s

There is a long history of work on various aspects of solar energy, primarily in architecture and thermal processes. Butti and Perlin[3], in their book *A Golden Thread*, present an interesting and detailed account of the history of solar energy applications, starting with solar architecture in Greek and Roman times, and including power from the sun, solar water heating, and solar house heating. The possibilities of utilizing the sun's energy has intrigued people for centuries, and many of the basic ideas we use today were devised by inventors many years ago, but the technology to make the ideas work effectively was not available.

For example, the effort in the early twentieth century by the American Frank Shuman to harness solar energy to drive a heat engine, using cylindrical parabolic mirror concentrators, led to his demonstration plant in Egypt. His system is of special interest because, superficially, it is similar to the LUZ solar power units set up in California in the 1980s, except that the LUZ unit is 4.6 times as efficient, i.e., the area of concentrator needed is reduced by this factor.

While there were many possibilities to be explored at the time, there was not much pressure to explore them. By the beginning of the 1950s, there was

---

[3] Butti, K,. and Perlin, J. A Golden Thread—2500 Years of Solar Architecture and Technology, New York: Van Nostrand Reinhold, 1980. ISBN 0-442-24005-8

still almost no recognition that fuel supplies might be limited and that burning them in ever-increasing quantities could seriously (and perhaps irrevocably) damage the world climate. As a result, there was little motivation to develop technologies to harness the sun. Exploitation of other renewable energy sources such as wind and hydro—which have a long history—was a matter of local convenience and availability. But this situation was about to change.

Thus, in the 1950s there were ideas and processes that needed development but also needed new technologies such as materials and design methods to make them practical. In the next section examples of progress in the years of the solar energy society—progress made in part by people active in the society—are noted.

1.2.1   Some Developments of the Last Five Decades—A Brief Summary

Advances in exploiting solar energy in the last five decades of the twentieth.century have been dramatic in two main areas: (1) the use of computers to optimize components and systems; and (2) advances in materials technologies.

Fig. 1: Jack Duffie, c. 1955

Architects have benefitted greatly in both these areas. New computational methods have made it possible to optimize the exploitation of solar energy in the heating of buildings on a seasonal or annual basis. Progress in materials technology has provided photochromic glasses that can control the ingress of solar energy into a building without blinds. New low-emittance surfaces on glass have provided windows with improved insulating properties (known as "low loss" windows).

Selective surfaces have improved the efficiency of solar thermal collectors, making solar water heaters competitive in almost any sunny region and even making solar thermal power (using a heat engine or turbine) nearly competitive. The LUZ[4] solar power stations in California, totalling 354MWe, would simply not have been feasible without the new technologies.

There were also advances in the geometry of optical systems for concentrating solar energy, for example, to yield a moderate degree of concentration without the need to "track," i.e., follow the motion of the sun continuously.

Fig. 2: Harry Tabor (Israel), c. 1955

The improvement in PV conversion has been even more dramatic. The earliest (nonsilicon) solar cells had conversion efficiencies of a fraction of 1%. A Bell Laboratories team developed their first silicon solar cells in 1953, achieving 2%, and had raised this to 6% when first publicly announced in 1954. They further increased the efficiency, in small research cells, to 11% by the time of the 1955 Arizona solar meetings. At that time, the Hoffman Electronics Corp. produced the first *commercial* cells, of 2% efficiency. Commercial cells with greater than 8% efficiency were available by 1957— which made them economical in many nongrid applications. Since then, silicon cells have been improved to over 20%, and multi-junction cells have been developed with conversion efficiencies of 30% or more. (These are expensive but have applications in the military and are used to power transmissions from satellites.)

---

[4] The LUZ project became possible because U. S. law gave a subsidy on added generating capacity. When the period of the law terminated, the LUZ company was caught with big commitments and failed. But the operation of the power stations was handled by a separate company (not burdened with capital costs), and power production has continued to the present day.

One area of R&D not related to new materials has been black-bottomed solar ponds—proposed by an Israeli team—which are large-area (liquid) collectors, where convection is suppressed by imposing a density gradient (by the dissolution of salt). Temperatures up to 93°C have been obtained, sufficient to operate new low-temperature turbines developed by the same team. Because these turbines, known as ORC (organic Rankine cycle) turbines, operate at temperatures below 100°C, they are suitable for the conversion of low-temperature *geothermal* energy, (where steam machines cannot be used). They are now used worldwide for this purpose.

Now we turn to consideration of meetings on solar energy that preceeded the formation of AFASE, and who participated in those meetings.

Fig. 3: Detailed view of the LUZ collectors in a California solar thermal power plant. There are more than a million square meters of collectors in the several plants. The receivers utilize selective surfaces and are enclosed in vacuum jackets.

Fig. 4: One of the LUZ solar thermal power plants in California

1.2.2   Solar Energy Meetings Prior to AFASE

In the early 1950s there were several small symposia in the USA and elsewhere that had a bearing on the formation in 1954 of AFASE. In 1951, the American Academy of Arts and Sciences organized a conference on the "Sun in the Servce of Man." Those participating were primarily from the Boston area and many were from Harvard and MIT, where Godfrey L. Cabot[5] was supporting research on these questions. Prof. Farrington Daniels[6] (University of Wisconsin-Madison) was there as a speaker on "Efficiency of Biological Photosynthesis." Prof. Hoyt Hottel[7] (MIT) was also on the program, discussing the possibilities of using solar power for meeting energy needs.

Fig. 5: Farrington Daniels, a key figure in the establishment of AFASE and the first president elected by the membership, 1964 – 67.

In 1952, an Ohio Academy of Sciences symposium included topics on solar radiation, heating, photosynthesis, photochemistry, photovoltaics, and optical systems. This one-day gathering, with a speaker on each of these topics, was a remarkably interdisciplinary meeting, and the program had strong similarities in its coverage to the first AFASE meetings.

In 1953, Farrington Daniels, with financial support from the National Science Foundation, organised a symposium at Wisconsin on solar energy that again covered a wide range of topics, with a broad range of speakers. Thirty speakers from five countries participated, with proceedings published in a book *Solar Energy Research*[8]. Farrington again spoke on photosynthesis

---

[5] G. L. Cabot, Boston industrialist who in the 1930s – 1950s supported solar energy research at MIT and Harvard

[6] F. Daniels: see section 3.2.1

[7] H. C. Hottel, authority on combustion, established the basis for calculating collector performance

[8] F. Daniels and J. A. Duffie (eds.). Solar Energy Research., Madison, WI: U. of Wisconsin Press 1955.

and also on solar distillation. The MIT group (Austin Whillier[9]—who subsequently participated in solar R&D at the Brace Research Institute of McGill University—and Hoyt Hottel), George Löf[10], and others spoke in detail about thermal processes. This symposium too, was a precursor of the widening interest in aspects of solar energy use other than by plants.

In 1954, the *Symposium on Wind and Solar Energy* took place in New Delhi, India, organized and supported by UNESCO. Participants included Farrington Daniels and Prof. Felix Trombe[11], the French solar scientist. This was followed by a tour of parts of India—to locales where the potential of solar energy to improve the lives of the population seemed particularly high. (It was on this trip that Daniels saw bullock-powered irrigation pumps, that his wife Olive was to paint in oils. He often stated that this was the picture that changed his life.)

Many of the participants in these symposia were involved in the planning and execution of the first major activities of AFASE—the 1955 Phoenix *World Symposium on Applied Solar Energy* and the Tucson *Conference on the Scientific Basis*. Hoyt Hottel, Felix Trombe, Eugene Rabinovitch[12], Charles G. Abbot[13], and Maria Telkes[14], were participants in the earlier meetings and in the programs at the Arizona events. Farrington Daniels was a keynote speaker at Phoenix.

Thus there was a group of scientists and engineers, mostly in America but with representation from other countries, who were known to each other and who participated in the early activities of the society while solar R&D gathered momentum.

1.3   AFASE/SES/ISES, 1955 to 1980

The history of the first twenty-five years of the society involved three distinct phases—which nearly coincided with the periods of its three names. The first of these phases lasted from 1955 until 1963, the AFASE years, when the Society was administered by officers and directors who were primarily

[9] A. Whillier, from South Africa, collector and radiation data and space heating research.
[10] G. O. G. Löf, Consultant, Denver, Air solar heating system design, distillation research. President of ISES 1973-75
[11] F. Trombe, Scientific Director of CNRS Solar Energy Laboratory at Montlouis, France. Responsible for design and operation of the large solar furnace, and for house heating and cooling research
[12] E. Rabinowitch, U. of Illinois, research on photochemical processes
[13] C. G. Abbot, Emeritus Secretary of Smithsonian Institution, known for solar radiation instrumentation, measurements, and analysis, and inventions of solar engines
[14] M. Telkes, of MIT and then New York University, research on solar house heating, phase-change chemical storage, and distillation

Arizona businessmen. The second phase was the seven-year SES period (1964 to 1970) spanning the presidencies of Farrington Daniels, Peter Glaser[15] and Roger Morse[16], the first three presidents to be elected by Society membership. During these years the major problem was survival of the Society. The third phase, ISES, after 1971, saw survival assured, growing membership, and major concerns with member services.

The first twenty-five years of ISES history was a time of dramatic changes and developments in the organization. How did it begin? What happened? Why? The answers to these questions involve the people who made the history, and the story of the society is to a significant extent the story of its early leaders.

1.3.1   The AFASE Years, 1955 to 1963

The first years of the Society's history were a far cry from those of most similar organizations, in that the individuals who were responsible for operation of the organization were not working in the field. These unusual arrangements persisted, with modification, for nine years.

1.3.1.1   The Origins of AFASE

Farrington Daniels—a visionary who dreamed of solar energy as a way to improve the human condition—in 1952 met Henry Sargent and suggested to him that there was a need for an organization to promote the development and application of solar energy—i.e., a solar industry. Two years later, on March 17, Sargent, with Walter Bimson and Frank Snell organized the Association for Applied Solar Energy, AFASE. Articles of incorporation, signed by the three founders, were filed with the State of Arizona on December 24, 1954. Sargent was the first president.

While Sargent, recognizing the importance of alternatives to oil and natural gas, saw the large business potential—Prof. Daniels saw the primary function of the association as educational, i.e., alerting the public to the need to find alternative renewable sources of energy. Thus its activities would be to encourage research (though carried out in other bodies), in organizing conferences, and in publishing articles on energy and the results of the research activities.

---

[15] P. Glaser: see section 3.2.2
[16] R. N. Morse: see section 3.2.3

The Association's objectives, as stated in the by-laws, were "to foster and encourage the research, development, application and education in fields related to solar and other energies."

Henry Sargent was in 1954 the president of Arizona Public Service Company—the Phoenix electric utility. In 1955 he moved to New York to become President of the American and Foreign Power Company. Walter Bimson was President of the Valley National Bank. Frank Snell was for many years a leading attorney in the Phoenix area. Jan Oostermeier, who succeeded Sargent as President of AFASE in late 1955 when the latter moved to New York, was a retired Vice-President of Shell Chemical Company.

Sargent in 1955 wrote of the founding of AFASE as follows:[17]

The idea for the Association was conceived as a result of conversations between Farrington Daniels and myself some two years ago. It seemed desirable to have an association which could form a vehicle, not only to encourage further scientific and engineering work in connection with solar energy, but also would serve as a means of presenting to industry and business accurate information on the present state of the art. Its purpose in doing so would be to enlist the support of private capital in the development and application of those phases of solar energy utilization which give promise of economic feasibility.

On March 17, 1954, in Phoenix, Arizona, the first meeting was held with a group of men of industry, agriculture, finance, and education who were interested in furthering the practical application of solar energy. Included in this group were representatives of Stanford Research Institute and the president of the University of Arizona. Everyone present felt that additional steps should be taken to meet the problem of greatly increased world requirements for energy. Expanding population and greatly increased per capita use of energy were putting increasingly greater demands for energy upon the non-replaceable sources of such energy, whether they were fossil fuels or nuclear energy. In order to supplement such sources initially and to replace them to a greater or less extent in the future, it seemed desirable to encourage aggressive investigations of tech-

---

17 Sargent, H., Proceedings of the World Symposium on Applied Solar Energy, Stanford Research Institute, 1956, p. 17.

niques for the economical application of the one great renewable source of energy—the sun.

These considerations led Sargent, Bimson and Snell to incorporate AFASE in December 1954. The Association's first activity was to engage the Stanford Research Institute to assemble and publish a directory of world activities and bibliography of significant literature on solar energy. The result, Applied Solar Energy Research, was a guide to the state of the art of utilizing solar energy at the time.

1.3.1.1a   The 1955 Tucson and Phoenix Meetings

The first public activities of AFASE were to take place in October and November 1955—the year that is usually associated with the beginnings of the Society's activities. Two closely related meetings were planned. The first was *The Conference on the Use of Solar Energy—the Scientific Basis* at the University of Arizona in Tucson, Arizona, on October.31 and November 1. The second was the *World Symposium on Applied Solar Energy*, held at Phoenix the following week. They were both supported by an impressive group of agencies: fhe National Academy of Sciences, the National Science Foundation, the Rockefeller Foundation, the Ford Foundation, the Office of Naval Research, the United States Air Force, and UNESCO.

The Tucson conference program was developed by the chairmen of five subject areas, including general papers, radiation, thermal processes, photo-chemical processes, and electrical processes. ninety-six papers were presented. The list of authors included many of the people active in solar energy R&D at the time. The conference was to set the scientific and technological stage of the status of solar energy. About 500 participated in the meetings. The Transactions were published in five volumes by the University of Arizona Press in 1958.

The Phoenix *World Symposium on Applied Solar Energy* was held the next week. It was organized for AFASE by the Stanford Research Institute. The program was designed to present to the business, industry, and govern-ment delegates the state of the art and the opportunities in solar energy. It was a major event, attended by about 900 registrants, many of whom had been at Tucson. A thousand people dined on pheasant at the banquet. The list of mem-bers of the advisory committee and program committee included many famil-iar names: Abbot, Hottel, Löf, Telkes, Trombe, Rabinowitch, and Heywood,[18] all of whom were participants in solar energy conferences in the early 1950s.

---

[18] H. Heywood, Mechanical Engineering, Imperial College of Science and Technology, University of London

Speakers at the Symposium included Harold Heywood from London, Valintin Baum[19] from the USSR, Austin Whillier[20] from South Africa, Gerald Pearson, Hoyt Hottel, George Löf, Richard Jordan,[21] and Farrington Daniels from the United States, Roger Morse from Australia, and others. Foreign delegates totaled 130 and represented 31 nations. The Proceedings of the Symposium were published by the Stanford Research Institute in 1956.

Accompanying the Phoenix Symposium was a major exhibition of solar energy–equipment—The Solar Engineering Exhibit, entitled *"The Sun at Work."* It included 85 exhibits from 50 exhibitors, and attracted 29,000 visitors. Key exhibits included the SOMAR solar engine, solar house designs, new solar cells generating electricity directly, and the first application of selective surfaces (to a solar flat plate collector producing steam at atmospheric pressure—without concentrating mirrors).

These meetings and the exhibit of AFASE made quite an impression and were widely publicized. They must be regarded as the jumping off point for solar R&D on a world scale.

1.3.1.2   The Board of Directors of the Association
The original Board of Directors of the Association included sixteen members, all leaders of business, industry, agriculture and education and mostly from Arizona. At a meeting of the executive committee of the board of AFASE in late 1955, a decision was made by AFASE and the Stanford Research Institute (SRI), to jointly employ an individual who would be the secretary of AFASE and an assistant director of SRI. This position was assumed by John I. Yellott on January 1, 1956. He was also elected to the board of directors for a three-year term. He came to AFASE from Bituminous Coal Research Inc, where he was Director of Development of their coal-burning gas turbine project.

The Board was made up primarily of Arizona bankers, utility executives, and other businessmen, and John Yellott who had a combined engineering and administrative background. The Board elected its own members and officers. The by-laws called for annual meetings of the Association and of the board of directors, and in the early years the directors regarded the board meetings also

---

[19] V. A. Baum, head of the Heliotechnical Laboratory of the Krzhizhanoz Power Institute in the USSR

[20] G. L. Pearson, Bell Telephone Laboratories, who together with D. I. Chapin and C. S. Fuller comprised the team that developed the Silicon solar cell for the practical direct conversion of solar to electrical energy

[21] R. C. Jordan, U. of Minnesota, solar power systems, radiation data analysis and processing

as Association meetings. In fact, the board was the organization in 1954 and 1955. Memberships were solicited in 1955 – 56, primarily from industry and business.

Fig. 6: Harry Tabor with a flat-plate selective-surface steam generator at the "Sun at Work" exhibition at Phoenix in 1955

Fig. 7: SOMAR pump (Italy) at "Sun at Work" exhibition at Phoenix in 1955

Fig. 8: Solar cookers on display at the Phoenix "Sun at Work" exhibition, 1955

In 1956, there was already an ambitious list of activities under consideration. It included establishment of a permanent Solar Energy Museum (based on the Phoenix Engineering Exhibit), establishment and maintenance of a library, publication of a quarterly newsletter (*The Sun-at-Work*), publication of a technical journal (*The Journal of Solar Energy Science and Engineering*), and a solar house architectural design contest. Development of a membership structure, to include individual memberships at dues of $10.00 per year, was also under consideration.

The membership structure changed from time to time, but always included two basic types of membership, "collective" (corporate, institutional) and individual. In later years, a student membership category was added. (Membership data are shown in Table 1 in the Appendix.)

By May 1956 there were 138 individual, two Institutional and seventeen corporate memberships in the Association. The library had been activated, with Ms. Jean Jensen as librarian. The first issue of the Sun at Work had appeared. Work on the first volume of *The Journal of Solar Energy Science and Engineering* (usually shortened to *Solar Energy*) had started. Negotiations for space for a proposed Laboratory of the Sun were under way.

Fig. 9: Walter Lucking,
Mrs. Frank Edlin, and W.
B. Gibson at Tempe
meeting of SES, 1967

AFASE offices were established in a Phoenix office building, which included space for the secretary, the office staff, and the library. An area of 10,000 square feet of roof area was available to the Association for a Museum of Solar Energy. The Association was involved in setting up solar energy exhibits at international trade fairs, notably in Greece and Morocco.

A proposed budget for 1957 included $50,000 income from corporate memberships and $10,250 from individual memberships. Major estimated expenses were for salaries totaling $35,500, publications $6,000, and other items, all adding up to $60,000. In late 1956 there were forty corporate members totaling $25,000 with contributions ranging from $5,000 to $50, at an average of a little over $600 per membership. There was also significant indebtedness; SRI had provided substantial services to the Association for which reimbursement had not been made, and funds had been borrowed from the Valley National Bank to provide operating capital.

The progress of some of the AFASE enterprises is noted below.

1.3.1.2a   The Solar Furnace Symposium
The Association convened a Solar Furnace Symposium in January 1957. Held at Phoenix, it brought together many of those active in this area, including Felix Trombe[22] and Peter Glaser (who was to become the organization's second member-elected president). Fifteen papers were on the program, and approximately 200 attended. The proceedings of this symposium were published as part of Volume 1 of the journal *Solar Energy*.

---

[22] Felix Trombe was the scientific director of the CNRS solar energy laboratory at Montlouis, France. He was responsible for design and operation of the large solar furnace at Montlouis and was active in research on passive house heating, cooling, and refrigeration. More later on Peter Glaser

1.3.1.2b The Solar Furnace Construction Project

President Jan Oostermeier (who had succeeded Henry Sargent) made a trip to Montlouis, France, to the solar furnace installation there and returned to the board with a recommendation that AFASE should build a similar facility in the Phoenix area, to be financed with industrial contributions. Oostermeier stated:[23]

> The furnace at MontLouis has given French Industry a magnificent tool for high temperature research. The Association can render a unique service to American industry by making available similar facilities in Arizona where 300 days of intense sunlight are available each year.

SRI, acting for AFASE, sent a team of three engineers to Montlouis to study the French furnace design. Negotiations with CNRS (the French government agency that operated the Montlouis facility) were undertaken to allow AFASE to use the Trombe furnace patents, and an advance royalty payment of $1,000 was made. A furnace of about 50 feet diameter was envisioned.

A group of scientists working in the solar field provided the Association with advice on the furnace design. A major recommendation was that the furnace should be designed to produce maximum temperatures, rather than to be very large. Cost estimates based on preliminary designs indicated that the investment would be of the order of $1,000,000. The Board was unable to generate the necessary level of industrial interest in the project, and the decision was made to terminate it.

1.3.1.2c The Library and Publications

The AFASE librarian, Jean Jensen, with considerable assistance from Maria Telkes and others, assembled a collection of some 5,000 items, including books, papers, periodicals, and patents relating to solar energy. Library services were made available to all comers, regardless of membership in the Association, although members were invited to use the facility.

---

[23] Oostermeier, J., report to the board of directors meeting of May 29, 1956, on his trip to Montlouis, cited in a review of the Board meeting dated June 5, 1956

Fig. 10: The Montlouis 50m solar furnace. The proposed AFASE furnace was to be of similar but smaller design

Fig. 11: The heliostats for the Montlouis furnace (not aligned when photo was taken)

Fig. 12: Frank Edlin, Jack Duffie, and Farrington Daniels at Montlouis, France, in 1958. They were attending the CNRS meeting on Applications Thermique de l'Energie Solare dans le Domaine de la Recherche et de l'Industrie, organized by Prof. F. Trombe.

Fig. 13: Valintin Baum (USSR), Farrington Daniels, Felix Trombe, and V. Storelli at Montlouis, France, 1958. A CNRS meeting organized by Prof. Trombe brought many researchers to the Laboratory in southern France

The Society's first periodical was the *Sun at Work*, a quarterly newsletter. The first issue appeared in March 1956. Volumes I and part of II were edited by Guy Benveniste, an SRI engineer who had participated in planning for the Phoenix symposium. After the first two issues he was joined by Jean Jensen as Associate Editor. She subsequently became the editor. This newsletter was an informative publication. It included information on a wide range of topics, for example:

- AFASE news of meetings, and activities and those of other organizations
- Reviews of activities of programs and laboratories, such as the MIT solar heating program and the US Army Quartermaster Corps solar furnace
- Historical reviews, such as that of John Ericcson, an inventor of solar devices
- Editorials and political developments relating to solar energy
- Reports of work of inventors, such as H. Thomason
- Information on solar equipment available for purchase
- Background articles on scientific topics, such as fundamentals of pyrheliometry

Fig. 14: Deer-layer solar still designed by George Löf at Daytona Beach, Florida. This and other experiments were noted in AFASE publications

In 1957 a quarterly technical journal was established: *The Journal of Solar Energy Science and Engineering*—later shortened to *Solar Energy*. Jean Jensen also became editor of this journal and was responsible for the first three volumes. For the first two volumes, there was an editorial board that included one name familiar to the scientific/engineering community at that time, Frank Edlin, an engineer from DuPont. For volume 3, the editorial board was expanded to include R&D people in the field. For volumes 4 and 5, A. B. Stafford of Arizona State University was editor, assisted by S. W. Wilcox. Charles A. Scarlott was the Society's editor starting in 1962, and served through six volumes of Solar Energy.

1.3.1.2d The Solar House Design Competition

The International Architectural Competition, launched in 1957, was a major initiative of AFASE—in ooperation with the Phoenix Association of Home Builders. The competition was financed by a $15,000 loan from the Valley National bank. The plan was to construct the building of the winning design on a site in the Phoenix area, and then operate and measure the performance of the heating system with the house occupied by a family. One hundred thirteen entries from thirteen countries were received by the Professional Advisor, J. M. Hunter,[24] of Boulder, Colorado. The five jurors met in September 1957, visited the site for the building, and flew to the Grand Canyon where they spent several days evaluating the entries.

Fig. 15: Drawing of Peter Lee's winning design for the AFASE solar house competition

The winning design, by Peter R. Lee, a student at the University of Minnesota and an employee of the firm Bliss & Campbell, had collectors that were in the form of rotating louvers so the slope could be adjusted to increase incident radiation over what it would be on fixed collectors. Engineering of the heating system was undertaken by Bridgers and Paxton, a leading consulting firm, and materials for construction of the heating system components were supplied by (among others) DuPont and Reynolds Metals.

A grant of $13,000 from the John W. Pierce Foundation of Connecticut provided for instrumentation and system performance measurements. With

---

[24] J. M. Hunter, Architect, designer of Löf solar house

financial support from the Phoenix business and construction community, the house was built. It was meant to be a showpiece, and it was open to the public for a month—until the neighbors complained about the traffic and took legal action. There were questions whether the design met zoning requirements for "conventional southwestern architecture." John Yellott commented that "Peter Lee's lovely house was certainly not southwestern in its architecture..." Action by the zoning commission upheld the complaint, ending the public phase of the project. Unfortunately, no operating data on the performance of the solar heating system were recorded. Monitoring and other equipment was turned over to Arizona State University and the house was sold. The unfortunate end of the project, reported in one newspaper under the headline "Sun Sets on Solar House," did not enhance the reputation of AFASE nor improve what was becoming a difficult financial situation.

John Yellott in 1980 recalled the situation thus:[25]

> The sun set not only on the solar house but on most of the paid staff of the Association because it became obvious that there was not sufficient financing to continue the operation in the manner originally contemplated. The writer's employment as Executive Secretary and later as Executive Vice President was terminated.

A book, *Living with the Sun*, included plans and drawings of sixty of the entries in the competition. They include the winning Lee entry, the next four runner-up designs, honorable mention designs, and others. It was published by AFASE in 1958 and is available from ISES Headquarters on CD.

Thus AFASE in its first years established an office with paid professional staff It embarked on ambitious publication and library service programs and other projects. These activities were to be financed by memberships, primarily corporate. When memberships did not materialize in sufficient numbers, economies were in order. As noted above, staff was reduced, and AFASE in 1960 moved to the Arizona State University at Tempe.

---

[25] ISES News, No. 33, Sept. 1980. After leaving the Association, John Yellott established his own consulting organization, was affiliated with the architecture department of ASU, and served as the ISES representative in Arizona for many years.

1.3.1.2e   The 1960 Affiliation with Arizona State University

With the 1960 reorganization, AFASE moved to offices on the ASU campus, to space donated by the University. Jan Oostermeier resigned as president and assumed a vice-presidency. Hal Walmsley was employed as president. Jean Jensen (the editor and librarian) and Lee McLean (who had been
hired as executive officer) resigned. University staff and faculty took on
responsibilities for some of the Association's activities. Milton Lowenstein
became the AFASE librarian. Prof. A. B. Stafford became editor of Solar
Energy, and S. W. Wilcox became editor of *Sun at Work*, arrangements that
lasted until 1962 when Charles Scarlott became editor of both publications.
AFASE would maintain its affiliation with ASU until the move of headquarters to Australia in 1970.

Fig. 16: The Denver house, designed by Hunter and occupied by the Löf family since 1957

1.3.1.3   The AFASE Advisory Council

The board of AFASE and its cooperating institutions (SRI and the
University of Arizona) called on ad hoc committees to plan its first three
meetings (Tucson, Phoenix, and the Solar Furnace Symposium). Included in
each were scientists and engineers working in solar energy. The programs that
were assembled were impressive and comprehensive. After the Tucson and

Phoenix meetings the committees had little formal input to AFASE and probably had little influence on its plans and activities. On paper there was an advisory committee, and at its meeting in May 1956 the directors decided to meet with members of the committee to review the Associations plans for 1957, but records of such a meeting have not come to light. Apart from that, and while there may have been personal contacts between directors and advisory committee members, the board was responsible for all of the decisions and activities of the Association.

Fig. 17: MIT House IV, with liquid heating collectors and water storage

The Advisory Council (which must have grown out of the committee) included among its members many of the scientists and engineers active in the field at the time. Members at various times included Farrington Daniels, George Löf, Hoyt Hottel, Harry Tabor, Maria Telkes, Charles G. Abbot, Dick Jordan, Felix Trombe, Roger Morse, Jack Duffie, and others. The Council's first organized function was to plan and carry out the scientific meeting in New York in 1959. Otherwise it was little involved as an organization in the operation if the Association—until the New York meeting.

1.3.1.3a. The 1959 New York Meeting

Members of the Council were conscious of the lack of contact between themselves and the board, and in 1958 George Löf made it known to the board that council members felt they were not being consulted by the Association. As a result, the council was expanded and plans were developed for the 1959 meeting.

The council's purpose was to meet in technical sessions, and also to make recommendations regarding the role of the Association in future solar energy developments. Some members of the advisory council were not satisfied with the direction in which the Association was going, and in an unscheduled gathering the discussion centered around basic questions: Should AFASE be abandoned, or should the organization be changed to a more traditional scientific/engineering society? Should the scientific members depend on their traditional scientific and engineering societies (like ASME, ASHRAE, APS) for forums to discuss solar energy matters, or would an interdisciplinary AFASE be a better forum?

Fig. 18: George Löf, long-time advisory council member and ISES President, 1973 – 75

AFASE had significant accomplishments to its credit. It had sponsored conferences (Tucson, Phoenix, and the Solar Furnace Symposium) that were effective in bringing people in the field together. It had a publication program, including a journal and a newsletter. At the same time there were problems. No one on the board of directors had experience or competence in the science and technology of solar energy. The editors of Solar Energy were hard working, but lacked expertise in the field. There was not an adequate reviewing system in place.

In spite of its difficulties, AFASE was very much a going organization. It was a unique organization, one that cut across usual disciplinary lines. Active members included chemists, physicists, mechanical engineers, chemical engineers, botanists, meteorologists, and others. Traditional professional organizations were not set up to absorb and serve such a variety of members. Also, there were members from countries other than the United States, and nationally based societies did not lend themselves to international and interdisciplinary memberships.

The Council's deliberations resulted in two actions that were to change AFASE over the coming four years. First, the responsibilities of the Council in AFASE were defined. Second, the members urged that AFASE undergo changes in its organization that would transform it into a society with a board of directors and officers elected by its members. This was a radical departure from the existing structure. In short, it would mean that the scientific community would assume from the Arizona business community the responsibility for the Association.

The Advisory Council met in April 1960 at Madison, with Hal Walmsley[26] (recently elected president of the Association by the directors). A set of by-laws for the Council was adopted, outlining the organization and responsibilities of the Council. In a section on Professional Assistance, the by-laws stated:

The Council will make recommendations to the Board and accept such other responsibilities as are mutually agreed upon by the Council and the Board. The Council will be mainly concerned with:
- Scope of all technical activities.
- Major financial matters and support having scientific and technical implications.
- Technical facilities, including library or laboratories.
- Cooperation with other organizations, state and national governments.
- Publications, including scientific, technical and promotional.

The Council will be responsible for:
- The review and approval of any proposed technical activities of the AFASE.
- The review of technical papers submitted to the AFASE and the establishment of publications policy and standards.
- Assistance in planning and conductance of symposia, conferences, and technical meetings of AFASE.

Particular concern was expressed at this meeting about the quality of the Association's publications, and an eight-member publications committee of the Council was formed. A. J. Drummond, who would play a key role in revitalizing the journal, Solar Energy, was a member.

Thus the newly organized Council outlined what it considered to be its growing role in Association affairs. The AFASE Board approved the Council by-laws in 1963, recognizing the importance of the scientific community in the affairs of the Association. This ultimately resulted in a new direction for

---

26 Hal Walmsley was a retired brigadier general who served in the U. S. Army's Chemical Corps.

the Association—a series of annual meetings organized by Council members and devoted to the science and technology of solar energy.

The proposal to reorganize AFASE was more far-reaching, and its progress more obscure. The essential fact is that the Council's ideas were approved by the board of directors at its meeting in January 1963, paving the way for officers and board members to be elected by the membership. The name of the society was changed to the SOLAR ENERGY SOCIETY, with the reorganization effective January 1, 1964.

As the new structure became effective in 1964, Hal Walmsley, the outgoing president, commented:[27]

> The execution of the new policies and organization will make the Society more responsible to the interests of the members, add to its world-renowned professional stature, and give it added force as the vehicle for dynamic progress in the science, technology and application of solar energy in all nations.

1.3.1.4   Other Concepts of AFASE

The advisory board was made up of scientists and engineers involved with solar energy research and was the group that developed the new concept of the organization. It is not surprising that the changes were to make it a society more along the lines of other scientific and engineering organizations (although a uniquely interdisciplinary one). There were a few dissenting voices, in particular of those who saw its potential as a more popular and more applied society. Harold Hay, for example, viewed the Sun at Work as more important than the Solar Energy journal and urged that the Society be more applications (and less research) oriented. These differences of opinion would persist over the lifetime of the organization.

1.3.1.5   Branches (Sections) of AFASE

Starting in 1955 there was international participation in AFASE meetings and symposia, although at a relatively low level. H. Tabor of Israel, V. A. Baum of USSR, F. Trombe of France, H. Haywood and John Page of England, and R. N. Morse of Australia were all at Tucson and Phoenix, and continued some level of AFASE activities. But the organization and its activities were largely American.

AFASE was a monolithic organization until 1962, when it first encour-

---

[27] Sun at Work, VIII, No. 2, 16

aged the formation of national or local branches. The first of these to be established was the Australia—New Zealand branch (later to be called section), with Roger Morse as its chairman. The next section to be organized was Chile, in 1963, with Julio Hirschmann as chairman. Italy followed soon thereafter, under the guidance of V. Storelli and G. Nebbia. Thus, by the time of the change from AFASE to SES, the concept of national sections, conducting their own activities but with close ties to the Association, was firmly established and the organization was taking on a distinctly more international flavor. (The move of headquarters to Australia in 1970 accelerated this trend.) Table 4, in the Appendix, lists sections and years of origin.

1.3.1.6   A Summary of the AFASE Years

The Association for its first five years was almost entirely the creature of the directors, a group of public-spirited Arizona businessmen. The input from the scientific community was primarily in program planning for meetings. AFASE plans and activities ranged beyond meetings, and included an architectural competition and solar home construction, a museum, a solar furnace, publications, and others. Financing was sought primarily from business and industry and secondarily from individual memberships. The board of directors was a self-appointed group not elected by AFASE members.

Beginning in 1959, the advisory council, as it became known, sought a greater role for the scientific community (the membership) in influencing the activities of the Association and its governance. The emphasis was shifted to improving the publications and to organizing meetings, i.e., to the exchange of scientific and technological information. The final step was to convince the directors to turn over control of AFASE to officers and a new Board all elected by the membership.

It took four years, but the Council's ideas were accepted and implemented. As of January 1964, the name was changed to the Solar Energy Society, and Farrington Daniels became the first president elected by the membership.

1.3.2   The SES Years, 1964 to 1971

The years from 1964 to 1971 were eventful years for the Society. Severe financial pressures and some organizational problems threatened its existence. That it survived and later prospered was due to the contributions of many unpaid volunteers who provided critical support. There were, however, three individuals whose service to the Society was extraordinary. They were its first three presidents elected by the membership: Farrington Daniels, Peter Glaser, and Roger Morse. They were three very different kinds of people with very different backgrounds.

Farrington Daniels played a critical role in the formation of AFASE and in keeping it alive during difficult years. He had a set of almost independent professional careers. He was a physical chemist who first made his mark in nitrogen chemistry. He worked in photochemistry and photosynthesis. During World War II he was the director of the Metallurgical Laboratory of the University of Chicago (where the first critical atomic reaction was carried out) and he was at Alamogordo when the first atomic bomb was exploded. His experiences in atomic bomb development drove him to seek alternative energy directions for the betterment of mankind. Based, perhaps, on his knowledge of photochemistry and photosynthesis, he directed his thoughts and efforts to developing and promoting solar energy.

He was generous, ingenious, inventive, and imaginative. He was widely respected and admired. He was a visionary. A trip to India for the 1954 Symposium on Wind and Solar Energy in New Delhi and the postmeeting tour where he saw water being pumped by bullock power broadened his interest in solar energy, and as he often said, "changed my life." One aim in his later years was to teach people in developing countries how to improve their lives by building and using solar cookers and stills.

Daniels was president of the American Chemical Society and vice-president of the U. S. National Academy of Sciences. He knew many people in many places. In 1953 he organized a symposium at the University of Wisconsin on "Solar Energy Utilization." This stimulated the interests of members of the engineering faculty, with the result that the U. W. Solar Energy Laboratory was established.

Peter Glaser was born and raised in Bohemia and educated in Czechoslovakia, England, and America. He was in the Free Czechoslovakian army during World War II. In 1955 he joined Arthur D. Little, a consulting organization in the United States, where he was a lunar scientist and worked with imaging furnaces and space power systems. He participated in the AFASE Solar Furnace Symposium in 1957 and was active in Society matters for many year thereafter.

Roger Morse was educated at Sydney University in Australia and had a half decade of experience in industry before his service with the Australian army in Papua-New Guinea during World War II. He was responsible for establishing the Engineering Section—later to become the Division of Mechanical Engineering—of CSIRO, and led its work on air conditioning, refrigeration, and solar energy applications. He was largely responsible for the work that led to development of the solar water heater industry in

Australia. A very practical, hands-on engineer, he could see in a minute what constituted a good or bad solar heater design.

Fig. 19: Roger Morse (Australia), Peter Glaser and Farrington Daniels (USA), the first three presidents of SES elected by society membership

In the normal course of their professional activities, these three would probably never have met, but the Society was (and is) very much an interdisciplinary organization and bridged these differences. Their backgrounds and work were different, but they shared the conviction that solar energy had promise for improving the welfare of mankind and that the Society was a useful vehicle for achieving that end.

1.3.2.1   The Daniels Presidency

Farrington Daniels assumed the presidency of the Society in 1964, and his (paid) predecessor, Hal Walmsley, became the executive secretary. The headquarters were at Arizona State University. The editor of the Society's two publications, the Sun at Work and the Solar Energy journal, was Charles Scarlott. As Daniels became president, the name of the Society was changed to the Solar Energy Society, to better represent the broader scope of the Society's interests (beyond applications) and put the word "Solar" first. Membership in the Society at the beginning of 1964 was 787. The Society had a dedicated and able secretary in Mary Weber.

Fig. 20: Farrington Daniels. Photo from
UW Archives

The new board of directors included a mix of fifteen directors from the previous board. It included Weldon Gibson as vice president of SES; he was Executive Vice President of Stanford Research Institute.. Five new members from the scientific community joined the board: Peter Glaser, George Löf, Roger Morse, Harry Tabor, and Felix Trombe. A mix of the new and old persisted until after 1967, when all of the directors were elected from the scientific community.

The new President wrote to a colleague in May 1964 as follows:[29]

...The situation is really very critical and it would be so easy for the newly organized Solar Energy Society and its journal to simply fold up and die. The financial situation is very precarious, but by cutting of $10,000 from Hal Walmsley's budget and bringing the total down to $50,000, we may be able to survive this year, but after this year our support of the journal by the National Science Foundation will be discontinued. In addition to loss of NSF support, we are losing some of our industrial memberships and there is a possibility that we may [...lose our donated space in ...] the build-

---

[29] Daniels F., letter to Duffie, J. A. (then in Australia), dated May 12, 1964

ing at the Arizona State University. The last blow was the cancellation by [NASA] of the previously approved support for our Solar Energy Symposium emphasizing terrestrial usages of space research. Perhaps the greatest worry of all, however, is the fact that Chuck Scarlott is not getting enough manuscripts to assure continuation of the Journal. If we do not have enough interest to justify the Journal, we do not have enough interest to justify a Society.

However, I will not accept these pessimistic views and I am doing my best to help the Society survive. …

Fig. 21: Farrington Daniels experimenting with solar stills at his summer home in Wisconsin

As Daniels took over the presidency, the Society's legal debts were large. The indebtedness to Valley National Bank was about $10,000, and tens of thousands were owed to Stanford Research Institute for services rendered to AFASE for the Tucson and Phoenix meetings, for solar furnace ventures, and for publications. One source listed the total debts as $120,000. The annual budget was of the order of $50,000, and membership income did not approach that figure. The financial problems were real and large.

In early 1965, Hal Walmsley, the Society's paid executive secretary resigned to pursue other activities. Frank Edlin agreed to replace him (at a salary of $5,000/yr). Frank was a chemical engineer who had retired from DuPont where he had been very active in solar distillation R&D and in materials for solar energy applications.. He was familiar with much of the technology and knew many of the scientists and engineers active in the field. He was to stay with the Society in this capacity until ill health brought on his retirement in 1968.

While the Society's fiscal and organizational problems persisted in the Daniels years, important functions continued. Meetings were held in Phoenix in 1965, Tempe in 1966, Boston in 1967, and in Palo Alto in 1968, with multiple symposia at each. The Solar Energy journal was published by the Society—although on an irregular basis. The Sun at Work continued. Thus the essential activities of exchange of information on the science and technology of solar energy provided motivation for people in the field to continue their memberships.

In the summer of 1965, the Society's day-to-day operations were at risk. At one point it was reported that there was a payroll of $500 to be met and a bank balance of $100. These were stressful times for both Daniels and Edlin, and for Mary Weber who had a deep personal involvement in these matters. That year a grant of $20,000 from the Rockefeller Foundation to support the Solar Energy journal provided some fiscal breathing room and enabled the Society to avoid bankruptcy. Headquarters were still in contributed space at Arizona State University.

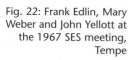
Fig. 22: Frank Edlin, Mary Weber and John Yellott at the 1967 SES meeting, Tempe

At the time of the SES board of directors meeting in March 1966, there were among the fourteen members four from outside of the USA: Harry Tabor from Israel, Gerald Ward from Canada, Roger Morse from Australia, and Valintin Baum from USSR. The growing international nature of the Society was becoming evident.

Daniels opened the 1966 meeting with remarks about changes in the previous year. Frank Edlin took on the post of executive secretary. Some growth in membership and subscriptions was reported. The ever-present financial problems were noted. Scarlott, the editor, reported that there was a steady flow of materials for the publications coming in, but that getting reviews was a problem.

On the international front, Valintin Baum told the board about the very active programs of solar energy research then under way in USSR. Roger Morse described a very active section of the Society in Australia, New Zealand, and surrounding islands, with most interest in thermal processes such as distillation and water heating. He noted that there was considerable interest in holding a 1970 meeting of the Society in Australia, that the government would extend a formal invitation to the Society if there were indications that the Society would be receptive, and that there would be some funds available to support the meeting. This news was received with enthusiasm by the board and action was taken to indicate the Society's interest in meeting in Australia in 1970.

At the 1967 board meeting, President Daniels opened the meeting with extensive remarks about the state of the Society. Starting with comments about the dedication of the staff (Frank Edlin and Mary Weber) and the fine relations with Arizona State University, he then spoke—as he had in the past—of the continuing dire fiscal situation of SES:[30]

> ...Finances are desperate. The National Science Foundation carried us for five years and said this was all. We borrowed $10,000 from the Valley National Bank to pay off back debts. ... We have reduced this to $9,000 but that is all. We hoped we could reduce it by selling our bound copies of the Journal. ...
>
> The only way we have been able to make it was for our executive secretary to forgo part of his token salary. And, that is what it is, a token salary. Many of our contributions are falling off and we are in a desperate situation. ... It is going to be difficult to cut expenses any further. The office force is cut to Frank [Edlin] and Mary [Weber] and this isn't enough to handle things. We got the Rockefeller grant, but this was all earmarked. Part of this is for printing abstracts of articles in the Journal in French and Spanish. ...

Frank Edlin was sufficiently discouraged in 1967 that he recommended the Society terminate its activities. This recommendation was rejected.

---

30 Minutes of March 19, 1967 board of directors meeting

The Society was still in trouble. But, even in those pre-OPEC times it had real strengths. It had a membership of about 1,000 that represented many disciplines. With members in many countries it was on the way to becoming a truly international organization. There were three national sections (Australia/New Zealand, Chile, and Italy). It had a going publications program. And it had a core of dedicated leaders. Peter Glaser was to assume the presidency and Roger Morse the vice presidency, and there was a real sense of determination to solve the problems and make the Society work.

Matters of concern to the Society at that time included (in addition to financial matters): how to form national sections, where in the world meetings should be held, and how to expand membership, There were continuing differences of opinion as to what should be the emphasis of the Society's programs and publications—to move in the direction of "high tech" and space applications, or to emphasize solar energy for developing economies.

1.3.2.2.   The Glaser Presidency

At the end of the 1967 Board meeting, Peter Glaser assumed the presidency and Roger Morse the vice-presidency. Frank Edlin resigned his post as executive secretary because of physical limitations and inability to handle the workload, although he was to stay on until a successor could be found.

Fig. 23: Frank Edlin, Farrington, Daniels and Peter Glaser at Tempe meeting, 1967

In December 1967 Glaser wrote to the membership:[31]

At the last meeting of the Board of Directors, new ways of handling the affairs of the Society were inaugurated. In the interest of economy, changes have been made in the administration of the Society, with all officers performing their duties without remunera-

---

31 Glaser, P., "An Open Letter to Members,"" dated December 1967

tion. Professor Carl Hodges has taken on the function of Secretary-Treasurer, and Mr. Frank Edlin has accepted the office of International Corresponding Secretary. Mrs. Mary Weber continues in her capacity of administrative secretary. Mr. Charles Scarlott has relinquished the function of Editor of the Society Publications, and our thanks go to him for his many years of devoted and superior service on behalf of the Society. We believe that such steps will … lead to the establishment of this organization on a sound fiscal basis without having to rely on outside subsidies, and one that is capable of expansion.

One such step of immediate interest to many members is the way we handle requests for technical information. In the future requests of this nature received at headquarters will immediately be routed to a recognized authority … (This was a simplification of functions, as headquarters itself had endeavored to act as a source for information for anyone who requested it.)

Thus, by 1968, there were substantial changes in the Society. The position of executive secretary had been abolished and replaced by a volunteer secretary-treasurer, with Carl Hodges, of ASU, in the new position. Publication of the Sun at Work was suspended to save money and for lack of an editor.

Fig. 24: Andy Drumond, editor of Solar Energy from 1970 to 1971, with Margaret (Mrs. Roger) Morse

Charles Scarlott, the paid editor (whose stipend was nominal and who did not always receive that stipend) was replaced by Andrew Drummond (who served without pay). Drummond was a physicist at Eppley Laboratories where he worked on problems of solar energy measurements, and he brought a new sense of high standards to the Journal. He visualized future issues in which papers relating to a single subject might be published, an idea that developed into the topical issues of recent years. He also sought review papers for the journal, and he appointed associate editors to help make the reviewing process more manageable.

There were also substantial changes in the Society's financial position. The dire prospects of 1967 were improving. The efforts of Farrington Daniels, Peter Glaser, Walter Bimson, and Weldon Gibson bore substantial fruit. The Valley National Bank agreed to reduce the size of the debt to the bank by $2,000 per year. Frank Edlin announced that he would forgo salary owed to him, thus in effect making a cash gift of $1,440. The Stanford Research Institute had been owed money for support provided to the Society in its early days, and this indebtedness was cancelled by SRI. Farrington Daniels personally paid $900 in interest on the Valley National Bank loan.

A significant part of the fiscal problems faced by the society was its expenditures on the Journal. From activities of Czechoslovakian nationals in London during World War II, Glaser knew Robert Maxwell, the founder and head of Pergamon Press. Glaser went to New York and discussed with Maxwell the society's need for a new approach to publication. The result was an agreement for Pergamon Press to produce the journal, starting in 1968. The terms of the contract were generous for the Society. Pergamon would produce and distribute to each member four issues a year at a cost to the society of $6—and contribute to the Society 25% of all profits generated by sales of the publication to nonmembers.

Irrespective of any later activities of Mr. Maxwell, the arrangement with Pergamon was a real helping hand to the Society. It continued, with modifications, into the 1990s. With a cadre of unpaid authors, editors and reviewers, SES put in the hands of its members a creditable journal at very low cost.

The agreement worked out by Peter Glaser with Pergamon Press resulted in major savings. The society had to pay only for copies of the Journal going to members and not for extra copies. This greatly reduced overhead and was a substantial step in moving the Society towards solvency. In addition, the "new" journal was a more attractive publication with wider circulation, and helped to obtain new members.

The vice president, Roger Morse, commented that there were times during the previous months that there were real misgivings as to whether the Society could survive. He stated that he believed it was mainly due to the efforts of Glaser and Hodges that we had managed this feat. Things were looking up, and the leaders could begin to devote more of their attention to memberships and meetings.

Plans to hold the 1970 meeting of the Society in Melbourne, Australia, called for a five-day congress, with emphasis on what had been accomplished in solar energy rather than on predictions for the future. This would be the first meeting outside of the USA and was to be on a scale that allowed special arrangements with airlines and hotels for attendees. The United Nations and other agencies would support attendance by representatives of developing countries. The meeting was to be the first significant international gathering since the Tucson and Phoenix conferences fifteen years earlier.

Many other issues were of concern. How should memberships for persons in developing countries be financed? (A characteristic of those countries is the lack of hard currencies to pay for journals and other services associated with joining the Society.) How could international sections be encouraged and developed? How could a balance be struck between high tech-applications, basic science, and applications? How could the Sun at Work or its equivalent be restarted?

1.3.2.3   The Morse Presidency

In 1969, Roger Morse became president, taking over from Peter Glaser. The new agreement with Pergamon Press was in place, the first issue produced by them with Andy Drummond as editor was in hand, and it was well received. There were still problems with the journal (then a quarterly), mostly concerning the supply of acceptable manuscripts and obtaining reviews, but the new editor's efforts were bearing very positive fruits.

Fig. 25: David Norris (Australia), Jack Duffie, Wal Read and Everett Howe inspecting an experimental CSIRO solar still at Griffith, New South Wales, Australia

Fig. 26: Roger Morse (Australia), Jack Duffie (USA), Taro Hisada (Japan) and Julio Hirschmann (Chile) examine a solar water heater at Melbourne, 1970

The Society had been maintaining a library at its offices at Arizona State University (ASU), with Mary Weber using it to respond to various inquiries. The decision was made to drop the library function and to turn the library facilities over to an appropriate organization. The collection was donated to ASU, that maintains it to this day.

Melbourne was the scene of the 1970 board of director's meeting, with members from nine countries in attendance. The Board meeting preceded the 1970 general meeting, and Roger Morse, the president, presided. Carl Hodges, the secretary-treasurer, was there, but had announced his resignation. This precipitated a discussion of future location for the Society's headquarters, since the secretary-treasurer should be at the same location as headquarters. Countries under consideration (in addition to the USA) were Australia, Japan, France, and the USSR. The decision was made by the board, in a later mail ballot, to move headquarters to Melbourne. The move was made, and Frank Hogg became the new secretary-treasurer.

The move to Melbourne was undertaken after considerable debate. The president and vice president wrote to the membership the following:[32]

---

[32] Morse, R. N. (President), and Duffie, J.A. (Vice President), Letter to Members of the Solar Energy Society dated June 16, 1970

At this time in the history of the Solar Energy Society, the Board of Directors has made extensive and careful study of the affairs of SES, from viewpoints of both scientific and technical programs of the Society, and its management and fiscal affairs. This letter is to inform you of the results of these studies and the changes we are making in the Society's activities. The recommended changes are considered to be in the best interests of the Society from both operational and financial viewpoints.

Late in 1969 our secretary-treasurer of the past several years, Mr. Carl O. Hodges, indicated that the pressure of other affairs made it desirable for him to resign during 1970. This decision, together with other operational considerations, led to the study by a committee of the Board of the location of the head office, its relation to the appointment of a new secretary-treasurer, and related questions of the structure and finances of the Society.

This special committee considered that the secretary-treasurer and the permanent staff of the Society should be in the same city, that there should be continuity for three to six years in the office of secretary-treasurer, and that the headquarters should be in a country which is active in solar energy research and development. The Committee considered that the Society, being an international organization, could operate effectively with its headquarters outside the United States, and found that important savings in operating expenses would accrue if the office were located in Melbourne. It recommended that a United States Section of the Society be formed without delay with its office in or near Washington, D. C. It further recommended that Mr. Frank G. Hogg be appointed as secretary-treasurer for a three year period, subject to reappointment, and that the office of the Society be established in Melbourne, Australia.

...This marks an important milestone in the Society's development in that it can now be claimed to be a truly international organization. The pattern of an international organization within which largely autonomous national societies can operate independently is an attractive one and has already been working very successfully in Australia for many years. Those members affiliated with a national group, such as the United States or the Australia and New Zealand Sections of the Society, will first and foremost be members of the International Solar Energy Society, but will, in addition, be free, and indeed encouraged, to organize their own national meetings and functions through their national or local headquarters. Those members not affiliated with a national group will continue to communicate with the headquarters of the Society.

A United States section of the Society is being organized, with the approval of the Board, and after July 1, 1970, the affairs of Society members in the United States will be handled through the assistance of Dr. William H. Klein. Bill has volunteered to act as secretary-treasurer for a U. S. Section ... This office will be operated by volunteers without payroll expense to the Society. ...

There were other problems associated with the headquarters move and the increasing internationalization of the Society, which was (and is still) incorporated under the laws of the State of Arizona. Annual membership meetings were required, and as the international meeting schedule evolved into a biennial pattern, it was necessary to hold general meetings in conjunction with a section meeting; this was often done with the American Section, the largest in the Society.

It was also necessary to have a representative in Arizona. John Yellott, residing in the state, volunteered to act in this capacity. Annual reports of the Society were to be prepared by headquarters and filed by Yellott with the Arizona Secretary of State.

The organizers of the Melbourne International Conference obtained about $35,000 in support for the Conference, including funds to support the travel of delegates from developing countries. It was truly an international affair, with 189 registered delegates from 26 different countries. Eight-three papers were presented (and preprinted), and the conference program included technical visits, a postconference tour, and social events. It led to consideration of changing Solar Energy Society to International Solar Energy Society.

Meeting plans included gatherings at NASA-Goddard (with Bill Cherry as chairman) in 1971 and Montreal (with Tony Ward as chairman) in 1972. The possibility was explored of a joint meeting in Paris in 1973 with AFEDES, the French solar energy society, with Georges Peri their main contact.

1970 marked the end of the SES home base in Arizona, and the end of Mary Weber's tenure as administrative secretary. She was a devoted and able employee of the Society. Mary and Carl Hodges were described by a board member as the administrative backbones of the organization.

The first issue of ISES News, dated September 1971, appeared with a photograph of the building housing the new headquarters on the cover. In a report on the 1971 Annual general meeting it was noted "... All long-term indebtedness has now been eliminated and, despite the costs associated with transfer of the headquarters, there was a modest surplus in the year's operations. Currently the Society is operating within its budget."

Thus, by a combination of contributions, economies, and publication arrangements, the Society was put on a sound financial basis. It went from perilously close to bankruptcy to having adequate cash reserves, and it survived to provide essential services to what would become a growing constituency.

1.3.3   The ISES Years, 1971 to 1980

In 1970 it had been proposed that the Society change its name, in recognition of its increasingly international nature. This change was formally adopted in 1971, so what started as the Association for Applied Solar Energy (AFASE) and then became the Solar Energy Society (SES), took on its present name, the International Solar Energy Society (ISES).

Fig. 27: Frank G. Hogg (Australia), secretary-treasurer of ISES from 1970 to 1985, and editor of ISES News

The primary concerns of the officers and board in 1971 and after shifted from survival to member services, i.e., what the Society should do for its constituents. Those services were primarily publication of *Solar Energy, ISES News,* and *SunWorld* (first published in 1976 as a successor to *Sun at Work*), and the organization of biennial world congresses.

1.3.3.1   The Energy World of the 1970s —OPEC and Other Outside Influences

It is of interest to briefly review what was going on in the world that affected ISES.

Solar energy had been used in applications like growing plants, salt production, and in architecture for ages, but interest in developing broader applications had been limited by availability of technology and by economic and other social considerations. Energy from other sources (coal, petroleum, natural gas, etc.) had been for many of the world's population readily available, cheap, and convenient. There had not been much incentive to develop alternatives like solar energy.

Three sets of circumstances changed the picture in the 1970s. The first of these was the environmental movement. The second was the rise of OPEC, the Organization of Petroleum Exporting Countries. The third need that spurred interest in a particular segment of solar energy technology, PV, was the unique energy requirements of space programs.

Concern for environmental considerations received a major boost in 1961 with the publication of Rachel Carson's book *Silent Spring*. The environmental movement became an important factor in the United States with the first Earth Day in 1970. A part of this movement was interest in renewable energies—the use of which would diminish pollution and wasteful expenditures of limited natural resources. As the movement gained steam, political decisions were made with environmental considerations very much a part of the decision-making process.

In 1960, OPEC was established, and included in its membership most of the Middle East and Latin American major oil producers. Primary aims were to establish a common price for crude oil and reduce tensions among its members. It took some years before it became an effective entity, but by the early 1970s it was an economic bloc of great influence on the international energy scene.

In 1973, OPEC sharply increased the price of crude oil, Middle-East members of the organization (the most dominant members) used oil prices as a political weapon in response to United States support of Israel during the Yom Kippur war of October 1973, and in December OPEC declared an embargo of oil shipments to the United States and to the Netherlands.

The result was shortages of gasoline and a reduction of the treasured mobility of the American people. This brought the energy economy very much into the forefront of American public policy and spurred a move (one that had already started) to develop alternatives to imported petroleum. In short, more funds became available for solar energy research, development, and applications, and more people moved into the field. In other parts of the developed world, similar combinations of concerns for the stability of energy resources and for environmental considerations led to increased availability of resources for renewable energy R&D and to more people working in the field.

ISES was not the only technical organization that had interests in solar energy, but it was the major broad-based, interdisciplinary one and provided appropriate forums for discussions of solar energy technologies. As activities in the field expanded, so too did membership in ISES.

The need for long-term energy supplies for space vehicles, the obvious availability of solar energy in space, and the early development of photovoltaic processes (as shown by Bell Laboratories at the 1955 Phoenix Solar Engineering Exhibition) resulted in major R&D programs on photovoltaic processes and converters. For decades, space satellites have been powered by photovoltaics, and the technology has made tremendous strides. Terrestrial applications are developing in the early 21st century. However, organizations other than ISES have provided the primary forums for work in this area, and PV activities of ISES have been an important but not major function of the organization.

1.3.3.2   ISES in a Growth Period

These events had a profound impact on ISES. With energy costs rising and supplies threatened, interest in alternative energy sources soared. The environmental advantages of "clean" energy sources added to the push. The results were increased interest on the part of the public; increased political support for exploring and developing alternatives; and increased research, development and applications. These added up to many more people actively working in the solar energy field—and ISES was on its way.

The ISES years covered in this section, from 1971 to 1980, saw five presidents presiding over the fortunes of the society. There were three engineers (all research-oriented, but with applications as the goals), and a chemist and a biologist. All were themselves involved in solar energy research and development.

Jack Duffie took over as president (1971 – 73) from Roger Morse, as SES became ISES, and as interest in solar energy started its period of rapid growth. Duffie, a Chemical Engineer by training, established the Solar Energy Laboratory in the College of Engineering at Wisconsin, and was its director until he retired in 1988. With Bill Beckman and Sandy Klein he wrote a series of books on engineering of solar processes. He was on the SES and ISES boards for many years, and served as editor in chief of *Solar Energy* for eight years from 1985 to 1993.

In 1971 – 72, Tony Ward, of the Brace Research Institute of McGill University was vice president. In the next year there were two vice presidents, Tony Ward and George Löf.

George Löf was president for 1973 – 75. He too is a Chemical Engineer, and established the Solar Energy Applications Laboratory at Colorado State University. Under his (and his successors') direction, the laboratory was a major systems development center for solar heating and cooling of buildings. Systems were designed, built, and operated, and their performance was measured. Löf also built a solar heating system on his own residence in Boulder, Colorado in the late 1940s. Then in 1957 he and his family moved into the Denver House with its solar air heating system (which is still keeping him comfortable in 2004).

The vice presidents for 1973 – 74 were Bill Klein and M. Perrot, of France. Professor Perrot, of the Laboratoire d'Électricité et d'Heliotechnique de l'Université de Provence in Marseille, was the president of COMPLES. In 1974-75 the vice presidents were Bill Klein and Fred H. Morse (USA). Fred was then on the Mechanical Engineering faculty of the University of Maryland.

Fig. 28: W.H. Klein, ISES President 1975 – 77, welcomes Prime Minister S. M. Desai to the ISES Congress in New Delhi. Dr. A. Ram, chairman of the India national Committee on Science and Technology is in the center of the photo.

Bill Klein was the ISES President in 1975-77. Bill is a plant pathologist and was Director of the Smithsonian Radiation Biology Laboratory in Bethesda, Maryland. Educated in the USA, Klein started his career with the Smithsonian in 1951. He was associated for many years with the classical work on solar radiation measurements of C. G. Abbot and developed an international network of stations measuring solar and ultraviolet radiation. He was a long time Director of ISES, and (with lots of help from his wife Winifred) served as assistant treasurer of ISES until 1992.

Reb Datta of India and Jim Eibling, (an engineer at the Battelle Memorial Institute in Ohio, USA, were the vice presidents during Bill Klein's term as president.

R. L. Datta, of India, succeeded Bill Klein for the 1977 – 79 years. Datta was educated in India and England, with his degrees in Chemistry and Applied Chemistry. He studied separation processes at the Max Planck Institute in Germany and worked at the Central Salt and Marine Chemicals Research Institute in India. His contributions in solar energy were in salt production by solar evaporation, solar distillation, solar ponds, and space cooling. He was active in a wide variety of energy agencies, including as chairman of the All-India Solar Energy Working Group, Convener of the Energy Research Committee of CSIR (the government of India), member of the ad hoc committee of the USA Academy of Sciences for Solar Energy for Developing Countries, and others.

Reb Datta's vice presidents were Bill Charters and Fred Morse.

Fig. 29: Bill Charters, of Melbourne University (Australia), president of ISES 1979 – 81

Bill Charters was president from 1979 to 1981 and was in a sense the bridge between this chapter of the ISES history and David Mill's history of the second half of the Society's existence. He received his early education in China and Australia, followed by university degrees from England and the USA, where he earned a master's in mechanical engineering from Princeton. He has had industrial and military experience in engineering R&D and has worked in Trinidad and in Canada at the Brace Research Institute of McGill University. His academic career is at the University of Melbourne, Australia, where he was chairman of the Mechanical Engineering Department. His international activities have been legion, in Bolivia, Pakistan, France, and many other countries. He is a Fellow of the Institution of Engineers Australia. He and his research group at Melbourne have contributed in collector design, heating and cooling systems, and heat transfer problems relating to solar energy processes.

The vice presidents in 1979 – 81 were Harry Tabor and Everett Howe. Howe was in mechanical engineering at the University of California at Berkeley, worked on solar distillation, and served ISES for years as Editor of *SunWorld*.

Thus the leadership of ISES in this decade was in the hands of a series of professional people with broad experience and knowledge of solar energy processes and their applications in various kinds of economies. They presided over the Society in a period of unprecedented growth, when meetings and publications, international sections, and the Society's organization and direction were major concerns.

1.3.3.3   Memberships and Dues

In the 1960s, members numbered in the 600 to 800 range, with most from the United States, a small percent from Australia-New Zealand, and the rest from other countries. Numerous calls for members to recruit new members went out, but the pool of people with active interests in the field was limited and there was little growth. The Society itself was not able to stimulate widespread interest, and it was not until the environmental movement and the energy crises of the 1970s that membership began to grow.

When growth began in 1973 – 74, it was rapid. Total membership went from 703 in 1970 to 815 in 1973 to 4,126 in 1975 to 8,854 in 1979. More data on memberships are shown in Table 1 of the Appendix.

There were several categories of memberships, including sustaining, and collective, but the large majority of the memberships were individual or student memberships. In 1979, out of the total of 8,854, 7,646 were individual and 648 were student memberships. Annual dues for many years were $15. In 1970 the board recognized the need for increasing dues and recommended an increase to $20 per year ($10 per year for students) to the membership. This was approved in 1971. However, the publication of the journal Solar Energy was still on an irregular basis, and the increase was not implemented until 1974 when the journal appeared in a more timely fashion.

Fig. 30: Wal Read, Bill Charters, Jack Duffie and Roger Morse at CSIRO in Australia

With its financial crises behind it and with growing membership, ISES turned its attention to other kinds of problems. among them conferences, publications, the nature of the organization and how it should function, and how it could best serve members from a variety of national and economic backgrounds.

1.3.3.4   ISES Publications in the Growth Period

Publications were matters of central importance to ISES in the growth period. A major function of the Society was to facilitate communications among the membership, with the aim of making solar energy R&D as effective as possible. Publications, along with meetings, were the major means of exchange of information among members. The journal *Solar Energy* was published during the ISES years. *SunWorld*, an applications-oriented news magazine that was in a sense a successor to *Sun at Work*, started its run in 1976. The *ISES Newsletter* (also referred to as *ISES News*) first appeared in 1971 and was published into the 1980s.

1.3.3.4a   The Solar Energy Journal

Solar Energy, the centerpiece of the ISES publication program, was in 1971 a quarterly edited by Andy Drummond and produced by Pergamon Press. The transition from the old arrangements (with Chuck Scarlott as editor) took several years. Drummond had to establish working relations with Pergamon, set up the procedures for handling manuscripts, and develop a cadre of reviewers. By the time of the 1971 meeting, the "new" journal was in its second year. Publication had not yet gotten on a regular schedule, as circumstances beyond ISES control conspired to delay the publication. Pergamon moved its office from Dublin to Oxford, United Kingdom, and a major postal strike in the UK interfered with shipments of manuscripts. The journal was on track, but the transition from the old format to the new was not yet complete. In this time of transition, manuscripts were available from the 1971 Goddard meeting, and the delays were in large part due to factors other than availability of papers.

The editor's tasks were considerable, and as the journal evolved the editor-in-chief (as he is now called) needed help. Four associate editors was appointed to cover specific areas. As the frequency of publication increased and the journal covered more of the diverse topics that are treated under solar energy, more associate editors were added. (In 2004 there are thirty-four working with the Editor-in-Chief.)

Solar Energy was a quarterly, and under Drummond's guidance it published carefully reviewed papers. In late 1971 ill health forced him to give up the position as editor, and Peter Glaser took on the responsibility, a post in which he served for fourteen years. ISES was indebted to Drummond for setting high standards for the Journal, and also to his company, Eppley Laboratories, for its support of the editorial activities.

The clerical tasks were formidable when significant numbers of manuscripts were being reviewed and prepared for publication. Most of this work was done on a voluntary basis or supported by the editor's employers. It was not until 1974 that ISES was able to make a small contribution (at first $3,000 per year) to meeting these expenses.

Four issues of the journal were published in 1974, but the number of pages fell short of expectations. The publisher pointed out that proofs of two manuscripts were not returned to Pergamon in a timely manner and that those papers could not be included in that volume. The editor's best efforts could not negate this kind of delay; fortunately there were not many of them,

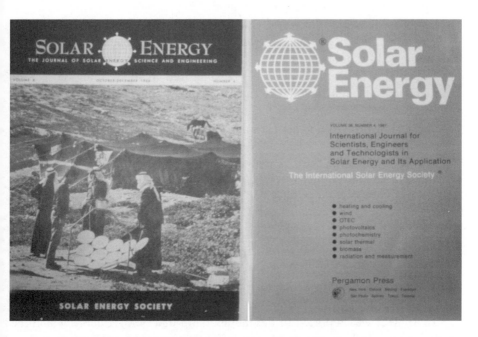

Fig. 31: New design of Solar Energy, instituted by Andy Drumond, on right.
Old cover design is on left

By 1976 the level of activity in the field had increased and the Journal appeared in six issues (380 pages) rather than four. At that time the board agreed in principle that the Society should itself publish the journal. Representations were made to Pergmon to this effect, and the result was revised agreements with Pergmon to publish the following two volumes on terms more favorable to ISES, and more agreements were to follow. In 1976, the six issues of volume 18 totalled 590 pages. The journal was on solid ground.

Growth in solar energy activities and in the supply of available mnuscripts for the Journal was resulting in excessive delays in publication of papers, and in 1978 it was agreed that publication should go to a monthly basis. *ISES News* No. 24, in June of 1978, reported the situation as follows:

In sympathy with an increase in contributed papers, the six issues of the Journal published during the year contained a total of

778 printed pages, as compared to 590 in 1976. Thanks to the dedicated work of Dr. Peter Glaser, Editor-in-Chief, ably assisted by the six Associate Editors, the high standards for which the Journal has become noted were amply maintained.

As a result of the worldwide growth in solar energy research and development activity, an increasing number of papers are being submitted for publication. On the other hand, the agreement that the Society has had with its publisher has imposed an upper limit on the size of each annual volume. In 1977 this limit was substantially relaxed, but even so, papers have been taking longer to pass through the review process and appear in print, and this has led to some dissatisfactions.

To improve this situation a new agreement has now been negotiated with the publisher, under which the Journal will become a monthly publication from the start of 1978. This in effect will double the number of printed pages per annum available to the Society, and authors are invited to take advantage of this improved facility. Due to the generous terms of the new publishing agreement, the Society should be able, at least for the present, to finance the enlarged publication without increasing members' dues.

In 1980 it was reported to the membership that *Solar Energy* was to be published regularly in issues of near uniform size and varied content. This achievement could be attributed to the editor-in-chief, his Editorial Assistant Anne Witkos, and to his associate editors. Much credit was also due to the many volunteer authors and reviewers who were major contributors to the success of the Journal.

1.3.4.4b   ISES News

The *ISES Newsletter* (with its name later shortened to *ISES News*) was designed to inform the membership of what was happening in the Society and provide some coverage of applications. It first appeared in September 1971, when the headquarters were established in Australia. For four years it appeared three times a year, with four pages, and was prepared by the secretary-treasurers, first Frank Hogg and then Wal Read. In contrast to other ISES publications, it was distributed only to members. In 1975, the frequency of publicaion was increased to four a year, and each issue was expanded to eight pages. The object then was to report to the membership what was going on in the Society, and also to report news of events outside of the organization. (At that time, *SunWorld* was still five years off in the future.)

ISES News was the means of distributing information about publications, meetings and congresses of the Society and its sections, organization of new national sections, and elections. Election materials, including biographies of candidates and ballot papers were included. Agendas for and reports of annual general meetings were included, as were budgets and auditor's reports. Thorough readings of the newsletter would result in members being well informed about the Society and its activities.

It cost more to distribute the newsletter from Australia than to produce it, so it was compact, small type was used, and it was printed on thin paper. All of this was to minimize the cost of air-mailing it to members from Melbourne three or four times a year. For a time, they were mailed in bulk to Section offices, with distribution from there to members carried out by the Sections.

1.3.4.4c   SunWorld

Fig. 32: Peter Glaser, Everett Howe, ISES vice president 1979 – 81 and editor of SunWorld, and George Löf

The *Sun at Work*, started in 1956, was an applications-oriented quarterly that also served as a newsletter. When the society's fiscal situation became perilous and economies had to be made in 1967, the *Sun at Work* was dropped (much to the dismay—understandably—of a segment of the Society that was most interested in news of applications). Replacing the *Sun at Work* was on the minds of the directors for years, and in 1975 the publications committee was exploring the possibility of producing a popular magazine-type publication having broad appeal to experimenters and individuals. Later that year, Bill Klein, then president of ISES, wrote in *ISES News*:

> And now it is our hope to round out further the activities of the Society by launching a new publication. Although as yet unamed, it is being designed to resume the function of *Sun at Work*, a magazine with more popular, less technical articles. It is our expectation that the first issue will appear in the spring of 1976, carrying reports of progress, new concepts, new installations, new applications in all aspects of solar energy and related fields around the world. Its success, as well as the success of our other undertakings, will depend upon the contributions and cooperation of our many members.

The new and more ambitious quarterly, called *SunWorld*, made its appearance as promised in 1976, with Everett Howe and Yvonne Howell as editors. In view of the very favorable response to the first issue, the board authorized that three further trial issues be prepared in order that it could reach a considered decision at its 1977 meeting on the future of the venture. From *ISES News* No. 24:

> Further issues of the new magazine *SunWorld* appeared in 1977, each fully maintaining the high standard set by the initial trial issue. The magazine has been enthusiastically received by readers everywhere, and in view of its success the Board has now agreed that it should become a permanent ISES publication.
> …As in the case of the Journal, no increase in Society dues has so far been found necessary due to the introduction of Sun World.

SunWorld was to be published for years by Pergamon Press. It was to be a staple of ISES publications for decades. It started as a quarterly, and by 1980 it had gone from four to six issues a year.

1.3.4.4d   Proceedings and Other Publications
There was an additional series of publications—proceedings of conferences—that started appearing in the mid-1970s. Once the meetings got large enough to justify the expense of their preparation (usually by obtaining camera-ready copy from authors) they appeared after each biennial meeting. Much of this was done by Pergamon Press, with ISES members serving as

editors. Also, for some meetings, preprints of papers were made available.

Thus ISES was deeply involved with publications of various sorts. As the situation evolved in the 1970s, much of this activity was done under agreements with Pergamon. There were extended debates in board meetings whether ISES itself should be its own publisher. In particular, Bill Klein and Peter Glaser advocated such a move, on the grounds that it would be an economic advantage to the Society to do so. The board in 1976 agreed to such a change, but Pergamon came back with revised terms that were too favorable to turn down. The Pergamon agreements took much of the risk out of the publications program and provided income to ISES from advertising that Pergamon was able to sell and from sales of publications to nonmembers.

In addition to the ISES publications noted above, many Sections had their own newsletters, magazines, and conference proceedings. These are noted in the Section histories.

1.3.3.5   Meetings and Congresses

ISES (and SES, AFASE) had from its inception sponsored scientific conferences. The first, those in Tucson and Phoenix, were large-scale meetings with many hundreds of attendees. Then for years, the conferences, all in the USA, attracted numbers more like 50 to 100 participants. Conferences did not show marked growth until the 1970 Melbourne meeting, when 189 registered. In 1973 ISES (in cooperation with AFEDES, the French solar energy society), met in Paris, with about 600 attendees. By 1975, the boom in interest in solar energy was at its height and the Los Angeles and Atlanta meetings had nearly 2,000 registrants.

Fig. 33: Bill Beckman, program chair for the Atlanta ISES Congress. ISES president 1985 – 87

A pattern of major conferences every second year developed. At first the plan was to hold every other conference in the USA, but it soon became evident that activities elsewhere were as vigorous as in the USA and the policy was changed to meet wherever the circumstances merited. Following Los Angeles, venues for the biennial meetings were New Delhi, Atlanta, Brighton, Perth, Montreal, etc. In addition to the ISES conferences (which have become referred to as Congresses), there have been numerous section meetings, some of which hosted the ISES annual general membership meetings that are required under Arizona law (ISES still being registered as a corporation in that state).

At Congresses, the usual pattern is for an opening session to be devoted to welcoming addresses by host notables and plenary lectures by outstanding authorities on topics of general interest. Then the scientific, engineering, and applications sessions start, with each session including as many as five or six papers on special topics. There may also be poster sessions at which authors discuss their topics—with the aid of posters—with those who come to him/her in the session hall. Throughout, there are coffee breaks, informal sessions, and other opportunities for one-on-one discussions that for many are the heart of the gatherings.

Fig. 34: Peg Bilston of the Melbourne ISES office, Winifred Klein and Bill Klein

At the New Delhi Congress in January 1978 there was an exhibit of solar equipment at the nearby National Physical laboratory of India, to which participants in the Congress were invited. As a part of the Atlanta Congress in 1979, there was an exhibition of solar devices, equipment, and publications that included ninety-five exhibitors and attracted several thousand visitors in addition to most of the 2,000 registrants. Exhibitions such as this became an integral part of subsequent ISES Congresses. (The precident was originally set by the "Sun at Work" exhibition at the 1955 conference in Phoenix).

Thus ISES (and its sections) provided many opportunities for its members to get together, present their new work, and engage in the all-important activities of informal give-and-take on technical matters that only personal contacts can provide. Workers in the field got to know their counterparts in other countries and in related solar energy fields.

At the 1971 meeting at NASA Goddard, W. R. Cherry, the meeting chairman, arranged for those at the banquet to be treated to a very special event. Dr. Charles G. Abbot, who was then a lively 99 years of age and had just received another patent on a solar engine, made a few remarks and then sang a song. His was a remarkable career, with his first publication on solar energy measurements appearing before 1900. It was a unique and special opportunity for ISES members to see and hear one of the true pioneers in solar energy.

1.3.3.6   Awards

By the time of the Los Angeles meeting in 1975, the Society was on sufficiently firm grounds that it could turn its attention to honoring the few who had made special contributions to the advancement of solar energy or the Society. The first award, the Farrington Daniels Award, was named in honor of the man who inspired the formation of the organization and who did so much to keep the Society alive during the crisis years.

> The award is conferred every two years for outstanding contributions in science, technology, or engineering of solar energy applications leading toward ameliorating the conditions of humanity, and for furthering this cause through the International Solar Energy Society.

It is customary for the award recipient to deliver an address to the Congress, on a topic of his/her own choosing. The first Daniels award was presented to Professor Hoyt Hottel at the Los Angeles meeting for his pioneering work on analysis of solar collectors—work that underlies all thermal applications of solar energy. His address was on a simplified model for atmospheric transmission of solar energy.

The second Daniels award went to Dr. Valintin Baum of the USSR and was presented at the New Delhi Congress in 1977. Professor Felix Trombe was the third recipient, at the 1979 Congress in Atlanta.

Fig. 35: Valintin Baum (USSR) receives the Daniels Award at the New Delhi Congress, 1978. The award was presented by ISES President R. L. Datta, with George Löf assisting

The second category of award of ISES, established in 1979, was to recognize outstanding papers published in Solar Energy. It was established through a gift to the Society from G. O. G. Löf and J. A. Duffie, with winning papers to be selected by the editors of the journal and the ISES board. The first of these awards was made in 1981.

1.3.3.7   Other Issues

ISES had made a major transition from the original organization (AFASE) to the more usual scientific and technical society (SES and ISES). There was one more major change to be made. ISES was an organization of individual members (many of whom were also members of Sections). An alternative structure, one in which ISES would become a federation of sections, was first noted in the letter to the membership from Morse and Duffie at the time of the move of headquarters to Australia. The idea was again brought forth in the November 1972 issue of ISES News. In 1977, the question of reorganization was again raised in ISES News, and a committee under the chairmanship of F. H. Morse was exploring the question. Two possibilities were suggested:[33]

---

[33] Duffie, J. A., guest editorial "ISES in the Future," ISES News, No. 19 (March 1977)

A first alternative is to retain the present basic structure of the Society, but elect members of the Board of Directors by Sections, rather than at-large. Members not affiliated with a Section would constitute a separate group analogous to a Section for purposes of electing Board members. The Board might then elect officers from its membership. ...

A second alternative would be to transform ISES into a federation of more independent national or regional societies, each carrying out its own activities and programs with relatively few constraints imposed by a constitution and by-laws of the federation. In this case individuals would be members of the constituent societies rather than of the federation. ... Constituent society memberships in a federation would carry with it the obligation to support the federation and make possible its international activities.

By 1977 there were ten ISES sections in various stages of development, some with active programs and some in their formative years: Australia-New Zealand, Holland, United Kingdom, United States, Southern Africa, Irish, India, Italian, Japanese, and German. There was also an "unattached" Section.

Practical problems arose out of the international nature of ISES. The abilities of sections to contribute a portion of membership fees to ISES varied widely. Some sections withheld 15 percent of dues for their local operations, and some withheld larger portions—and were still subsidized in their activities by individual members.

Funds were coming into the organizations from a variety of countries. The headquarters were in Australia, and many of the functions were being carried out in the USA. The relative value of currencies fluctuated, and it is costly to transfer funds from one currency to another. To minimize the adverse effects of these problems on the Society's finances and to make dealing with Pergamon easier (their offices in New York were handling much of the Society's publications programs), W. H. Klein was appointed assistant treasurer in 1977. In effect, a second treasury was established in the USA, reporting to the secretary-treasurer in Australia, and operations were set up to minimize currency conversions and maximize the ease with which the Society's business could be conducted. Winifred Klein (Mrs. W. H. Klein) did much of the work in running the assistant treasurer office, attended board and membership meetings, and was always a source of useful current information.

Fig. 36: The Solar Energy Society Directors meet at NASA Goddard in 1971

1.3.3.8   The Society Loses Leaders

In the early 1970s, the Society lost several outstanding members. Farrington Daniels, who had played such a key role in keeping the Society alive during the crisis years and who served as its first elected president, died in June 1972. Andrew Drummond, the first Editor-in-Chief of the new Solar Energy, who set the standards for future editors, died in August 1972. Harold Haywood, a participant in the first Arizona meetings and a director of the Society, died in December 1971. Matthew Thekaekara was a distinguished physicist who made substantial contributions to the measurement and spectral distribution of solar radiation; he died in 1977. Walter Bimson, who died in 1980, was one of the founders of AFASE and was an active participant in Society affairs throughout the first twenty-five years of its existence. He was an honorary director until his death, and it was through his intervention that the Valley National Bank forgave the Society's debts to the bank.

1.4   Authors' Notes and Acknowledgments

The authors have relied on three major sources of information in preparing this history.

The Daniels archives at the University of Wisconsin have been a major source for anything involving Daniels; they are extensive and very well organized, and it has been possible for one of us (J. A. D.) to go into these records.

Arizona State University at Tempe maintains the AFASE archives and has extensive collections for the years before Society headquarters moved to Australia. James Allen, at the Archives and Special Collections of the Architectural and Environmental Library, has been most helpful in finding, copying, and sending to the authors a variety of files on AFASE. (Neither of the authors has been able to visit ASU to use the collections, so Mr. Allen's assistance has been invaluable.)

ISES headquarters in Freiburg has also been of substantial assistance in providing copies of publications and other materials. Christine Hornstein has been most helpful. She has searched the files at headquarters in Freiburg and found for us many of the photographs appearing in this chapter.

A fourth source has been our own files and memories. Both of us participated in the 1955 Phoenix and Tucson meetings and have been active in Society affairs most of the time since.

We are also glad to acknowledge the help of George Löf, Peter Glaser, Winifred and Bill Klein, Bill Charters, and Morton Prince. Neil Duffie and Peter Schmitz helped us with the intricacies of Word.

1.5   Other Histories of ISES

Several other histories of the International Solar Energy Society have been written. They are less detailed, but each contains insights and information that is unique.

Strum, Harvey, "The Association for Applied Solar Energy/Solar Energy Society, 1964 – 1970. "*Technology and Culture* 1985; 26: 571.

Duffie, J. A., "An Early History of ISES." *SunWorld* 1999 June; 23 (2): 9.

Howe, E. D., "IES Roots." *SunWorld* 1979; 3 (2): 32.

Yellott, J. I., paper presented at the Atlanta ISES Congress (1979). "The International Solar Energy Society (ISES)." (This paper was part of a set entitled "Historical Notes." Others in the set were very brief histories of Sections.) See also Yellott, J. I.,) "Twenty Five Years Later." *ISES News* 1980 Sept; 33.

Postscript

The authors prepared a Postscript to this history of the first twenty-five years, but it seemed more appropriate that it cover the entire fifty-year history of the Society. Thus at this point the reader is referred to the final section of David Mill's history of the second twenty five years for a Postscript authored by all three of us—a look in retrospect at what the Society was and what it has accomplished.

Appendix

Table 1 shows membership data by years. The early data come from minutes of board of directors meetings or correspondence. Data for the years 1974 and after were compiled by the secretary-treasurer (F. G. Hogg or W. R. Read) and were reported each year in *ISES News*. Note that an additional data point would be for 1955, when the membership of the board of directors, 16, was also the membership of the society.

Table 1. Membership

Date	Individual	Student	Group	Total
AFASE				
5/56	138		19	157
9/57				864
12/61				663
SES				
1/64				787
10/65				649
1970				703
ISES				
4/73				815
4/74				1,808
12/74	1,959	160	352	2,471
12/75	3,321	291	514	4,126
12/76	4,317	402	539	5,258
12/77	6,029	544	654	7,227
12/78	6,747	550	636	7,933
12/79	7,646	648	560	8,854

The Officers and Staff

Table 2, adapted from Yellott (1979) indicates the officers of the society for the first twenty-five years. Some explanation helps to appreciate what occurred. John Yellott was the half-time executive secretary of AFASE, at a salary of $15,000 per year, with the balance of his time at the Stanford Research Insitute (SRI). He resigned in 1958 and E. Lee McLean was employed to fill the position. McLean stayed as executive vice president until a major reorganization at the end of 1959, when AFASE affiliated with Arizona State University. (At that time, Jean Jensen, the librarian and editor, also resigned.) Effective at the beginning of 1960, Jan Oostermeier resigned as president (while continuing as vice president), and Hal Walmsley was employed as president. (Walmsley was a retired Brigadier General, U. S. Army Chemical Corps.) These arrangements persisted for four years, until the restructuring of the organization in 1964.

Table 2. Officers of the Society

Year	President	Vice President	Secretary or Secretary-Trreasurer	Executive Officer or Assist. Treasurer
AFASE				
1955	H. Sargent	W. R. Bimson	F. L. Snell	
1956	J. Oostermeier	W. T. Lucking	J. I. Yellott	
1957	J. Oostermeier	W. T. Lucking		J. I. Yellott
1958	J. Oostermeier	W. T. Lucking		J. I. Yellott (to 6/58) E. L. McLean (6/58)
1959	J. Oostermeier	W. T. Lucking H. Sargent	F. L. Snell (Sec'y)	E. L. McLean
1960	H. Walmsley	J. Oostermeier W. T. Lucking H. Sargent	F. L. Snell	
1961	H. Walmsley	J. Oostermeier W. T. Lucking H. Sargent	F. L. Snell	
1962	H. Walmsley	J. Oostermeier W. T. Lucking H. Sargent	F. L. Snell	
1963	H. Walmsley	J. Oostermeier W. T. Lucking H. Sargent	F. L. Snell	

Table 2 Continued

Year	President	Vice President	Secretary or Secretary-Trreasurer	Executive Officer or Assist. Treasurer
SES				
1964-65	F. Daniels	R. Krause (to 3/64) W. B. Gibson		H. Walmsley
1965-66	F. Daniels	W. B. Gibson		H. Walmsley (to 5/65) F. E. Edlin (9/65)
1966-67	F. Daniels	W. B. Gibson		F. E. Edlin
1967-68	P. E. Glaser	R. N. Morse		F. E. Edlin
1968-69	P. E. Glaser	R. N. Morse	C. N. Hodges	
1969-70	R. N. Morse	J. A. Duffie	C. N. Hodges (to 2/70)	
1970-71	R. N. Morse	J. A. Duffie.	F. G. Hogg	
ISES				
1971-72	J. A. Duffie	G. T. Ward	F. G. Hogg	
1972-73	J. A. Duffie	G. T. Ward G. O. G. Löf	F. G. Hogg	
1973-74	G. O. G. Löf	W. H. Klein M. Perrot	F. G. Hogg	
1974-75	G. O. G. Löf	W. H. Klein F. H. Morse	F. G. Hogg	
1975-76	W. H. Klein	R. L. Datta J. A. Eibling	F. G. Hogg	
1976-77	W. H. Klein	R. L. Datta J. A. Eibling	F. G. Hogg	
1977-78	R. L. Datta	W. W. S. Charters F. H. Morse	F. G. Hogg	W. H. Klein (asst. treas.)
1978-79	R. L. Datta	W. W. S. Charters F. H. Morse	F. G. Hogg	W. H. Klein
1979-80	W.W.S. Charters	E. D. Howe H. Tabor	F. G. Hogg	W. H. Klein

Table 3. shows a list of meetings and Congresses of the Society The data on attendance are incomplete, as it was not until publication of ISES News began that regular reporting of this information occurred.

In addition to these meetings, AFASE organized a Junior Solar Symposium in March 1956, where students aged 12 to 18 displayed the results of their ingenuity in designing and building solar furnaces, cookers, water heaters, stills, and other devices.

Table 3. Meetings and Congresses

Year, Place	The Meeting
AFASE	
1955, Tucson AZ	Conference on the Use of Solar Energy
	Approx 500 registrants, 93 papers
1955, Phoenix AZ	World Symposium on Applied Solar Energy
	900 registrants
	Sun at Work Exhibition; 29,000 visitors
1957, Phoenix	Solar Furnace Symposium
	Approx 200 registrants, 15 papers.
1959, New York, NY	First Meeting of AFASE Advisory Council
	Sponsors: AFASE, SRI and New York University
	Approx 130 in attendance
SES	
1965, Phoenix, AZ	Annual Meeting of SES
	Approx 50 papers, 110 in attendance
1966, Boston, MA	Second Annual Solar Energy Society Conf.
	Approx 43 papers
1967, Tempe, AZ	Industrial Aspects of Solar Energy
	General Chair: P. E. Glaser
	Approx 100 in attendance, 40 papers
1968, Palo Alto, CA	4th Annual meeting of SES
	General Chair: W. B. Gibson
1970, Melbourne, Australia	1970 International Solar Energy Society Conference
	General Chair: R. N. Morse; Conf. Organizer: F. G. Hogg
	Approx 190 in attendance; 62 papers
ISES	
1971, Greenbelt, MD	Goddard Space Flight Center
	General Chair: W. R. Cherry
	180 in attendance, 40 papers
1973, Paris, France	Theme: The Sun in the Service of Mankind
	Organized jointly with AFEDES and COMPLES
	General Chair: P. Auger
	Approx. 600 registrants, 300 papers, 60 countries represented
1975, Los Angeles, CA	Theme: Solar Use Now; a Resource for People
	General Chair: E. L. Ralph; Program Chair: J. A. Duffie
	Nearly 2,000 registrants, 280 papers.
	Daniels Award to H. C. Hottel
1977, New Delhi, India (January 1978)	Theme: Mankind's Future Source of Energy
	Secretary: J. Gururaja, Program Chair: F. de Winter
	1,100 registrants, 342 papers
	Daniels Award to V. A. Baum
1979, Atlanta, GA	Theme: Silver Jubilee Congress
	General Chair: W. Shropshire, Program Chair: W. A. Beckman
	2,000 registrants, 430 papers
	Daniels Award to F. Trombe

Table 4 lists Sections of the Society and the approximate year in which each was established. The information is from notes on section histories presented at the Atlanta ISES Congress in 1979.

Table 4.   Sections and Year of Establishment

Section	Year
Australia - New Zealand	1962
Chile	1963
Italy	1964
India	1967
American	1970
Japanese	1973
United Kingdom	1973
South Africa	1974
Dutch	1975
Irish	1976
Scandinavian	1976
Arab	1977
Belgian	1977
German	1977

Chapter 2
Argentina Solar Energy Society 1974 – 1980

by
Graciela Lesino
INENCO
Universidad Nacional de Salta-Conicet
lesino@inenco.net

Abstract

The Argentina section of ISES was created in 1992. Most of its members are also members of the Asociación Argentina de Energías Renovables y Ambiente. This society was founded in 1974 under the name of Asociación Argentina de Energía Solar, ASADES. The name of the society was changed to its present name in 1997 to include a broader scope of subjects, but the acronym has been kept to ensure continuity and is spreading widely among the renewable energy community aided by their familiarity with its acronym, ASADES.

2.1   Introduction

The first works on applications of solar energy started in Argentina in 1970 (Moragues, 1976). In 1974 UNESCO and the Comisión Nacional de Estudios Geoheliofísicos (CNEGH, later CNIE), National Commission for Geoheliophysics Studies, organized a workshop for young astronomers and scientists on Solar Physics, in the Observatorio Nacional de Física Cósmica (Cosmic Physics Observatory) in the city of San Miguel, province of Buenos Aires. During that workshop a foundational document was drafted and signed by 68 of the seminar participants (Fig.1). It reads, in English translation, "... the undersigned, convinced that the study and application of Solar Energy constitutes an essential basis for the economic and social advancement of the nation and understanding the need for creating an association on a national level for all people involved in teaching, research, and implementation of Solar Energy, unanimously agree on creating the Asociación Argentina de Energía Solar (ASADES) with the following aims:

- To encourage the study and development of science and technology related to peaceful applications of Solar Energy
- To guide and promote research to find solutions for the energy problems of Argentina
- To optimize the use of all resources, human, technical and industrial in Argentina
- To bring together all research groups in the country through co-operation and exchange
- To promote and encourage education in Solar Energy
- To coordinate and distribute all information on Solar Energy. ..."

2.2   Organization

A provisional committee integrated by Jorge Guerrero, Jaime Moragues Jorge Rieznick, and Jorge Serrano was in charge of obtaining broader consent and membership, drafting the by-laws of the society, obtaining a small financial support from members, and establishing the date for a General Constituent Meeting. The first meeting of ASADES, with 23 members, took place in the Observatory, in San Miguel, in November 1974. Fig.1 shows the Foundational Act. ASADES was formally constituted during the First Latin-American Congress in Solar Energy, in April 1975. The first president elected was Dr. Jaime Moragues. Fig.2 shows participants in the Congress.

That same year the Secretaría de Ciencia y Técnica de la Nación

(SECYT) organized a meeting in Vaquerías, Province of Córdoba, to set the bases for a National Program (von Wuthenau, 1977).

Acta Fundacional de la ASADES

En la Ciudad de San Miguel, provincia de Buenos Aires, a los tres días del mes de junio de 1974 y en ocasión de realizarse la Escuela UNESCO-IAU y CNEGH para jóvenes astrónomos y científicos latinoamericanos en el área de la Física Solar, en el Observatorio Nacional de Física Cósmica, los abajo firmantes, convencidos de que el estudio y aplicación de la Energía Solar constituye una base indispensable para el progreso económico y social del país, y comprendiendo la necesidad de crear una entidad a nivel nacional que agrupe a todas las personas vinculadas al campo de la enseñanza, investigación y aplicación de la Energía Solar, acuerdan por unanimidad la creación de la Asociación Argentina de Energía Solar (ASADES), con los siguientes propósitos:

1. Alentar el estudio y desarrollo de la ciencia y la tecnología relacionados con la aplicación pacífica de la Energía Solar.
2. Orientar y propiciar las investigaciones hacia la solución de reclamos energéticos en la Argentina.
3. Procurar el aprovechamiento de los recursos técnicos, humanos e industriales existentes en la Argentina.
4. Fomentar la integración de los distintos grupos del país a través de programas coordinados y/o conjuntos.
5. Promover y estimular la educación en el campo de la Energía Solar.
6. Coordinar y distribuir toda información relacionada con la Energía Solar.

Se designa una comisión provisoria integrada por: Jorge Guerrero, Jaime A. Moragues, Jorge Rieznik y Jorge Serrano, encargada de:

1. Difundir y recurrir adhesiones a esta carta de Creación, a nivel nacional.

2. Realizar un censo de las personas o grupos de trabajo en la materia.
3. Requerir la contribución de $ 10,00 (pesos diez) a los abajo firmantes para cubrir los gastos administrativos que demande esta gestión.
4. Elaborar un proyecto de Estatuto.
5. Establecer la fecha y lugar de la Asamblea General Constitutiva de esta Asociación.

Lista de Socios

1. ARGUELLO, Carlos Oscar Felipe
2. CORBELLA, Oscar
3. CRIVELLI, Ernesto Santino
4. DIAZ, Mario
5. FERNANDEZ SARMIENTO, Norberto G.
6. GARIBOTTI, Carlos R.
7. GRINSTEIN, Fernando
8. GUERRERO, Jorge Luis
9. MORAGUES, Jaime
10. PEÑA, Noemí
11. PIACENTINI, Rubén
12. RAPALLINI, Alfredo Tomás
13. RIEZNIK, Jorge
14. SCHEUER, Walter
15. SERRANO, Jorge
16. ALANIS, Elvio
17. ALBERO, Miguel
18. ALBISU, José Antonio
19. ARIS, Hugo
20. AUCIELLO, Orlando
21. BARAGIOLA, Raul Antonio
22. BARBARROLA, Ricardo R.
23. BARRAL, Raúl Héctor
24. BARROSO, Eduardo W.
25. BAZTERRICA, Carlos E.
26. BIANCHI, Juan Carlos
27. BRAGAGNOLO, Julio A.
28. BROSENS, Pablo Renato
29. BRUNE VIGNOLA, Aníbal
30. BUGNA, Luis
31. CARDONA, Alberto F.
32. CARDOSO, Juana María
33. CASELLA, Jorge
34. DE GIACOMI, Atilio
35. DE LUCA, Jorge Gustavo

36. DIAZ DORADO, Diego
37. DI BERNARDO, Elio Ricardo
38. FABRIS, Aldo
39. FASULO, Amílcar
40. FOLLARI, Jorge Alberto
41. FIORE, Antonio
42. GARCIA, Norberto Omar
43. GARCIA PULO, Edgardo R.
44. GASPAR, Roberto
45. GUTIERREZ, Juan Alberto
46. JAOAND, Alfredo
47. KRAFT, Siegfrido
48. MARONE, Víctor Jorge
49. OBIOL, Elía Elvira
50. ODICINO, Luis Antonio
51. OVEJERO, Roberto
52. PADILLA, Evaristo
53. PARFAIT, María Cristina
54. PEREZ DE ALBENIZ, Marta
55. PONCE, Víctor Hugo
56. RABBAT, José Alberto
57. RAMOS, Edmundo D.
58. REGGINI, Horacio
59. GUZMAN S. Susana
60. SARAVIA, Luis
61. SILVA, Néstor Homero
62. SOUTO, Jorge A.
63. TACCHI, Victorio
64. TEDESCHI, Enrico
65. WOISZKO, María Inés
66. ZABALA, Juan Elías
67. GAGGIOLI, Néstor Gustavo
68. FRADE VARELA, Cándido

Fig. 1: Minutes and foundational document of ASADES

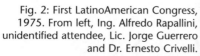

Fig. 2: First LatinoAmerican Congress, 1975. From left, Ing. Alfredo Rapallini, unidentified attendee, Lic. Jorge Guerrero and Dr. Ernesto Crivelli.

The group of researchers present established a plan for collaboration, distributing the different lines of work among the participants to avoid duplication of efforts but recognizing that areas such as bioclimatic architecture, drying, etc., required an analysis tailored to the various climatic conditions in the country. This organization has continued to the present. The National Program started in 1977, later became a subprogram in the area of natural resources and was discontinued in 1996. In fact, all National Programs were discontinued then and were substituted for by a five-year programming system steered by a committee of six Ministers (Lesino and Saravia, 1998).

The annual meetings of ASADES started in 1975 in Vaquerías and have continued up to now, being held in different cities where research groups existed. The XXVII Meeting will take place in 2004, in La Plata, province of Buenos Aires. The number of attendees was 23 in 1975, 112 in 1977, and 159 in 1980. The proceedings of all the Meetings have been published, digitally (in CD and on paper) since 2001, and previous ones are in process of digitization. The number of papers presented in the meetings grew from 30 in 1976 to 60 in 1980, but those published were around 25.

The topics discussed were:

- Solar drying of fruits, vegetables, tobacco, and grains
- Flat collectors
- Solar ponds, convective layers, electricity generation
- Climate and radiation
- Bioclimatic architecture
- Water distillation
- Concentrating collectors (CPC and others)
- Selective surfaces
- Solar cells
- Simulation

2.3   The Activities

The activity started with a great momentum, powered by the 1973 crisis, reasonable funding, and a group of scientists and engineers deeply involved in renewable energy dissemination. To have an idea of what they believed and thought at that time, I include some parts of a letter from Dr. Moragues, first president of ASADES:

2.4   The Reasoning

"It was 1974 and many of us were worried by the issues set up by The Club of Rome in 1972 (and their document *The limits of growth*). Great emphasis was put on the apparent oil crisis, the finiteness of natural (energy) resources, and the demographic explosion. We looked anxiously for energy alternatives to mitigate the announced crisis. In that context, the press reported that CNEGH had organized a course on 'Helioenergetics,' sponsored by UNESCO and IAU and to be held in the Observatorio, in San Miguel. The lecturers were Dr. Georges Peri from France, Dr. J. Boehm from Germany, and Lic. Jorge Guerrero, an Argentinian who had studied solar energy in the Soviet Union and who conducted a research group in the CNEGH. So we attended the course, a large group of professionals from different institutions and with different orientations, some with experience in solar energy, but all enormously motivated to learn how to harness this renewable energy that would allow humanity to overcome the impending crisis."

During the course, Dr. Peri suggested that we should do as the French in AFEDES (Association Française pour l'Étude et le Développement des Applications de l'Énergie Solaire) and join our forces and cooperate with the research groups working on the subject, organizing us at a national level. The idea was enthusiastically accepted, and a provisional committee was appointed.

Two issues were discussed and approved, and they have very probably been the reason for the survival of ASADES for almost thirty years, in spite of the terrible crisis the nation has gone through. The society should not have formal conferences but working meetings where the work done during the previous year would be discussed and evaluated by all participants, to promote the dissemination of ideas and projects, no matter the degree of advancement attained. Second, the meetings should take place every year in a different city or province, provided there was an active group working on the subject there.

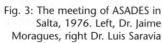

Fig. 3: The meeting of ASADES in
Salta, 1976. Left, Dr. Jaime
Moragues, right Dr. Luis Saravia

Cooperation and coordination also have been fundamental elements for
the survival of ASADES. Figs. 3 and 4 show participants in the II and III
Annual Meetings of ASADES in 1976 and 1977.
The members of the board of directors were:

1975 – 1977   Dr. Moragues, Arch. Ricardo Serrano and Ing. Alfredo
               Rapallini
1977 – 1979   Dr. Moragues, Ing. Alfredo Rapallini and Dr. Walter Scheuer
1979 – 1981   Ing. Alfredo Rapallini, Ing. Mónica García and Arch. Manuel
               Net

Fig. 4: III Meeting of ASADES
hosted by LAHV, Mendoza, 1977

The meetings were planned by ad-hoc organizing committees and an editorial board was in charge of publishing the proceedings.

2.5.   Acronyms

ASADES   Asociación Argentina de Energía Solar, afterwards, Asociación
          Argentina de Energías Renovables y Ambiente

CNEA   Comisión Nacional de Energía Atómica. National Atomic Energy
          Commission

CNEGH   Comisión Nacional de Estudios Geoheliofísicos. National Geoheliophysical Studies Commission

CNIE   Comisión Nacional de Investigaciones Espaciales, previously GNEGH. National Space Research Commission

CONICET Consejo Nacional de Investigaciones Científicas y Técnicas. National Science and Technology Research Council

CRICYT   Centro Regional de Investigaciones en Ciencia y Tecnología, CONICET, Mendoza. Science and Technology Research Regional Center

INENCO   Instituto de Investigación en Energías No Convencionales, UNSA-CONICET. Non-Conventional Energies Research Institute

LAHV   Laboratorio de Ambiente Humano y Vivienda. Human Environment and Housing Laboratory

SECYT   Secretaría de Ciencia y Técnica de la Nación. State Science and Technology Secretary

UNSA   Universidad Nacional de Salta

Acknowledgements

I want to thank all the colleagues and friends who contributed to this chapter with information, photos, and memories, very specially Dr. Jaime B. Moragues and Dr. Luis R. Saravia.

2.6.   References

Moragues, J. (1976). Discurso Inaugural. *Actas de la 2a. Reunión de Trabajo de la ASADES*, V-VI.

Lesino, G., y Saravia L., Solar Energy In Argentina: Past, Present and Future Activities, *Proceedings of SOLAR 98*, ASES, New Mexico, USA, 15-20.

Von Wuthenau, G. (1977) Planificación en Ciencia y Tecnología. Caso: Plan Nacional de Energía Solar, *Actas de la 3a. Reunión de Trabajo de ASADES*, 1-8.

Chapter 3

ASES

American Section of ISES

By
Karl W. Böer
Distinguished Professor of Physics and Solar Energy, Emeritus
University of Delaware
Newark, DE 19716
e-mail: solpax@aol.com

Abstract

The American Section of ISES was formed and named first when the head-quarters of ISES moved to Australia in 1970. The Section was operated from the desk of Bill and Winifred Klein at the Smithsonian Radiation Biology Laboratory, with Chairman Roger Morse, followed by Jack Duffie, George Löf, and Bill Klein, between 1970 and 1977. The American Section elected its own chairs, starting in 1971 with Bill Cherry, Jim Eibling, and Walter Shropshire during the formative years to 1975. In 1976 under the Chairmanship of Karl Böer, the ASES office was moved to Florida with a full-time director, and the Section was incorporated in Florida as the International Solar Energy Society, American Section Inc., later referred to as the American Section of ISES (AS of ISES). The Society was then defined as a technical society with technical divisions in the different solar energy fields. The service of lay-people was delegated to local chapters. A publications office was created and housed at the University of Delaware, with the first set of Proceedings for the Winnipeg Conference produced there, generating a modest income for the society. In 1978 the ASES Office was moved to Killeen, Texas, and in 1982 to its present location in Boulder, Colorado. Under chairmanship of Frank deWinter in 1978 and of Doug Balcomb from 1979 to 1980 the Society gained further attention and more visibility in Washington, DC. The membership increased from 703 in 1970 to over 5,000 in 1980; the budget increased from about $5,000 in 1970 to over $100,000 in 1980. The American Section was fiscally on solid footing, and most of its members were also members of ISES.

3.1   Introduction

Most of the solar activities of ISES in the years before 1970 were taking place at national conferences in the United States. National Section meetings were held in Tucson, Arizona in 1955, in Phoenix, Arizona in 1955 and 1957, at the New York University in 1963, again in Phoenix in 1965, in Boston, Massachusetts in 1966, in Tempe, Arizona in 1967, and in Palo Alto, California in 1968. The first International Solar Energy Congress was organized in Melbourne, Australia in 1970, organized by Frank Hogg, with R. N. Morse as the general chairman. From there on out, ISES became a truly international society.

The Society's financial basis was in dire need of help. Staff personnel were cut drastically and a bank loan was taken to help bridge the gap until more income was expected. Three national Sections were created, (Australia/New Zealand, Chile, and Italy) but did not bring much needed income to ISES' headquarters. There were substantial doubts in 1970 whether the Society could survive. At this time, and at the Melbourne meeting, the decision was made to move the headquarters to Australia, with Frank Hogg as the secretary-treasurer. The move was considered to be in the best interest of the Society from operational and financial points of view. The move was made in the summer of 1970.

At the same time, a United States Section of the Society was organized, and on July 1, 1970, its affairs were handled by Bill Klein as secretary-treasurer, and his office was operated by his wife Winifred Klein, without pay, as volunteers (Fig. 1). This also marked the end of the home office of ISES in Arizona.

Fig. 1: Winifred and Bill Klein with Peg Bilston (on the left) from the Melbourne office

It was the start of the American Section of ISES. Its first annual meeting was held at NASA Goddard in Maryland (1971), with Bill Cherry as chairman. The following year's (1972) meeting was held in Montreal, with Tony Ward as chair. In 1973 the first joint meeting of ISES and its national chapters took place in Paris (1973), organized by the French solar energy society (AFEDES) under Georges Peri. It was voted that ISES would conduct its international conferences (later referred to as Congresses) every second year, with the national Sections meeting every year, and joining with ISES in a combined meeting whenever it was held in their respective country.

The national Sections were expected to operate in close relationship with ISES and to each have a substantial number of its members also as members of ISES. This was, to a large extent true for the American Section and, initially, also true for many of the other Sections. Later, a minimum number of 20 joint members were required to qualify as a National Section of ISES. A list of their names was to be sent with an official application form to ISES headquarters for official approval. This, however was unnecessary for AS of ISES since they originated at the beginning from ISES and were by far its strongest National Section.

3.2   Development of the American Section of ISES

3.2.1   William R. Cherry Chairmanship

William R. (Bill) Cherry (Fig. 2) had worked at the U.S. Signal Corps in 1954 when the modern solar cell was invented and later was used to power the first US satellite. He then became the leading photovoltaic scientist at the NASA Goddard Space Center and helped shape the solar cell program for space satellites. He recognized early that photovoltaic panels should be used for large-scale terrestrial application. In 1972 he became one of the principals in the NSF/NASA Solar Energy Panel Project. He co-chaired, together with Lloyd Herwig, the White House Office of Science and Technology panel to explore solar energy as a national resource and developed the panel's groundbreaking report "Solar Energy as a National Energy Resource." He then moved to ERDA and became the liaison officer between ERDA and SERI until his untimely death in 1979.

Fig. 2: Bill Cherry

Bill Cherry was elected chairman of the American Section of ISES in 1971 and served as its chairman until 1973.

Publications sponsored and edited by ISES at that time were the Journal of Solar Energy, with Dr. Peter Glaser as the first editor-in-chief, published under contract with Pergamon Press, and the Section's newsletter, with Everett Howe as editor. This newsletter was intended to be returned to a "Sun at Work" type of publication that was published earlier by ISES. It was issued by the American Section twice a year as Solar News and Views.

The total income of the American Section from July 1970 to December 1972 was $6,496.22 including an NSF Grant of $5,100, with expenditures of $5,168.34, including $5,054 for travel assistance to the annual conference. The total of office expenses was a mere $62.94 during the entire 18 months, for stamps, letterheads, paper and forms, and $50 for clerical fees.

In the following year (from January 1 to September 24, 1973) the income increased to $11,311.83, including a grant from NSF of $10,000, while the expenses were $1,211.85 for office expenses (mostly for a membership drive) and $10,000 for the printing of the Paris Conference Proceedings.

Steve Baer proposed the creation of local chapters with members paying a nominal fee of "less than $5," and they would not have to be a member of

ISES. Harold Hay proposed the restructuring of the Society into committees in the fields of the environment, meteorology and hydrology, biology and medicine, chemistry, physics, engineering, commerce, and public relations. Each of these Committees was to be enacted when requested by at least 10 members. A questionnaire was consequently sent to all members with a more detailed and appropriate listing, but the results were inconclusive and did not result in any board action.

The membership in the American Section of ISES increased from 240 in January 1971, to 309 in January 1972, to 411 in January 1973, and to 560 in June 1974.

3.2.2   James A. Eibling Chairmanship

Fig. 3: James A. Eibling

Jim Eibling (Fig. 3) became president of ASES in January 1974. He got his B.M.E at Ohio State University and later became professor of architecture at the Arizona State University. He was chief of the Thermal Division at Battelle, and manager of the Thermal Energy Programs Office. He is internationally recognized as a pioneer in solar energy and conducted solar research since the early 50's. He is the author of fifty technical papers. He is past chairman of the ASME Solar Applied Energy Division (1962–65) and vice president of ISES. He was a member of the National Bureau of Science advisory panel on solar heating and cooling systems and participated in the US/USSR and U.S./Japan solar exchange programs. His research activities covered a wide range of solar activities, from solar heating and cooling to desalination to thermal storage, Stirling engines, a rotary vane solar heat pump, and the impact of photovoltaics on central power stations.

During his tenure as president there were five established membership categories in the American Section:

Individual	at $15
Supportive	at $50
Corporate	at $100
Student	at $10, and
Ladies	at no charge

It was suggested to raise the charge for individuals by $5 to pay for the local office; the rest would go to ISES. A major membership drive was started to substantially increase the membership in the Society, resulting in a membership total of 815 at the end of 1974.

A committee suggested a number of suitable locations as headquarters for the American Section of ISES including AIAA, New York, Arizona State University, and Argonne National Laboratory. Other locations were mentioned as alternatives. ISES headquarters was informed that the American Section of ISES intended to form a separate headquarters in the USA.

The printing of three or more issues of *Solar News and Views* was approved. A closer tie to *"Sun at Work"* was encouraged.

The Charles G. Abbot (Fig. 4) Award was established as the major award of the American Section.

Fig. 4: Charles Greeley Abbot in front of his solar trough collector

3.2.3   Walter Shropshire Jr. Chairmanship

Walter Shropshire, a biophysicist with a PhD in plant physiology/photo-biology; a former piano teacher, creative in music, an ordained Methodist minister; and an ardent tennis player was chairman of the American Section during the calendar year 1975.

At the board meeting at the Museum of History and Technology of the Smithsonian Institution in Washington, D.C. on January 13, the creation of local chapters of the American Section of ISES was approved for such chapters that had at least 20 members, with chairman and members being associate members of the American Section. The by-laws of the chapters were to be approved by the ASES board, and $5 per member of their membership dues had to be transferred to AS of ISES.

The first chapters of the American Section were represented at the Los Angeles board meeting at U.C.L.A. on July 18; these were Northern California, Los Angeles, San Diego, New England, Ohio, Illinois, New Mexico, Oregon, Colorado, Mexico, Puerto Rico, and Virginia.

The American Section dues were increased to $10 with an additional $10 for the obligatory ISES membership. The membership increased to 1,603 at the beginning of 1975 and to 1,975 by June 1975. The budget of the American Section increased to a total of $9,300.47 (no grant) with a disbursement of $4,828.65 for office expenses ($1,516.67), printing ($2,761.89), and committee and traveling ($550.09). Total cash in hand at January 1, 1994, was $12,994.99.

The American Section of ISES was accepted as the Corresponding Society of the Assembly of Life Sciences at the National Research Council.

A joint annual meeting of the American Section was held together with ISES in Los Angeles at U.C.L.A. with almost 2,000 registered participants. Dr. Jack Duffie was technical chair, Gene Ralph was general chairman.

Next year's meeting was to be a joint meeting between the American Section and the Solar Energy Society of Canada, to be held in Winnipeg. Karl Böer was invited to be the technical chairman.

At this meeting, the first Abbot Award was presented by Walter Shropshire to Dr. William H. Klein for his activities in ISES, most recently as its elected President, and his dedicated help to the American Section, for which he served as secretary-treasurer, as well as for his longtime research at the Smithsonian Institute, where he became director of the Radiation Biology Laboratory in 1958 and where he set up a national network to determine the solar spectral irradiance values. The Award plaque was handed by Dr. Shropshire to Dr. Klein at the Award dinner (Fig. 5) attended by 600 invited guests.

Fig. 5: Dr. William H. Klein was presented with the Charles Greeley Abbot Award by Walter Shropshire. Left is Mrs. Duffie, and at the right is George Löf

A North American User-Oriented Technology group was created to conduct local and regional workshops and publish in Solar News and Views.

3.2.4   Karl W. Böer Chairmanship

Karl Böer (Fig. 6) was professor of physics and engineering at the University of Delaware, the former director of the Institute of Energy Conversion, and CEO of SES Inc., a subsidiary of Shell Oil. He is a prolific author with over 300 publications in the field of solid state physics and photovoltaic devices, with 18 patents in the field; a fellow of the American Physical Society and of IEEE, AAAS, and ASES. He has been awarded the Charles G. Abbot Award of ASES and recently the Farrington Daniels Award of ISES. He was president of the American Section of ISES during 1976 and 1977.

Fig. 6: Karl W. Böer

The first board of directors meeting took place in the Conference Center of Clayton Hall at the University of Delaware on January 19, 1976. New officers were K. W. Böer as chairman, and J. I. Yellott as vice chairman. The new directors were B. Anderson, F. de Winter and J. Farber. D. S. Halacy, Jr. was appointed to fill the vacancy, resulting from the chairman's election.

The perennial discussion continued of whether ISES and its American Section was to conduct its affairs as a professional society or should attempt to also inform lay persons, and therefore should be titled appropriately. After a lengthy heated discussion the board accepted a proposal from Karl Böer that the education of lay people should fall exclusively to the local chapters while the American Section of ISES would address professionals in the field. Therefore it should clearly be termed a Professional Society. In order to emphasize this, Böer proposed the creation of technical divisions within ASES that would cover the main established fields of solar energy conversion and its socio-economic implications. The by-laws committee was instructed to prepare an addendum to permit, on a petition of at least 20 members, the creation of new divisions.

The relocation of the Society's office was discussed and only the offers from the Arizona State University and from the Florida Energy Center were to be given further consideration. The chairman was instructed to negotiate with these candidates and report back to the board.

Solar News and Views was offered for subscription to nonmembers for $10 per year. A 30-page magazine was proposed to be created in late spring of 1976. John Yellott (Fig. 7) was appointed editor of a 20-Year History of ISES book.

Fig. 7: John I. Yellott, vice president of ASES and editor of a 20-Year History of ISES

A "user technology" resolution was approved, and Robert Murray was invited as chair to assemble an implementation committee.

The board voted to accept an invitation from the University of Delaware to create a publication office with Karl Böer as the director and Barbara Bradley as editor. The first task was to prepare a complete set of volumes (12) for all accepted presentations (400) for the next annual conference in Winnipeg, to be readied and presented to all registered full participants. This became the first income-making function of the American Section and laid the foundation for added services to its membership.

During the Winnipeg conference, Dr. John A. Duffie received the second Charles G. Abbot Award with the citation "For his outstanding contribution to the conversion of solar energy for the needs of mankind and for the guidance and inspiration he has given to many workers in the field." It was presented by Karl Böer at the banquet of the joint conference of AS of ISES and SES Canada, in Winnipeg, Manitoba, Canada, on Thursday, August 19, 1976.

The next board meeting took place during the annual conference in Winnipeg on August 14. The bid of the new office of the Society from the Florida Energy Center was accepted, and Howard P. Harrenstein, the dean of the School of Engineering and Environmental Design at the University of Miami in Coral Gables, was appointed as the new secretary treasurer and the director of the office. W. Klein reported as the outgoing secretary treasurer of the American Section of ISES. The assets of the American Section were $42,866.35 cash on July 12, 1976 (a substantial increase over the cash on hand on January 1, 1976 of $15,448.32). The membership at the end of 1975 had increased to 2,800. The fiscal years (July 1, '76-June 30, '77) budget called for total expenditures of $81,410, with $19,500 for the American Section and $61,910 for the Florida headquarters.

The new office was established in May and started officially on July 1, 1976. Marian Bert was hired as administrative assistant and Ed Fordyce joined the headquarters office.

Responding to a request for proposals, Kurt Wasserman and Bruce Anderson of Solar Vision proposed that the American Section adopt Solar Age, published quarterly, as its official publication. Extensive discussion evolved as to whether to adopt the magazine and under what conditions. The affiliation with Solar Age was finally voted on and accepted overwhelmingly, with Kurt Wasserman as publisher and Bruce Anderson (Fig. 8) as executive editor. A distinguished Editorial Advisory Board of present and former members of ASES was established.

Fig. 8: Bruce Anderson, executive editor of Solar Age

Heated discussions were held in respect to the improvement of the Journal of *Solar Energy* and whether its subscription should be obligatory for all members. This was answered in the positive. Journal improvement related mostly to the commitment of the publisher and required intensive further discussions and direct negotiations.

The number of local chapters was growing rapidly. The American Section was accepted as an Affiliate of the American Association for the Advancement of Science within the Sections of biology, physics, chemistry, engineering, and industrial science.

The need to present short technical workshops in conjunction with the annual conferences was suggested and voted to be implemented at the next conference.

Solar energy "advocacy" and "lobbying" in Washington was discussed but was judged to be counter to the professional image of a society seeking to avoid overselling and to the legal limitations against lobbying by a nonprofit organization.

In response to a question by Jim Rannels, Karl Böer wrote, "in respect to our status as a professional organization, it is my personal desire to strengthen and solidify its roots and to provide the basis for strong and sound professional activities. For this reason we suggested the creation of topical divisions, which was approved at our January board meeting."

A weekend brainstorming session (up to three day's duration) for members of the board was suggested and approved by the board.

Dr. Harrenstein suggested incorporation of the American Section in the State of Florida. The board approved.

The membership meeting on August 17 was attended by a large number of members with very active participation. The Winnipeg meeting drew in excess of 1,200 participants. The budget of the Winnipeg meeting was quite modest, with a total income from participants and exhibitors of $39,447 plus $16,472 from the proceedings, with expenditures of $49,972, showing a modest surplus of $5,947.

The third board meeting of this year took place on December 5 and 6 in Orlando, Florida. Dr. Harrenstein resigned as the director of the Florida office and accepted a position at ERDA. There were also indications that the University of Miami might not honor the contract with ASES; consequently, the American Section reopened the bidding for its office. Ed Fordyce accepted the position as acting secretary-treasurer, assisted by Del Ward.

Extensive discussion with Mr. Maxwell and Mr. Straka of Pergamon were reported in respect to purchasing the left-over proceedings of the Winnipeg conference ($50,000 for these proceedings were received from Pergamon, increasing the above cited annual surplus from $5,947 to $59,473). The improvement of the production and distribution of the Solar Energy Journal was promised. The board's recommendations were all accepted by Pergamon. The financials of the preprinted Proceedings of the Winnipeg Conference were very encouraging, with a total sale of $96,403.75, versus a total expense of $77,799.06, resulting in a net income of $18,604.69.

The board also agreed to negotiate a contract with *Solar Age*, making the society part owner (10%) of the stock and declaring it as the official magazine of the American Section of ISES.

Incorporation of the American Section of the International Solar Energy Society in Florida, using Leonard Spielvogel as attorney, was approved. It was incorporated on July 1, 1977, as the "International Solar Energy Society, American Section, Inc.," commonly referred to as AS of ISES. A contractual relation with ISES was signed, reaffirming the continuation of the American Section as a Section of ISES, with membership proceeds divided as a 25% to 75% ratio for the American Section and ISES, respectively. The societies assisted each other as they did before the incorporation of AS of ISES. Membership in the American Section required membership in ISES in good standing.

Publications of AS of ISES that were to be provided to members were announced in its membership drive: *The Solar Energy Journal, SunWorld,*

ISES News, *Solar News and Views*, the *ASES Directory* and *Solar Heating and Cooling of Buildings*. Individual membership fees were listed as $20 for ISES and $10 for ASES (Students $12 and $6, respectively).

During early spring 1977 a new contract proposal from the AS of ISES headquarters in Florida arrived that modified substantially the financial conditions to the disadvantage of AS of ISES. Consequently, the board of directors decided to take legal action against the State of Florida for breach of contract.

At this time, other offers to house the office of AS of ISES were actively pursued, including Argonne National Laboratory/Northern Illinois Solar Energy Association; American Technological University, Killeen, Texas; and the New Mexico Solar Energy Institute, Las Cruces, New Mexico.

For the 1977 annual meeting, "A Solar World," in Orlando 236 abstracts were accepted. The meeting was attended by over 1,200 participants. The Conference Proceedings were preprinted and distributed at the conference. The sale of additional Proceedings resulted in a modest $2,000 exceeding the production cost, with over 300 sets available for later sales. At the meeting, an increase of the membership dues to $40 was announced, including the subscription of *Solar Age* ($10). Half of the membership dues were collected for the obligatory membership to ISES.

That year's (1977) Charles G. Abbot award was presented by Karl Böer to Dr. Maria Telkes, one of the pioneers in solar energy conversion who began at the MIT under Hoyt Hottel with research and experimentation on three model solar houses. She also designed the Dover, New Jersey solar-heated house. She worked on solar cooking and solar distillation and was internationally recognized for her extensive work on heat storage.

The next board meeting was held at the Smithsonian Radiation Biology Laboratory on October 28, 1977. The board decided to vacate the Florida office by December 31 of that year.

The (full) membership of AS of ISES has increased to 3,815, with income exceeding expenses by $13,000. With 9,000 paid subscriptions to Solar Age a new membership group was initiated: the associate members of AS of ISES. The relocation of the AS of ISES office was extensively discussed, with two offers on the table, one from the Northern Illinois Solar Energy Association, with a distinguished consortium of industry and city government backing the proposal, and the other one from the American Technological University in Killeen, Texas, with substantial private funding (the New Mexico offer was withdrawn). The board voted that the Killeen offer be accepted (Fig. 9), subject to a background check and a satisfactory site visit.

Fig. 9: ASES Headquarters in Killeen, Texas

The changes of the Society during Dr. Böer's tenure as chairman, is summarized in his chairman's message in *Solar News and Views*:

- The Society will provide to the professionals in the field the opportunity to exchange knowledge and to engage in discussion through its professional conferences and through the *Solar Energy* Journal and will be assisted by topical divisions, with the expectation to sponsor publications, technical reviews, and periodic assessments.
- The Society will distribute to the lay-person well-prepared information, and through its regional Chapters, it will reach out into the communities with lectures, seminars, and materials designed for local conditions. There are currently 21 local Chapters established with a total membership of 9,200. Most of them charge $10 per member (these are also listed as Associate Members of ASES).
- The *Solar Age* magazine will assist in this education and was accepted as the official Magazine of the Society.
- The Society's operation will change from the assistance of a group of volunteers to a Professional Office with paid staff.
- The financial basis of the Society will be based on membership fees and income from publications. Through careful budgeting of conferences it will attempt to obtain additional income from conference surplus.
- Short and long-range planning was, for the first time, conducted in a board meeting without a business agenda, labeled as a "brainstorm meeting." Its success indicates the desirability to make it an annual event.

3.2.5   Francis de Winter Chairmanship

Francis de Winter got his education in The Netherlands, Argentina, and the USA (at MIT). He started his solar energy work in 1966 at the Jet Propulsion Laboratory; then worked extensively on solar water heaters. He published well-received books on flat-plate collectors. With over 90 publications in the field, he is a well-recognized expert in heat exchange. He has devoted most of his professional life since 1978 to leadership positions in ASES, ISES, and civic organizations dealing with renewable energy. He is a recipient of the Charles Greeley Abbot Award and a member of the Solar Energy Hall of Fame and is a fellow of ASES. He is a registered engineer and former president of the Altas Corporation. His hobbies include sailing and cooking. His recent photo (Fig. 10) shows him in front of his extensive library of cookbooks. de Winter was elected chairman of ASES and started his term on January 1, 1978.

Fig. 10: Francis de Winter in front of his cookbook library

During the first few months of his chairmanship there were two important conferences, the ISES Solar World Congress in New Delhi in January, where he was technical program chair and general chair of the AS of ISES Annual Meeting in Boulder, Colorado, during the last week in August.

The move of the Society's office to Killeen was accomplished starting smoothly on Dec. 15, 1977, and it began full operation in June 1978. It was to be supported with $45,000 in cash and $75,000 in in-kind services. John J. Kincel was appointed executive director and treasurer of ASES, Patty McDaniel as office manager, and Robert D. Philips as an associate.

The membership had grown to 5,000 by mid-1978. Eight topical divisions had been established: agriculture (C. Dirilee Baird), biology and chemistry (James R. Bolton), engineering (Noam Lior), passive systems (J. Douglas Balcomb), physics (Karl W. Böer), socio-economics (Keith Haggard), solar radiation (Kinsell L. Coulson), and wind (C. G. Justus).

At the Denver conference 300 papers and 150 poster papers were accepted. The number of registered participants at the conference exceeded 1,200. The expenditures at the Denver conference were $102,000 and the net receipts were $80,000, for a net deficit of $22,000.

On October 20 the second board meeting started at 2:30 pm in the Goodstay Center in Newark, Delaware; on the first day it dealt with the leftover motions of the fifty motions of the Denver meeting that had been tabled. It was agreed that the next year's annual conference would be a joint conference between AS of ISES and ISES and would be held in Atlanta Georgia. Bill Beckman was appointed technical chair. It was voted by the board that in the future the technical Chair of all annual meetings would make an all-out effort to include all solar technology areas. In order to ease the organization of future conferences it was decided that the ASES office would write a handbook for conferences that detail every step necessary to conduct the preparation of conferences.

A map of the United States was presented showing boundaries of chapters. Where an overlap existed, negotiation between the chapters was suggested to remove such overlap. In areas where no chapter existed, the creation of chapters was to be stimulated. Subchapters would only be permitted in the region assigned to the respective chapters. These conditions were introduced as amendments to the AS of ISES by-laws.

For a membership drive, it was approved that the membership fee of individuals who bring in new members would be decreased by one month per new member.

It was suggested that AS of ISES publish periodic updates of the state of the art of solar energy conversion. AS of ISES would also prepare periodic news releases of new developments in the field of solar energy conversion.

It was observed that the board meetings this year had a very large number of motions (63 in Denver and 103 at the Goodstay Center in Newark), indicating the increasing tendency of the new board to engage in micro-management. The need to delegate more to committees was recognized.

2.2.6   J. Douglas Balcomb Chairmanship

On January 1, 197,9 Dr. Balcomb became the chairman of the American Section of ISES (Fig. 11). He retired in 2003 as a Research Fellow at the National Renewable Energy Laboratory. Thirty-one years research in passive solar energy. Author of six books and 143 papers. Developed the Solar Load Ratio method for predicting passive solar performance. Author of the Energy-10 design tool computer program. Chairman of ASES and 9 years on the ISES board of directors. Founded the Passive Solar Division of ASES. Recipient of the DOE Ericsson Award, the ASES Charles Greeley Abbot Award, and the PLEA Lifetime Achievement Award.

Fig. 11: J. Douglas Balcomb and his wife Sara

Doug Balcomb's goals were to "broaden the scope of AS of ISES and to increase the base of its membership to better achieve the Society's objectives and to stabilize the office operation and its financial status." His first priority was to "strengthen the chapters and to integrate the chapter activities closer to the Section." He saw a "strong professional core of AS of ISES encouraged by high publication standards and the activities of the topical divisions." He advocated a "closer relation between the Section and the chapters to join the professional part with the grass roots community and the related socio-economic community."

The Annual meeting of AS of ISES was jointly sponsored by ISES and held in Atlanta, Georgia from May 28 through June 1, 1979. More than 1,000 abstracts were submitted, of which 350 were selected for oral presentation and 100 for posters. The conference drew in excess of 2,000 participants, with 700 coming from overseas. The conference proceedings were readied before the conference (Fig. 12) and distributed to the registered participants free of charge.

Fig.12: Proceeding (l. to r.) editors Barbara Glenn and Gregory Franta (seated), with production personnel Kathy Durrant and Barbara Bradley in the Delaware publication office looking on

The highlight of the conference was the announcement of Omi Walden, assistant secretary of Conservation and Solar Application at the US Department of Energy that a budget of more than $600 million was being considered to support the federal renewable energy program in fiscal year 1980. This represented another very large budget increase for the department's solar energy activities during the Carter administration.

Lee Salmon (Fig. 13) was appointed chapter coordinator, responsible for coordinating the twenty-seven chapters. With a background of physics, and working in the field of electro-optics, he brought a solid base to the job; and his involvement in solar education made him well-suited to bring together the work of the chapters and their relation to the Section.

Fig. 13: Chapter coordinator Gordon Lee Salmon, recently appointed as the new executive director of AS of ISES, together with his wife Nancy

The 1979 Charles Greeley Abbot Award was presented to Professor Everett D. Howe (Fig. 14) for his exceptional service to the Society and for significant contributions in his field. He was editor of Solar News and Views and for Sun World and a contributing to the ISES Newsletter. He investigated distillation for seawater desalination and installed numerous solar distillers on coral atolls and islands. His most recent book was Fundamentals in Desalination, published in 1974. Howe was one of the organizers of the 1955 AFASE conference in Arizona. He developed the by-laws of ASES. He worked in Brazil as well as in Egypt and in Australia for the development of solar energy.

Fig. 14: Abbot Prize Winner: Everett D. Howe

Currently *Solar News and Views* is produced by the AS of ISES Publication Office at the University of Delaware (Fig. 15)

Fig. 15: Karl W. Böer presents the newest issue of the Solar News and Views to the members of the Publication Committee: l. to r. standing K. Coulson, J. Farber, E. Howe; front K. Böer, F. deWinter.

3.3   The Renaissance of Solar Energy Conversion in the '70s

The genetics and interaction of the American Section of ISES with its members cannot be separated from the dynamics of the U.S. federal solar energy research and development activities in the remarkable epoch of the '70s. Therefore a short summary will now be provided to point out the general status of solar energy technology development before 1970 followed by a brief review of some of the most important developments during this period of solar R&D, including its influence on ASES and ISES.

The general technical outlook before 1970 was that solar energy utilization would be largely limited in importance to some special needs and applications in developing countries with good solar resources and potentially to a small role in providing power for space exploration. A few groups of academic researchers were working on various thermal applications of solar energy for heating water, residential buildings, and agricultural uses (e.g., MIT, Wisconsin, Delaware, Florida, Arizona, and Colorado). Several of these groups had small support grants from the Agency for International Development to research solar energy applications for developing countries (e.g., solar cookers, water distillation and purification, water pumping, and hot-water systems). Prior to 1970 all US federal funding for solar energy research had been estimated to have averaged on the order of $100,000 per year from all sources.

However, for a limited time in the 1930s and '40s a modest commercialization of solar water heating systems for residential buildings existed in several regions of the United States (e.g., in or around Florida, California, and Arizona). However, the solar water heater sales almost completely stopped by 1970.

Early economic estimations by Hottel and later by Löf and Tybout were, in general, disappointing for the widespread use of solar energy for heating of buildings and marginal for water heating. Conventional resources (oil, gas end even electric) were much more convenient and less expensive.

It was not until late in 1970 that at the National Science Foundation a new evaluation of the large potential for the utilization of solar energy technologies was initiated. With the recognition of the possibility of solar energy to provide large scale energy and power sources for the United States, feedback from the Nixon administration and, with congressional support, a move to push research results more rapidly to commercialization.. As a result, a new NSF program initiative, called "Research Applied to National Needs"

(RANN), was started. This was the basis for starting a large and broad energy research program, including solar, however, all with a relatively small staff at NSF.

NSF's project manager, Lloyd Herwig (Fig. 16), immediately signed on to the RANN project and became an advocate for supporting the role of solar energy as a large national energy resource. Herwig organized the initial NSF research grants for universities in solar energy and became project manager of the NSF/NASA Solar Energy Panel (consisting of forty-five university and industry experts), covering the entire field of direct and indirect solar technologies, including heating, cooling, solar thermal, wind, photovoltaic, bioconversion, and ocean.

Fig.16: Lloyd Herwig, at the helm of early government support of solar research

Bill Cherry (see Fig. 2), NASA Space Center's lead engineer for photovoltaic technology and the chairperson of AS of ISES, was the executive secretary of the NSF/NASA Solar Energy Panel. Fred Morse (Fig. 17), a professor of mechanical engineering of the University of Maryland, was NSF research grantee for logistics and panel meetings. More than half of the panel experts were members of AS of ISES.

Fig. 17: Fred Morse

In September 1972, the NSF/NASA Solar Energy Panel published a seminal evaluation of the potential of solar energy technologies, titled "Solar Energy as a National Energy Resource." This report provided the major foundation for the early planning and budgeting of the NSF solar program.

David S. Freeman, as the science advisor to Nixon, was very sympathetic to solar energy research, but in FY 1970 and '71 only limited resources were available.

The NSF solar energy research budget started with approximately $350,000 in FY 1970, increased to $1 million in 1971, to $3 million in 1972, $5 million in 1973, $15 million in 1974, and $50 million in 1975.

The oil crisis in late 1973 provided an additional impetus to increase the solar energy budget during the Nixon administration. In the early years through FY 1973 all NSF/RANN awards were required to be made to academic institutions with possible subcontracts to industry. In special areas they were also permitted to be given to NASA or other DOE national laboratories. This changed after 1973 when as a result of congressional actions grants could also be made directly to industry.

The Federal Office of Management and Budget (OMB) established NSF in 1973 as the lead federal agency for solar energy research and development. Lloyd Herwig was named as its director with a staff of about twelve program managers.

In 1975 the bulk of the NSF solar energy budget and its staff was transferred to the newly organized Energy Research and Development Administration (ERDA). The ERDA solar energy budget was administrated within the DOE in 1977.

The first large solar energy research grant was made to the University of Pennsylvania under the directorship of Dr. Altmann as the principal investigator.

3.3.1   Photovoltaics as a First Device to be Evaluated

The climate changed rapidly as the oil embargo continued. Many new assessment groups were formed under Lloyd Herwig to develop extensive five-year plans for each of the many potential solar energy technologies. A major task was the evaluation of photovoltaics (PV), that was known at that time as yielding working devices (most of the satellites were powered by PV). But it was also clear that at present they were much too expensive to be considered for major terrestrial deployment.

Top scientists and engineers were invited for several days of evaluation of the different kinds of PV devices (Si, Poly-Si and thin-films) and the consensus of the group was that, with mass production, there was feasibility that the price of PV, currently at $500/Watt, could be reduced by three orders of magnitude. That would make it competitive with the conventional supply of electric energy, if the PV devices would have a service life of at least 20 years. Preference, at that time was given to thin-film devices, were mass production in a continuous production line seemed feasible. $CdSCu_xS$ cells were the first candidates, and several pilot production companies (mostly with oil company sponsorship) sprang up. Most visible was SES, Inc. with Shell Oil as sponsor and Karl Böer as CEO.

3.3.2 Other Solar Conversion Devices and Systems

Broader evaluation of a large variety of solar energy conversion means were done initially under NSF, later under ERDA, sponsorship. These evaluations produced results that eliminated few, but showed a wide range of conversion means to be in the same ballpark of techno-economical feasibility.

Consequently, a large number or proposals were submitted to ERDA for all kinds of conversion means such as solar heating (buildings, water, agricultural crops, industrial, solar tower), wind, ocean thermal, bio-conversion, ocean waves and tides). It was a time of great creativity to propose new materials, machines, principles. Many new research groups were formed at universities and in industry.

3.3.2.1   Increased Research Funds Became Available

With results progressing, more daring advances were proposed, as (sometimes rather large) demonstration projects. Increased funding of the solar energy projects continued from the federal government. During the relatively short period of the Ford administration limited attention was given to solar. This all changed when Jimmy Carter became president. Carter was an engineer and understood the need to accelerate research and development in the field of energies, especially renewable energies. He had solar collectors installed on the White House, promoted solar energy in many of his speeches, and signed laws that the U.S. Congress was encouraged to pass. The national solar budget increased from about $15 million under Nixon to more than $600 million at the end of the Carter presidency.

3.3.2.2 Increased Awareness of Solar Worldwide and its Influence on ISES and ASES

As a result of the US government's leadership in solar energy research and development through the 1970's, worldwide attention and cooperation increased rapidly in both developed and developing countries. Governments, research institutions industrial companies, and scientists and engineers worldwide initiated efforts aimed at developing and utilizing a broad range of solar energy technologies. The recognition of the large potential of solar energy became worldwide.

This had a direct influence on the growth of the professional solar energy societies, of ISES and of AS of ISES. Conferences in this field were attended in the late '60s and early '70s by only a handful of participants (seldom more than 200) but now had increased to over 2,000 participants. The Society's membership had increase by much more than a factor of ten. National Sections of ISES had been created in almost fifty nations worldwide. The general public became stimulated, and in many general questionnaires the response was overwhelmingly in favor of energy conservation and for the use of renewable energies.

3.4   Solar Energy Research

The research of various types of solar energy conversion devices, sponsored first at NSF, was quickly expanded to other fields by physics and engineering departments of universities. Fertile grounds for research were generated by early support from NASA for photovoltaics for space application, for flat plate thermal panels by mechanical engineering departments and HUD, windmill research from aerodynamics departments and industry, and for investigation of the use of biomass by biology departments and agricultural colleges. It was a field *in statu nascendi*, when some of the most intuitive researchers found open opportunities to develop their creative ideas and compete for government support.

This was also the time when some industry researchers saw an opportunity to branch out from their work, often related to outer space application, into terrestrial application, proposing feasibility studies and future production economics analyses. Here many of the early researchers found a forum in government evaluation panels to promote their ideas and have them critically reviewed by a panel of experts.

First larger grants were given in 1970 from the NSF to Altman at the University of Pennsylvania, who had assembled a team of experts in the field of solar thermal conversion, and in 1971 to Böer at the University of Delaware, who was investigating with his team thin-film solar cells and hybrid collectors.

3.4.1 Photovoltaics Development

In the early '70s the oil industry became interested in sponsoring research and development of photovoltaic panels, with Exxon, Mobil, Arco, and Shell as early investors.

The main materials that were under development early in the '70s were single crystal and polycrystalline silicon and, as thin-film, the CdS/Cu_xS solar cell. For all material the cost reduction for producing solar cells was the dominant research subject.

3.4.1.1   Silicon Solar Cells

First, Eugene Ralph from Heliotek suggested reducing the materials demand by employing solar concentrators. In the silicon cell technology much early emphasis was devoted to finding benign impurities that could be tolerated for reasonably efficient cells (so-called solar grade Si) and thereby simplify the otherwise costly purification process. Another means suggested to reduce materials demand was the pulling of Si-sheets out of the melt rather than slicing single crystal rods. Tyco later, with financial assistance from Mobil, developed this method. Other methods to produce Si-sheets directly from the melt were developed by Westinghouse, IBM, and Motorola.

Another way to simplify the Si cell production was by slowly cooling the melt and thereby producing polycrystalline Si that in turn again was cut into slices and processed by doping to solar cells. Solarex was first using this process commercially.

Solar Power Corporation under Elliot Berman was first to explore the terrestrial market with Si solar panels, composed of a series connection of several Si-cells. Lindmeyer with Solarex started one year later. Also Spectrolab entered the terrestrial market; it offered cells for terrestrial use that were rejected for the outer space market. Then Solar Technology International, with J.W. Yerkes and sponsored by Arco, entered the market.

3.4.1.2   Thin-Film Solar Cells

Thin-film CdS/Cu_xS solar cells that were originally developed by a group of Shirland at Harshaw and Clevite were further developed at the Institute of Energy Conversion of the University of Delaware and later by SES, Inc. under Böer, with Shell sponsorship. These cells were plagued by early degradation due to copper nodule formation in the copper sulfide lattice. Research efforts were under way to prevent such nodule formation by avoiding nucleation centers at high-field spikes inside the cells and at the electrodes. With the development of graphite-coated electrodes and by avoiding deep grooves in the polycrystalline CdS, this goal could be achieved, though with yet insufficient production yield because of the difficulty to reliably clog deep CdS grooves. Further process development indicated some promise; however, the principal limitation of the cell efficiency being below 10% because of the lattice mismatch of both cell components, finally gave the signal to terminate development when other thin-film cells, notably amorphous silicon, copper indium diselenide, and cadmium telluride, showed promise to easily exceed 10% efficiency (some of them are now approaching 20% solar conversion efficiency).

Shell then formed a joint venture with Motorola but folded a few years later when the Motorola thin-film Si process proved to be unattractive.

3.4.1.3   Other Thin-Film Solar Cell Development

In the mid '70s at several laboratories almost simultaneously, first feasibility was shown for amorphous Si (RCA, Carlson, and Wroski), $CuInSe_2$ (Boeing, Chen, and Michelsen), and CdTe (University of Southern California, Panicker, et al.) for thin-film solar cells.

The a-Si cell attracted early commercialization by ECD, later Photon Power (Ovshinsky) and by Solarex (Carlson). Main problems with the a-Si cell was its rapid degradation by photochemical processes (Stabler-Wronsky effect that could be minimized by using a special doping profile and/or multilayer cells) that partially anneal out during dark periods and could be made acceptable by preaging the cells, thereby reducing the severity of the remaining degradation.

The $CuInSe_2$ cell was astonishingly rather insensitive to various deposition methods (evaporation, sputtering, electroplating, selenization) and found early commercialization interests in a number of companies with ARCO solar (Choudary, Mitchell). However, production yield and uniformity issues prevented inexpensive production of larger panels.

The CdTe cell made by electro-deposition was favorably judged for commercialization of p-type CdTe followed by n-type CdS (Ametek); later ARCO Solar, then Monosolar, acquired by BP. Problems still related to large-area homogeneity and the stability of the contact on the p-type CdTe.

3.4.2   The Initial Solar Cell Market

The solar cell market in the '70s was marginal. It was related to small-scale energy consumers for electronic gadgets, for water pumping, remote telephone highway installation, cathodic oil and gas line protection, street traffic warning signs, and the like. The market for houses that were far from power grids opened slowly, with photovoltaic energy supplementing diesel generators. The price per watt was still well in excess of $10, too high for becoming attractive to compete with the electric power provided by the grid. It took almost two more decades to bring the photovoltaic price down to an attractive figure.

3.5   Solar Thermal Collectors

The sheet metal and glass industry early in the '70s became interested in sponsoring the development of solar thermal panels. Olin Brass, Revere Copper and Brass, Alcoa, Pittsburg Plate Glass, and Libby-Owens-Ford were some of the companies that tried to enter the market of flat plate panels early. Research subjects early on were the development of stable selective black coatings, inexpensive collector materials and fabrication (black polymers), finning of collectors for air as heat transport fluid, glass covers with high optical transmissivity, and materials compatibility.

Entrepreneurs who carried out the early development in collectors were Freeman Ford, creating FAFCO for polymeric solar pool heating panels; Harry Thomason, who moved along another path, building several solar houses using trickle collectors in which an open flow of water percolated over a black absorber behind a glass sheet, as an example, and licensed these for others to copy. Löf, on the other hand, combined his own experience in his solar air heated home with techno-economic studies (with Tybout and Duffie) and thereby exerted positive influence (he later, together with his son commercialized solar pool heater and evaporation barriers). Other industries in the mid-'70s began activities in the collector field, at Grummar, Martin Marietta, Raypak, and General Electric, for examples.

3.6   Innovation and Demonstration

The first years of the solar renaissance gave an opportunity to realize some new ideas. One such was the Solar One House of the University of Delaware. Its basic idea was to build a house designed by a systems approach, in which many interacting facts were taken into consideration and connected to each other in order to arrive at a much more cost-effective solar building.

3.6.1   The Solar One Hybrid System with Built-in Collectors

The Solar One house (Fig. 18), built in 1973, was the first house worldwide that had hybrid solar collectors, that were not mounted on top of the roof but were built-in between the nude struts of the roof and provided sealing against the weather and strength of the roof against shearing by means of their box-like construction. Such boxes were used as air-ducts for collecting the heat from the sun-exposed solar cells into the house. The heat transfer surface from the bottom of the solar cells was equipped with specially designed fins, to increase the efficiency of the solar cells by "cooling" them effectively and by harvesting the maximum possible heat for comfort conditioning of the house during the heating season. They were also designed to still minimize air resistance to decrease the electric load for air pumping. Surplus heat was stored by melting eutectic salts in containers located in big boxes in the basement. During the summer months heat was ventilated to the outside and coolness during night hours was also collected to freeze other eutectic salts that could be used later during the day for cooling the living space. Both means could assist a heat pump that was used for comfort conditioning during inclement weather.

Fig. 18: Solar One House of the University of Delaware

The house was super-insulated and also designed as a passive house by orienting its main windows to the south and by properly designing the window overhang. Photocell-controlled window shades prevented unnecessary heating in the summer or assisting heating in the winter while the occupants were away. Other features included venting of the refrigerator in the kitchen in the summer and using DC in the house whenever possible to avoid unnecessary losses by inverting to AC.

A major feature of the house was its heat and coolness storage by freezing and melting salt eutectics, designed by Maria Telkes (Fig. 19), one of the outstanding early pioneers of solar energy conversion, who helped to design several features of the Solar One House.

Fig. 19: Maria Telkes

The house was equipped with CdS/Cu_xS solar cells that were obtained from Harsha and further developed first at the Institute of Energy Conversion at the University of Delaware (Fig. 20) and later at SES, Inc. a subsidiary of Shell Oil, located adjacent to the Institute of Energy Conversion at the University of Delaware.

Much of the data were obtained by simulation since, at the time the collectors were only partially filled with solar cells, and many of the air-duct boxes were periodically exchanged for further development of the heat transfer surfaces. Very encouraging results were obtained, including peak shaving for power utilities, using the prevalent solar radiation later in the day, and some storage to maximize the output during peak utility hours.

The results of the experiments in the house were presented at many of the ISES and AS of ISES conferences and provided stimulation for systems development. But it took decades to develop devices and solar panels that permitted such system installation (e.g., hybrid collectors).

Fig. 20: Karl Böer delivers to President Trabant of the University of Delaware the first working CdS/Cu$_x$S Solar Cell developed at the Institute of Energy Conversion.

3.7   Solar Demonstration Projects

In order to accelerate the commercialization of solar energy technologies (particularly through solar heating and cooling of residential buildings) the U.S. Congress initiated and passed legislation and budgets for a relatively massive demonstration of a wide range of solar heating and cooling systems throughout the United States in the late 1970s and early 1980s. In addition, Congress passed legislation providing substantial tax incentives for individuals, businesses, and institutions to install solar energy systems.

3.7.1   Solar Power Tower

In the 1970s, academic groups and industrial engineers and researchers evaluated several approaches for central electric power generation using solar thermal energy. While some preferred solar trough fields, as promoted early by the Meinels, others preferred a solar boiler located on a tower in the focal point of a surrounding mirror field. Aerospace Industry consulted with ERDA on the topic, and later DOE continued to sponsor such solar power projects. Research teams at the University of Houston in the Physics Department together with McDonnell Douglas developed the first concepts. Sandia Laboratories in Albuquerque became involved in the mid '70s to further develop the Solar Power Tower. In time a design was developed by McDonnell Douglas, Martin Marietta, and Honeywell, using water steam as transport fluid and stone/oil as heat storage, with silver-coated glass heliostats as solar reflectors. Southern California Edison constructed the solar electric power plant at Barstow in the California desert (Fig. 21). For more, see Holl and DeMeo (1990) and Mener (2000).

As the result of this demonstration project, electric power utilities became interested in using central solar power plants to feed electric power into the grid. At that time their conservative approach called for a centralized power plant rather than for a distributed system that was later introduced by other power utilities. Several approaches were realized as demonstration objects: large arrays of PV panels; concentration of sunlight through a field of mirrors onto a boiler on top of a tower; and fields of concentrating troughs that heated a transport fluid that was in turn collected at the main heat exchanger to produce the steam for running generators. All three approaches were successful, but the field of concentrating troughs showed the most economic attraction and was commercially used (see below).

Fig 21: Solar Power Tower Installation at Barstow in the Mojave Desert by Southern California Edison

The results that were presented at several ISES congresses were encouraging, even though the specific results at Barstow indicated the need for further research for a more effective heat transport fluid (sodium or molten salts), higher life expectancy in the mirror field, and a larger plant to make the electric output more cost effective. Nevertheless the demonstration indicated feasibility.

3.7.2   Thermal Power Plants with Focusing Devices

There were two types of focusing devices used to generate steam for electric power generation, paraboloids and parabolic troughs requiring two- and one-axis solar following mechanisms. Fig. 22 shows a typical paraboloid mirror to create heat for running a Stirling engine (supported by the Jet Propulsion Laboratory). For more, see Holl and DeMeo (1990) and Mener (2000).

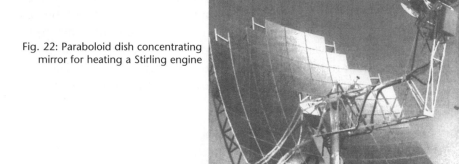

Fig. 22: Paraboloid dish concentrating mirror for heating a Stirling engine

Fig. 23: Parabolic mirror field for inter-connecting generated steam with a hybrid installation using fossil fuel to increase and stabilize operation temperature. The steam was used to process heat and generated electric power (400 kW(el) rating) in Shenandoah, Georgia, by Georgia Power Company (supported by Sandia National Laboratory)

The most successful installations used focusing troughs to collect heat within the central tube and deliver it through the heat transport fluid to a heat exchanger for generating steam and consequently generating electric power. The most well-known installation that started early and expanded to a multi-Megawatt plant is shown in Fig. 24. The collector field was designed and built by LUZ Industries in Israel, with support for the extensive design and development activities from the U.S. Department of Energy during the years 1975 to 1984 and mainly from tax credits. This installation also demonstrated the success of a hybrid installation that used fossil fuels to supplement thermal storage at times of insufficient insolation.

Fig. 24: Field of trough collectors for the Solar Electric Generating System (SEGS) placed in service by the Southern California Edison Company

3.8   Wind Farm Demonstration

Early efforts to show economical feasibility of wind turbine generators were supported by NSF program funds, transferred to NASA Lewis Laboratory, where relatively small wind turbines of 100 and 200 kW were designed and tested. They showed an engineering proof of concept during the late 1970s. A General Electric designed MOD-1 machine of 1 MW output provided valuable technical information for further development.

The first wind farm was installed in California in a stage of early development of wind machines. Still, the demonstration farm was impressive and provided information sufficiently attractive to open a most successful branch of solar energy (wind should also be classified as solar energy since it is generated as the result of solar radiation on terrestrial surfaces) conversion worldwide. The first large wind installation from the Pacific Gas and Electric Company in the Altamont Pass, shown in Fig. 25 was a "wind farm" in California. The phrase wind farm was used to indicate that usual farming, e.g., with cattle grazing, could continue to go on at the fields on which windmills were installed, hence the traditional farmer could reap additional revenues from his fields. This wind farm was later extended to 740 MW with unsurpassed performance because of its optimal wind condition throughout this Pass.

Fig. 25: The first larger wind farm at the Altamont Pass in California

3.9   Photovoltaic Demonstration

During the early '70s photovoltaic development made rapid progress and it became feasible to initiate a number of demonstration projects, from single-family house roofs (Fig. 26) to large fields of interconnected panels, feeding directly into power utilities (Fig. 27). These were designed to test longtime reliability for a variety of solar panels supplied by different manufacturers and at different locations with their specific meteorological environment.

Starting first with small panels and arrays as laboratory tests and simulated accelerated degradation, these tests were soon enlarged to substantial panel sizes in the mid to late '70s, with deployment from airports, to mountain tops, to oil drilling platforms in oceanic environments. The amount of data analyzed increased the confidence in many of the PV-panel types, especially single crystal or poly crystal silicon, to be reliable and maintenance-free to permit factory warranties in excess of 20 years.

With this and the payback guarantee and with many power utilities to permit net metering, two major conditions were fulfilled to make photovoltaic conversion a near-term competitor for the terrestrial market. Tax incentives that were provided by a number of states helped the industry further.

Unfortunately, the government support that was given decisively under the Carter administration, dwindled under Reagan's watch and gave the wrong signal worldwide.

Fig. 26: Rooftop installation of photovoltaic panels at the Los Angeles Department of Water and Power's "Optimum Energy House." This house was established in 1984 after many earlier PV-equipped houses showed technical feasibility. This indicated the growing interest of power utilities to generate hands-on experience.

There were several examples of positioning photovoltaic panels between side mirrors to enhance insolation (Clarisa Plains PV Power Plant) or on one- or two-axis trackers; an example of a two-axis tracker is shown in Fig. 24. Mixed results of these installations indicated the need for further research (undesirable heating in Clarisa with consequent degradation, and undesirable cost penalties for most of the trackers).

Fig. 27: Platte River flat-plate photo-voltaic panels mounted on a two-axis tracker to increase the daily output

Field installation of a large number of interconnected single-axis tracking panes with proper spacing were provided by the Sacramento Municipal Utility District (SMUD), and are shown in Fig. 28. After the first two of the planned five phases were installed, the next phases were postponed indefinitely because of economical concerns.

The first installations were simple fixed-elevation flat panels, deployed at a proper angle and distance between the panel rows, and they showed most promising results.

Fig. 28: SMUD PV1 Photovoltaic Power Plant

3.10   The Political Climate as a Major Influence

For more information, see Mener, 2000.

3.10.1   The Kennedy Administration

The first solar energy impulse started with energy study initiated by President Kennedy in 1963 that was completed in 1966, and President Johnson consequently authorized his science advisor to include solar energy into their plan. Reasons were the steady increase of energy demands and the evaluation of future options for alternative energy supply. Few studies were initiated by NASA but little was accomplished until President Nixon took office in 1969 and David Freeman, in the newly established division of Energy Policy in the White House, started to interact with solar scientists in the USA to evaluate potentials for larger scale terrestrial applications.

3.10.2.   Nixon Administration

Starting in 1971, with Senator Mike Gravel (Alaska) leading the way an initiative was passed in the US Congress to sponsor solar research. NSF (since 1969) and NASA became active in the field, based on several evaluations (University of Delaware, Böer, Oct 8 and 9, 1971; and NSF/NASA, Herwig and Cherry, evaluation of photovoltaics for terrestrial use in early 1972) and on two speeches that President Nixon gave in January and June 1971 in which he indicated a new emphasis on including solar energy with its long-term potential. In the office of energy policies, a renewed effort to support solar energy evolved. David Freeman consequently started to encourage the work of solar scientists. The results of the "Assessment of Solar Energy as a National Energy Resource" became available at the end of 1972 (Donovan et al.). A goal was set for the development of flat-plate collectors for comfort conditioning and hot water, as well as for solar thermal electric energy generation and for photovoltaic conversion. The start of commercialization was predicted for between 1975 and 1980. Emphasis from NSF was given to photovoltaics. The cost for such a five-year program was estimated in 1972 in the NSF/NASA "Solar Panel Report" at $196 Million and later in 1973 by the NSF solar energy planning staff at $409 million and still later at $1,050 million. As a result of planning under the Nixon Energy Independence effort, a small part of these planning budgets was initially included in the NSF budgets for 1973 and 1974.

Sponsorship from NSF in FY 1970 under Denton and Herwig and from NASA (especially the Lewis Research Center) under Woodward was then combined with other similar efforts. These were in the Department of Housing and Urban Development (HUD); the General Service Administration (GSA), the Atomic Energy Commission (AEC), later the Department of Defense (DoD), and the National Bureau of Standards (NBS) into a new Program at RANN (Research Applied for National Needs) in 1973. Still, under Nixon, solar energy ranged after nuclear energy (Dixie Lee Ray, report on December 1973) and all other conventional energy forms at last position. This changed in 1974 with the oil embargo and the proclamation "Energy Independence." Again, solar central power stations and solar heating and cooling development ranged with high priority.

The funding increased at NSF from a miniscule $1.2 million in 1971 to $13.2 million in 1974. At ERDA the budget in solar energy in 1975 increased steeply to $42.9 million and in 1976 to $114.9 million.

Congress enacted the "Heating and Cooling Demonstration Act" on September 3, 1974, with HUD responsible for private houses and NASA for industrial buildings. The Act was financed by $60 million for a duration of five years.

Congress also enacted the "Solar Energy Research, Development, and Demonstration Act" on October 26, 1976, with $1 billion for the duration of five years, with emphasis on solar-thermal and photovoltaic development.

In addition, the creation of a central solar energy research institute was to be established.

In the following two years few activities were initiated from the White House—during the last year of the Nixon and the interim Year of the Ford Administration. Most activities in support of solar came from the different states, mostly related to sometimes substantial tax incentives.

3.10.3   The Carter Administration

This all changed when Carter was elected in 1976. A visible step was Carter's address at the UN in May 1976, proclaiming an increased use of solar energy with a reform of the United States Energy Policy. Based on a critique of the previous administration's energy assessment, Carter demanded a much increased national support for solar energy research and development, now housed in the newly created Department of Energy. On April 20, 1977, the Carter plan delineated the concept of his energy policy in which 2.5 million houses should utilize solar energy by 1985. He proposed up to 40% tax incentives for solar. He also proposed substantially increased support for solar research.

During the years 1977 and 1978 several laws were enacted by the Carter administration that had a major influence in accelerating commercialization of solar. These included the ease of credits for small business. In the "Veteran Housing Benefit Act" additional credits were available for installation of solar systems. Attractive credits were also available for solar demonstration in agriculture. The DoD provided financial support for government buildings that included solar installations. The "National Energy Act" became law on November 9, 1978. This included the "Energy Tax Act," the "Public Utility Regulatory Policy Act" (PURPA, and the "National Energy Conservation Policy Act." All became law immediately, except PURPA, which was delayed until 1982 because of a lawsuit brought by the power utility companies.

Each one of these laws was rather complex in respect to the benefits and the duration of their applicability's, but it was a positive step in providing immediate incentives and it caused major commercialization efforts. Long discussions had predated by years these laws that were finally enacted, and the result was almost immediate. Especially small consumers profited substantially (tax benefits of 30% for installations up to $2,000 and of 20% up to $10,000). The market exploded at that time. Unfortunately, the end of the support period, and hesitation to extend it, played havoc with many parts of the industry.

Substantial benefit was offered to conservation means. Other measures included the guaranty of markets when specific conditions of conservation were fulfilled. Special financial benefits were given to schools, hospitals, and community buildings when energy-conserving means were installed. The economic method of "life cycle cost" was introduced to judge eligibility for financial benefits. Much of the benefits were paid partially by the federal and by the local government. Some hindrance in the implementation, however, still came from DOE in 1977. But commercialization of photovoltaics was, in general, supported, e.g., by inclusion of the life cycle cost in the tax support and by opening of the market for federal and DOD installations.

Pressure from the Congress and Senate on the Carter administration to further increase the budget for solar, resulted in the "Solar Photovoltaic Energy Research, Demonstration and Marketing Act" that was signed on November 4, 1978. For this it was planned to set aside $1.5 billion during the next ten years.

A visible sign of acceptance of solar energy was the installation of solar water heating collectors on the roof of the White House on recommendation of Carter's advisors Schlesinger and Eizenstat in 1978.

Another sign of increasing the visibility of solar energy research was the creation of the Solar Energy Research Institute in Golden, Colorado on March 24, 1976, with Paul Rappaport as its first director that started operation on July 5 of the same year. President Carter visited the newly formed Institute in the following year during the Sun Day celebration (Fig. 29).

Fig. 29: Dr. Paul Rappaport explains to President Carter the site for the new Solar Energy Research Institute

A major publicity effort was connected by the Carter administration with "Sun Day" on May 3, 1978, when festivities were celebrated in the entire United States. On that day, Carter said that a Domestic Policy Review would be initiated in relation to support for solar energy. A bit more than a year later (delayed by initial opposition from HUD and by the Treasury), on June 20, 1979, Carter presented the results of this review before Congress. He proclaimed the goal to have 20% of the US primary energy demand supplied by solar by the year 2000. This was to be achieved by tax incentives and substantial support for research and development.

However, others in the field of environmental concern voiced demands, e.g., by Amory Lovins, that such a goal could not be achieved without deviation from the conventional energy supply establishment. Carter did not respond to such a demand, in fact in 1980 he responded with the "Energy Security Act" to promote development of synthetic fuels.

Still, with the Energy Security Act and the "Windfall Profit Tax Act," that reduced the profit of the oil industry during the time of steeply increasing oil prices, Carter also spoke for the solar industry and proposed further help that substantially exceeded the previously installed tax credits:

1) all such credits were to be extended to the year 1985;
2) private housing that includes passive solar features were given a tax credit of 25% for such features;
3) the tax credit for solar panels was again increased, to 40%, and
4) a 25% tax credit was to be given to industry for solar installations to produce process heat. In addition, he proposed the creation of a solar bank.

3.10.4   Solar Financing from the US Government

The financial support for terrestrial solar from all government sources combined showed a dramatic increase between 1971, when essentially all support came from NSF, to the year 1980 under President Carter. This is shown in Table 1 in the first set of columns (Source: Larry Kazmerski, NREL). The second set of columns shows the dramatic cuts that were made under the Reagan, and during the first year of the Bush administrations (for more see Volume 2 of this Book).

Table 1
U.S. Government Solar Energy Budget

Year	Total Solar	PV Only	Year	Total Solar	PV Only
1971	1.1	0.0	1981	487.0	133.2
1972	1.9	0.33	1982	268.0	74.0
1973	4.0	0.79	1983	202.0	58.0
1974	16.0	2.4	1984	181.0	50.2
1975	55.0	5.0	1985	180.0	56.6
1976	149.0	28.6	1986	145.0	47.8
1977	290.0	51.9	1987	124.0	46.7
1978	408.0	61.7	1988	97.0	35.0
1979	456.0	118.5	1989	92.0	35.15
1980	550.0	151.1	1990	91.0	35.3

3.10.5   The After-Effect When Tax Incentive's Stopped

As discussed in more detail in the ASES chapter of the next volume, the after-effect of stopping the Carter-initiated tax cuts in the early 1980s was dramatic. Many of the small companies producing solar panels as well as larger groups selling solar energy went out of business. The flat-plate collector market that went from almost 120,000 square meters in 1974 to over 1.8 million square meters in 1981, collapsed to less than 455,000 square meters in 1985. Later, reinstating tax incentives on local or federal government levels still had an initially negative effect when some of the negotiation became known early on; little of the market that was still there almost completely disappeared in expectation of the forthcoming tax break; but many small companies could not bridge the time gap until the market would reappear. The lesson learned is how sensitive of the industry is to reliable support in time and in magnitude.

3.11   Influence on Membership of ASES

The membership of ASES was steadily increasing in the '70s based to a large extent on the substantial increase of support for research and development. Many universities and industry laboratories created groups working in the solar field, and their members were eager to present their results at national and international conferences. ASES and ISES were the preferred forums for many of them to discuss these results with colleagues and offer their help for others in need of good advice.

On a local level, many trades were eager to learn about solar, and local chapters were growing rapidly to teach and spread knowledge about a rapidly maturing field to all people interested in learning and utilizing the new tools. Local workshops, conferences, and exhibitions drew large numbers of participants, and the membership in local chapters grew rapidly. Many of these new members were subscribing to local solar magazines that were created, and also to the literature offered at a discount by ASES.

The end of the '70s saw a healthy organization of ASES and its chapters, and the success of the development in the field was visibly demonstrated in larger and larger conferences, permitting sponsors to weed out marginal submitted papers. The quality of all of these conferences increased and attracted professionals of adjacent fields who were eager to obtain first-hand information and to have their probing questions answered by experts. This in no small measure was an effect of the carefully orchestrated solar energy support given by the Carter Administration in the late '70s and this had dramatic reverberations worldwide.

During the height of the solar research and development activities it also became established that ASES and ISES provided attraction to solar specialists who had their main meetings in the topical specialists conferences, e.g., in ASME, ASHRAE, ASME, APS, IEEE, etc. Careful attention was given to compose the plenary sessions— in which quality review papers were presented that had been selected with regard to meeting the needs of the audience, from specialists who needed to obtain a summary of the latest results from one type of review, to professionals who were interested in systems approaches to evaluate the potential of combining different fields of solar conversion, to those who appreciated more general reviews. These plenary sessions covered a wide range from technical to economic to societal and political presentations. The technical conference chairs were also careful to avoid unsolicited technical papers that were rejected from specialists conferences for lack of quality. With such a conference philosophy it will be possible to attract the core of solar professionals and maintain membership in ASES and ISES through periods in which government sponsorship fluctuates.

References

Holl, Richard J, and Edgar A. DeMeo. *Status of Solar Thermal Electric Technology,* Advances in Solar Energy (K. W. Böer, ed.) New York; ASES, Boulder, and Plenum Press, 1990. pg. 219–381.

Mener, Gerhard , PhD Thesis, *Between Labor and Market; History of Solar Energy Utilization in Germany and USA, 1860–1986.* Munich, Germany: Ludwig Maximilian University, 2000.

Chapter 4

The Passive Solar Division of the American Solar Energy Society (ASES, The American Section of the International Solar Energy Society)

by
John S. Reynolds
Department of Architecture
University of Oregon
Eugene, OR 97403
jreyn@darkwing.uoregon.edu
and
J. Douglas Balcomb
Retired
cdbalcomb@earthlink.net

Abstract

In this part we review the twenty-four year history of the Passive Solar Division of the American Solar Energy Society. The Passive Division grew on the demand of a large number of architects and a few engineers and builders who were focused on designing solar heating, natural cooling, and daylighting elements into the architecture of the building itself. The most significant accomplishment of the Passive Division has been the organization of a series of highly successful National Passive Solar Conferences, beginning in 1977 and continuing each year up to the twenty-ninth in 2004. We also trace the evolution of the passive solar movement in the United States, including impacts on education and the architectural profession, design tools, and national awards or recognitions.

4.1   Introduction: The Passive Solar Movement in the USA and the Formation of the Passive Solar Division of ASES

Passive solar, as a term, originated in the USA in the 1970s as a large-scale reaction among building designers against the prevailing concept that solar energy for buildings necessarily consisted of collectors on the roof connected through piping or ducts to a heat storage tank or bed in the building. By intentional contrast, the latter approach was disdainfully dubbed "active solar." Although there was a lot of debate over these names and their definition, the terminology stuck and has persisted. Some of the passive solar advocates objected to the unsightly hardware of active systems. Others objected to the unreliable reliance on outside electrical energy for the system operation. Others objected to "tacking" a system onto the building rather than embedding the system design within the building architecture. And still others focused on using the ordinary materials of building construction--glass, mass (bricks, concrete, etc.), and insulation—instead of imposing unfamiliar elements. A significant divide appeared between the two camps. Architects tended toward the passive approach, while the active system advocates were predominantly engineers.

Because all buildings are passive to some degree, the term passive solar came to be applied to buildings in which the designers had intentionally modified the design to take advantage of solar heating or natural cooling, for example by window placement, added mass, or ventilation strategy. Inevitably, some designs relied on both passive and active elements and came to be called "hybrids."

Certainly, there were many passive solar buildings constructed prior to their flowering in the 1970s. The Keck Brothers had been designing passive solar ranch-style houses in the Chicago area. In 1947, Libbey Owens Ford (LOF), in an effort to encourage the use of more glass, sponsored leading architects in all forty-eight states and the District of Columbia to design a solar house for that state. The result was *Your Solar House*, edited by Marion Simon, Simon and Schuster, 1947. LOF also built and distributed an elegant slide rule to educate designers about the sun-path across the sky in different seasons. Victor Olgyay's *Design with Climate* (Princeton University Press 1963) was in most university libraries, if not in most offices. In 1969, two influential books appeared: Baruch Givoni's *Man, Climate, and Architecture*

(London: Elsevier Press) and Ian McHarg's *Design with Nature* (John Wiley & Sons). Ironically, the landmark active solar system research, done by the team of Hottel, Whillier, and Bliss at MIT, was preceded by a series of little-known passive test cells, built at MIT by Albert Dietz. These performed equally well as the active cells built by Hottel, Whillier, and Bliss but were simply before their time.

But the 1970s saw a tidal wave of passive designs. A whole terminology was coined to describe the basic system types—direct gain, thermal storage wall, roof pond, and sunspace. Although isolated passive solar buildings showed up in other parts of the U.S., in England, and in France, the epicenter was in New Mexico, where the counterculture enthusiastically endorsed the approach. This tended to further polarize the technical and academic community working on funded active solar research, who wanted hard data and definitive experiments and dismissed anecdotal accounts as fanciful wishful thinking. This impasse was overcome by a group of engineers at the Los Alamos National Laboratory (LANL), who had been working on active solar but in 1974 ventured a few hour-by-hour computer simulations of simple passive concepts. The results proved so encouraging that the group, led by J. Douglas Balcomb, a nuclear engineer, swung over to working entirely on passive solar. They built and instrumented a series of test cells to verify their calculations and published the results. The LANL group did not invent anything new, but they legitimized passive solar to a skeptical technical audience.

The single event that put passive solar on the map was the National Passive Solar Conference held in Albuquerque in May 1976. This was funded through LANL by the Energy Research and Development Administration, predecessor of the US Department of Energy: co-chairs were Balcomb and William Mingenbach, an architect from Taos. The conference was coordinated with the help of the New Mexico Solar Energy Association. It is difficult to overestimate the excitement as 585 attendees strained to hear 51 all-invited papers describing all the major buildings and evaluations. The 355-page proceedings, edited by Balcomb and published by LANL, were highly sought. Prior to this conference, funding from the government was only for active approaches. The conference started the process of balancing the scales between active and passive solar research, development, and dissemination.

4.1.1   The First Steps of the Passive Solar Division

The first official step occurred at the 1977 Annual Meeting of the American Section of the International Solar Energy Society (AS of ISES, which later became ASES), held in Orlando, Florida, in June 1977. There was a lot of interest in passive solar at the conference and a whole section of the proceedings was devoted to the topic.

Upon action by the board of directors, AS of ISES Chairman Karl Boer invited J. Douglas Balcomb (Fig. 1) to initiate the formation of a Passive Solar Division as one of several new divisions being formed. Balcomb post-ed signs in the hallways inviting those interested to an evening meeting. A standing-room-only crowd, filling the large room, ratified the selection of a provisional division board of directors to be chaired by Balcomb and to include Bruce Anderson, Don Aitkin, Drew Gillett, Jeffery Cook (Fig. 2), and Fred Dubin (Fig. 3).

Fig. 1: Doug Balcomb making his final point at a national conference under a rainbow

Fig. 2: Jeff Cook lecturing to a fascinated group of students

Fig. 3: Fred Dubin

4.1.2   Initial National Passive Solar Conferences

The Orlando meeting described in 1.1 also selected Philadelphia, Pennsylvania, as the site of the next conference devoted entirely to passive solar. This conference, called the 2nd National Passive Solar Conference, was the first actually organized by the AS of ISES. The conference was coordinated by the Mid-Atlantic Solar Energy Association and chaired by Don Prowler, Doug Kelbaugh, and Harrison Fraker.

The conference was held in March 1978. The proceedings show an attendance list of 678, slightly outnumbering attendance at the AS of ISES Annual Meeting of that year held in Denver, Colorado. The 157 papers filled 942 pages printed in three proceeding's volumes, edited by Don Prowler. Unlike the first conference in Albuquerque, nearly all of the papers were in response to a call for abstracts rather than being invited.

Thus began the trend that prevailed for the next several years. Until 1983, the AS of ISES held two annual conferences, one the Annual Meeting and the other the National Passive Solar Conference, which often had a larger attendance. The Passive Solar Division took responsibility for selecting the site of the Passive Solar Conference, which was subsequently coordinated by a local state or regional solar energy association. Although there were traditional researchers from universities and laboratories presenting papers, most were written by architects, builders, or do-it-yourselfers not accustomed to the rigid discipline of refereed technical publications. The process was accommodated to serve these division members—papers to be presented were selected on the basis of abstracts submitted, but the final papers, due only at the time of the conference, were not reviewed, only screened to assure that they met minimum requirements. They were not held to the same standard as Journal publications and thus could more accurately be described as simply a record of what happened at the conference. This served the needs of a rapidly evolving field well and reduced the lead time required between abstracts submittal and presentation. Outsiders might have objected to this method of operating, but not the division members.

The proceedings of the National Passive Solar conferences, all published by the AS of ISES, form the backbone of the literature of the passive solar movement in the United States. The initial conferences, held separately, were as follows:

Conference	Year	Location
1st	May 1976	Albuquerque, NM
2nd	March 1978	Philadelphia, PA
3rd	Jan. 1979	San Jose, CA
4th	Oct. 1979	Kansas City, MO
5th	Oct.1980	Amherst, MA
6th	Sept. 1981	Portland, OR
7th	Aug. 1982	Knoxville, TN
8th	Sept. 983	Santa Fe, NM
9th	Sept. 1984	Columbus, OH
10th	Oct. 1985	Raleigh, NC

The fifth conference, on the University of Massachusetts campus in Amherst, deserves special comment. It was a multi-ring circus in some ways, with an overall claimed attendance of 2,500. In addition to the regular technical sessions, there were large sessions dedicated to builders, government officials, the Women In Solar Energy Organization (WISE), numerous workshops, and a large exhibition. The conference was held in an American election year and occasionally took on political overtones. Certainly, attendance, whether or not it was actually 2,500, peaked at this conference.

In addition to these conferences, there was a very significant conference sponsored by the AS of ISES. This was a one-of-a-kind event, the International Passive and Hybrid Cooling Conference, held in Miami Beach, Florida, in November 1981, the same year as the conference in Portland, Oregon. Principal organizers were Arthur Bowen, Eugene Clark, and Kenneth Labs. The focus, both on passive cooling and on the international scene, was unique. This conference was the predecessor of conferences of a separate group called Passive and Low-Energy Architecture (PLEA) that went on to sponsor international conferences around the world, although never again in the United States. The 1,050-page proceedings is the landmark publication in passive cooling.

4.1.3   Later National Passive Solar Conferences

By 1986, attendance at both the Annual Meeting and the National Passive Solar Conference had declined to the point that the AS of ISES Board decided to co-locate the Annual Meeting and the National Passive Conference, in Boulder, Colorado, where the national ASES office was located. However, the Passive Conference maintained a separate identity, held distinct presentation sessions, and published separate proceedings.

This formula proved to be successful, largely because it recognized and fostered the unique flavor and character of the passive movement, and has been continued ever since. The twenty-ninth National Passive Solar Conference was held in Portland, Oregon, in 2004, in conjunction with the ASES Annual Meeting. The Passive Division has maintained oversight of the Passive Conference, selecting the technical organizing committee, which has maintained its separate identity.

In 1988, the ASES Board of Directors instituted a reorganization of the Section division structure. In the process, the Passive Solar Division was broadened and renamed the Building Division.

Fig. 4: Susan Luster, Mike Nicklas, Jeff Cook, and Edna Shaviv

4.2   Our Impacts on Education and the Professions

4.2.1   Curriculum

Before 1970, the typical architecture school curriculum had two quite separate and unequal parts: design, and everything else. [This continues today at some schools.] The design faculty held the positions of prestige and privilege. Students were most likely to encounter a few examples of passive architecture in history class, because design studios concentrated on the current work of the best-known architects. Reference documents in studio were the architecture magazines rather than books. Courses in environmental –technology—called mechanical and electrical equipment in those days—concentrated on formulae and hardware. They were something to suffer through, and too often served primarily as a "weeding-out" mechanism. There was little to appeal to either social or esthetic concerns: such equipment was ugly, and energy was plentiful and getting cheaper. Indeed, nuclear power was touted as soon to become "too cheap to meter."

In the early 1970s, two forces helped reshape the architecture curriculum: the environmental movement began by Rachel Carson's *Silent Spring* and the Mideast oil embargo of 1973. Energy was suddenly no longer plentiful, and its production and use spewed environmental damage. Biology became as influential as physics for the designer, and the dreary "mechanical" courses sprang to life with design criteria such as energy conservation and designing with the climate. Those schools that gave a faculty member an assignment in both studio and tech courses benefited first and most, as such faculty could speak the language of design in the lecture, and bring technical criteria to direct application in studio.

In 1975, the Association of Collegiate Schools of Architecture [ACSA] sponsored a seminar on "Energy and Architecture," followed by a special issue of the *Journal of Architectural Education* in 1977. This resulted in the book *Energy Conservation through Building Design* (McGraw-Hill, 1979), edited by Don Watson, with fifteen entries.

Stung by its energy vulnerability and by growing criticism of pollution, the U.S. government rushed to invest in energy conservation; renewable energy investments increased as well. The Solar Energy Research Laboratory was established, as well as a set of regional offices called the Solar Utilization Network. Solar energy received favorable treatment until 1980, when a new administration hostile to conservation and solar energy took office. By then, a vibrant infrastructure had been established, so research and education continued despite governmental disfavor.

One outstanding example of federal contribution to passive strategies was the ambitious and wide-ranging curriculum reform project, funded by the U.S. Department of Energy, Office of Solar Applications in Buildings (Mike Maybaum and Robert Shibley). "Teaching Passive Design in Architecture" was directed by Donald Prowler and Harrison Fraker, of the University of Pennsylvania. Participants included many leading passive educators and practicioners: University of California at Los Angeles, Murray Milne, Baruch Givoni; Carnegie-Mellon, Vivian Loftness; Georgia Tech, Charles C. Benton, James Akridge; Kent State, Jack Kremers, Peters Oppermann; Massachusetts Institute of Technology, Edward Allen, Douglas Mahone; New Jersey Institute of Technology; David Elwell, Barry Jackson, Doug Kelbaugh, Steve Zdepski; North Carolina State, Henry Sanoff, Graham Adams; University of Oregon, G. Z. Brown, John Reynolds (Fig. 5), Susan Ubbelohde; Rensselaer Polytechnic Institute, Walter Kroner, Harvey Bryan, Russell Leslie; Rice University, Gordon Wittenberg; and Yale University, Donald Watson.

Fig. 5: John Reynolds, the co-author of this review

The architecture magazines soon recognized the new order, instituting annual issues on energy-conserving architecture, later to be widened and christened "green architecture." A competitor appeared, *Solar Age*, published by Bruce Anderson, running from 1976 through 1985, featuring color photos and technically accurate write-ups of the latest examples of conservation and climatic design. Design awards began to include research; the 1983 *Progressive Architecture* thirtieth Awards program gave a citation to "Teaching Passive Design in Architecture." In the Pacific northwest, the Portland AIA and Bonneville Power Administration established the Energy and Design Awards, beginning in 1993, ending in 2002.

Schools not mentioned in the "Teaching Passive Design in Architecture" project, but highly influential in the early passive movement, include: Arizona State, Jeffrey Cook, John Yellott; California Poly San Luis Obispo, Polly Cooper, Keith Haggard (Fig. 6), Phillip Niles; San Jose State, Don Aitken; State University of New York at Buffalo, Dennis Andrejko, Robert Shibley (Fig. 7); Trinity University (San Antonio), Gene Clark; University of California Berkeley, Edward Arens, Charles C. Benton, Richard Peters; University of Miami, Arthur Bowen; University of Southern California, Ralph Knowles, Marc Schiler; University of Washington, Joel Loveland, Marietta Millet.

Fig. 6: Keith Haggard and Doug Balcomb

Some outstanding contributions from individual educators include Edward Mazria, who brought passive solar to Oregon, wrote a popular book, and returned to New Mexico to practice; Harold Hay, pioneer of the roofpond, at Arizona State and Cal Poly San Luis Obispo; William Shurcliff, Harvard professor of physics who compiled his personal sketches in a "Directory of

Solar Buildings," and continuing through 13 rapidly updated editions between 1974 and 1977; and Tim Johnson at MIT, an early proponent of low-emissivity glass.

Fig 7: (standing from left to right) Bruce Hunn, Robert Shibley, Frank DeWinter, Doug Balcomb, and Jeff Cook. Dennis Andrejko is seated.

4.2.2   Design Tools: Publications

Within a decade following the Mideast oil embargo, several books became widely available to designers and educators. Edward Mazria's *The Passive Solar Energy Book* was published by Rodale Press in 1979, and achieved great market success. David Wright's *Natural Solar Architecture* (Van Nostrand Reinhold), appeared in 1978. Doug Balcomb, Robert Jones, et. al. prepared three volumes of the *Passive Solar Design Handbook*, released by the U.S. Department of Energy, Assistant Secretary for Conservation and Solar Energy, Office of Solar Applications for Buildings, from 1980 to 1982. This set presented detailed design criteria for a wide number of US and Canadian climate zones, for direct gain, sunspaces, and Trombe and water wall systems. Phillip Niles and Ken Haggard's *California Passive Solar Handbook* was published by the California Energy Commission in 1980, complete with recommended details of particular use to architects. Richard Stein's *Architecture and Energy* (Anchor Press, 1977) raised awareness by including embodied energy information on a wide variety of typical building materials. Ralph Knowles', *Sun Rhythm, Form* (MIT Press, 1981) approached urban form with solar access design criteria.

To provide a forum for the rapidly developing research, the *Passive Solar Journal* began publication in January 1982. With four issues annually, it continued through 1987.

An ambitious 12-volume set, *Solar Heat Technologies: Fundamentals and Applications*, Charles Bankston, editor-in-ehief was published by MIT Press, beginning in 1989. Three volumes: *Passive Solar Buildings*, Doug Balcomb and Bruce Wilcox, editors 1992; *Passive Cooling*, Jeffrey Cook, editor 1989; and *Solar Building Architecture*, Bruce Anderson, editor, 1990, were especially of interest to members of the Passive Division.

In the schools, the 6th edition of the widely-used textbook by Benjamin Stein, William McGuinness, and John Reynolds, *Mechanical and Electrical Equipment for Buildings*, appeared in 1980, the first edition to include design data on energy conservation and passive solar design. In 1983, McGraw-Hill published Donald Watson and Kenneth Labs' *Climatic Design: energy-efficient building principles and practices*. G. Z. Brown's *Sun, Wind and Light* (Wiley, 1985), took a designer's approach to passive guidelines. Fuller Moore's *Environmental Control Systems: Heating, Cooling, Lighting* (McGraw-Hill, 1993), and Norbert Lechner's *Heating, Cooling, Lighting Design Methods for Architects* (Wiley, 1991), gave two more perspectives on solar design for architects.

Architecture programs rely heavily on visual images, so the set of color slides provided by the New Mexico Solar Energy Association proved highly popular and influential as a teaching tool.

4.2.3   Design Tools: Software

Many of the books mentioned above contained design rules of thumb, and more elaborate step-by-step design analysis procedures. With the advent of hand-held calculators, then programmable ones, designers gained the ability to rapidly sharpen their designs for better energy performance. Early innovators included Total Environmental Action in New England, and the Berkeley Solar Group in California, whose CalPas software gained wide usage. For integrated design decisions in the earliest design stages, Energy Scheming software was developed by G. Z. Brown at the University of Oregon. For analysis of buildings beyond the formative stages, Energy 10 became the most widely used software. Thanks to Lawrence Berkeley Labs, accurate and rapid daylighting analysis programs became available.

4.3   Buildings

There is a tension of long standing in the design community, between an emphasis on energy conservation versus solar energy. Because windows are one of the greatest threats to thermal performance, those emphasizing conservation often see the large windows associated with solar heating as counterproductive. Solar advocates decry the small windows and stuffy air associated with the conservation examples. Although seen as a conflict between "light and tight" and "glass and mass," both approaches aim to conserve nonrenewable energy and reduce pollution. The solar approach, however, establishes a stronger link between inside and outside.

4.3.1   Design-Build

New Mexicans were among the first builders of self-designed solar homes, including Zomeworks inventor Steve Baer, sunspace advocates Bill and Susan Yanda, and developer Wayne Nichols, whose multiple solar residences include the widely influential Balcomb house in Santa Fe. Later, Mike Reynolds added earth-bermed, tire-walled Earthships to New Mexico's solar heritage. Elsewhere, Jersey Devil Steve Badanes became famous for creative, highly unconventional residences from coast to coast. In Vermont, the Yestermorrow school was established on the design-build model, unlike typical architecture programs. Pliny Fisk's Center for Maximum Potential Systems near Austin, Texas, innovates in both building products and building forms, residential and beyond.

The best-known residential solar development remains Village Homes in Davis, California, developed by Mike Corbett. Streets are laid out so that every house has excellent solar exposure; most homes (by various architects and builders) have passive solar gain and solar water heaters. Community-owned gardens are woven throughout the subdivision, retaining rainwater in the semi-arid climate. The homes have increased substantially in value compared to those in contemporary neighboring subdivisions.

4.3.2   Residential Architecture

One of the earlier architect-designed solar homes in the U. S. was Doug Kelbaugh's own home in Princeton, New Jersey. Built in 1975, dominated by a Trombe wall with large direct gain openings, it also has an attached sunspace. David Wright designed his early direct-gain home in Los Alamos, then many more in New Mexico and California. Don Watson's own direct gain solar home is in Connecticut. Perhaps the largest and most expensive solar home is in Sun Valley, Idaho, the Dennis house by Arnie Bystrom. This is a lovingly-detailed example of direct gain with concrete thermal mass and solar water heating. The federal government funded the Brookhaven House, designed by Total Environmental Action. It illustrates direct gain, Trombe wall, and sunspace strategies.

4.3.3   Commercial and Institutional Architecture

During the solar heyday of the late 1970s, the office of the State Architect of California (directed by Sym van der Ryn) designed the Gregory Bateson office building in Sacramento. Filling an entire city block, this prominent solar example includes a daylit atrium, exterior sunshading appropriate to orientation, and night ventilation cooling of exposed concrete structure. Another early example is the office building of the Society for the Preservation of New Hampshire Forests, Concord, designed by White, Banwell, and Arnold. Elongated east-west, the building combines direct gain, double envelope sunspace, eutectic salt storage, and water tube storage. In 1974, Alvar Aalto's library opened at Mt. Angel Abbey in Oregon, prompting a daylighting awakening among U. S. architects.

Other notable early examples include the Tennessee Valley Authority offices in Chattanooga, elongated east-west with a daylit atrium and lightshelves; Ed Mazria's Mt. Airey Library in North Carolina, integrating direct gain and daylighting; and the Center for Regenerative Studies at Cal Poly Pomona, where John Lyle inspired a new curriculum and the innovative solar buildings that house it.

Two office buildings of the 1980s reflect utterly different solar approaches. The Occidental Chemical headquarters in Niagara Falls, New York, by Cannon Design, is a nine-story glass cube. On all four sides, a wide air space between the outer layer and an inner layer of glass contains moveable shading fins that can reflect daylight as well as blocking unwanted sun. Heat build-up within the space can be harnessed as needed for space heating. In Eugene, Oregon, The Emerald People's Utility District headquarters, designed by John Reynolds and Dick Williams, is elongated east-west with no east-west windows, uses deciduous vines on trellis for south shading, and integrates thermally massive structure, daylighting, lightshelves, direct gain solar heating, and night ventilation cooling.

Later notable solar buildings include the Audubon Society's New Canaan (Connecticut) Nature Center, Buchanan-Watson Architects, which takes the greenhouse form and adapts it to serve direct gain and solar water heating.

The Famolare Warehouse in Brattleboro, Vermont, probably has the largest Trombe wall in the US. Sym van der Ryn's Real Goods store in Hopland, California, features not only direct gain and daylighting, but environmentally friendly products and landscaping. The Visitor Transit Center at Zion (Utah) National Park, designed by the Park Service Denver office, beautifully integrates daylighting, passive downdraft cooltowers, direct gain, Trombe wall, and photovoltaic panels.

4.3.4   Earth Sheltering

In 1975, a conference—"The Use of Earth Covered Buildings"—was held in Ft. Worth, Texas. Many of the advocates of earth sheltering are careful to simultaneously advocate daylighting and passive solar heating. Prominent among these proponents are Lester Boyer, Texas A&M; Walter Grondzik, Florida A&M; architect Malcolm Wells in Cherry Hills, New Jersey, and architect-researcher Ken Labs. One example is the Antelope Valley California Poppy Preserve, Lancaster, California, by Colyer-Freeman Architects, featuring earth berms and an earth covered roof, direct gain, Trombe wall, and a 150-foot earth tube whose supply air gets a bit of evaporative cooling as it enters this small visitor center.

4.3.5   Straw Bale

The recent attention to "green buildings" has increased interest in straw bale construction, using an otherwise waste product to provide well-insulated walls. Solar applications need care, because the bales cannot be simultaneously thermally massive and insulative, so a rather thick coat of interior stucco, or at least a concrete slab floor, are necessary for thermal mass.

Architects who skillfully combine passive solar, daylighting, and straw bale include Polly Cooper and Ken Haggard, San Luis Solar Group, who have designed many solar homes in California, including their own home-office complex featuring direct gain, water wall, PV, and low-head hydro power.

4.4   Other Things of Interest

4.4.1   Awards

The Passive Division instituted the Passive Pioneer Awards in 1979 to "honor those in the passive field whose pioneering work set the stage for others to follow. Honorees are men and women who developed the theories, early research efforts, new concepts, and opportunities for later researchers to develop. Their foresight, innovative thinking, and creativity opened the doors for others."

Passive Pioneer awardees:

2004   David A. Bainbridge, Alliant International University
2003   Ralph Lewis Knowles, University of Southern California
2002   Donald Prowler, Donald Prowler & Associates
2001   Murray Milne, UCLA
2000   Pliny Fisk III, Center for Maximum Potential Building Systems
1999   Robert Keller, Kalwall Corporation
1998   Bill and Susan Yanda, New Mexico
1997   John Reynolds, University of Oregon
1996   Ken Haggard and Polly Cooper, San Luis Obispo Solar Group, California
1995   Anne Dunning, SOLARCON, Santa Fe, New Mexico
1994   Edward Mazria, Albuquerque, New Mexico
1993   Phil Niles, Cal Poly University at San Luis Obispo
1991   Native Americans
1990   Bruce Anderson, Earth Day, USA
1989   Steve Baer, Zomeworks Corp.
1988   Norman B. Saunders, Weston, Massachusetts
1987   John I. Yellott, Arizona State University
1986   Harold Hay, California
1985   Jeffrey Cook, Arizona State University
1984   J. Douglas Balcomb, Los Alamos National Laboratory
1983   Peter Van Dresser, New Mexico
1982   Wendell Thomas, Celo, North Carolina
1981   Loren Neubauer, Davis, California
1980   Albert Dietz, Massachusetts Institute of Technology
1979   George and Fred Keck

4.4.2   Influence on Other Organizations

The Passive Division has encouraged a network of activists to further organize the spread of renewable energy, energy conservation, and responsible design.

In section 1.2, the founding of PLEA—Passive and Low Energy Alternatives—was discussed. PLEA's first international conference was held in Bermuda in 1982. Pergamon Press published the conference Proceedings. The first International Daylighting Conference was held in Phoenix in 1983. Again, many passive division members helped organize the event. As an outgrowth of both the passive conferences and the daylighting conference, the Society of Building Science Educators was organized in 1983. This influential group of architecture professors continues to hold its annual meeting during the Passive conference, and introduces many students to ASES.

Another outgrowth of Passive division activism is the Sustainability division, formed in 1992-93. Many of its organizers were Passive division members.

A final example, albeit with less Passive division influence, is the U.S. Green Buildings Council. An organization of manufacturers and designers; few of the industrial members are overtly solar oriented. But many of the founding architects are familiar faces at ASES conferences.

Chapter 5

Australia-New Zealand Section of the International Solar Energy Society (1954-80)

by
Garry F. Baverstock, B Arch, MSc, FRAIA
Adjunct Associate Professor Murdoch University,
Director of Wise Earth P/L t/a Ecotect-Architects
and www.solar-e.com,
P.O. Box 3322, Broadway, Nedlands
Western Australia, 6009
e-mail: solartec@iinet.net.au

Abstract

The formation of the ANZ Section of ISES began very early. In fact Australians, led by the CSIRO scientist Roger Morse, attended the Arizona conference in 1955, which was the first meeting that eventually led to the formation of the Solar Energy Society. In Australia he was a pioneer in solar water heating, working closely with colleagues Bob Dunkle, Terry Hollands, Don Close, and Wal Read. ANZSES, or ISES (ANZ) as it was then known, evolved from this early prominence in the formation of ISES. Roger Morse became president in 1970 after financial problems prompted a move from the USA to Melbourne, Australia. He was honored for his pioneering work, including an Order of Australia (the Australian equivalent of a British knighthood), Fellowship of the Academy of Technological Science and Engineering, and the Premier Medal of the Institution of Engineers, Australia. Other leaders came forward, with Wal Read seeing the formal incorporation of ANZSES through its embryonic stage to its role as an active, well-respected organization. The socio-economic climate for the development of solar energy during the first thirty years was adverse and difficult. It took a large personal and economic commitment by the early champions of research and of industry to persist in their work on solar energy. We all owe a debt of gratitude to the many scientific and industry pioneers who laid the foundations for future generations.

5.1   Introduction: Solar History in Australia and First Steps Toward the Formation of ANZSES

Fig. 1: Early Australian pioneers in the late 1970s.
From the left: Wal Read, Bill Charters, Jack Duffie, and Roger Morse at the CSIRO Division of Mechanical Engineering, Highett, Victoria

Australia had an important role in the development of solar energy in the modern era since World War II. To understand how this occurred, a number of historical eras are discussed. These eras help to define the many influences that world events had on the history of the Solar Energy Society, specifically in Australia, as well as globally:

1954 – 63:   American genesis
1963 – 73:   Emergence of Australia (early beginnings)
1973 – 79:   Energy crisis

Early pioneers of solar energy in Australia (Fig. 1) had a large impact on the world scene and the formation of the solar energy society. The following summary shows how this impact occurred.

5.1.1   1954-63, American Genesis

The International forerunner, the "Association for Applied Solar Energy" (AFASE), was formed on 24 March 1954 and then incorporated on 24 December that year, after the initial actions of a group of American industrialists and agricultural leaders to host a world conference in Phoenix, Arizona, USA. Their functions were to gather and disseminate information, foster research, and encourage industry expansion. Henry Sargent, the first president, led the organization after the famous Dr. Farrington Daniels, who had originally sowed seeds of the idea, as early as 1952.

5.1.1.1   International Focus

The world symposium of Applied Solar energy, 1–5 November in Phoenix in 1955, attracted 900 delegates from 36 countries. An international focus had arrived.

Australia, Roger Morse, chief CSIRO Div. Mech. Eng. (Fig. 1), attended the 1955 Phoenix conference and was involved in the early formation of the Solar Energy Society. Other key technical players from that division of the CSIRO were Wal Read, Bob Dunkle, Terry Hollands, and Don Close. (Refer to short biography of Roger Neil Morse by Bill Charters. This can be sourced from the full version of the ANZ history on the ANZSES web site.)

After nine years of activity support, the interest began to dwindle. Led by the visionary Farrington Daniels, they reorganized and re-formed as "The Solar Energy Society" in 1963, with Daniels becoming president from 1964-1967.

5.1.1.2   Australian Interest

During the early '60s, interest in SES had spread throughout Australia. This was to be significant, as the embryonic branch of SES (later to become ANZSES) was to become a potent force for solar energy research and development on the world scene.

In 1959 an interesting connection of the oil industry with solar energy development occurred. The involvement of retired president of the Shell

Chemical Corporation, Ian Oostermeyer, in 1959, was significant. The involvement of Shell personnel in Australia as well as globally was to set a path and attitude toward the development of solar energy that was to prevail for decades.

Interest grew in Australia through administrative people like Frank Hogg, who became the honorary secretary of the Australian and New Zealand Section. He complemented the technical expertise of Morse and his colleagues. Eventually, Wal Read (Fig. 2) took over the job and managed the Australian contingent for many years. Wal Read was an integral part of the history of solar energy development in Australia for the next two decades.

Fig. 2: Wal Read in his latter years (the late 1990s) (photo supplied by the family simply notated Granddad)

5.1.1.3   Early Technological Innovation

From the late '40s, Australia's interest in solar had been growing. There was an enthusiastic group of thermal engineers, innovators, and inventors just waiting for an opportunity. All that was needed was an industry focus and a forum for sharing ideas and information and for making contacts. During the early days cross-fertilization of expertise between academic researchers and industry innovators was ad hoc and unstructured. This mode of operation was to change with the birth of the Solar Energy Society. Dissemination of information through the publication "Sun at Work," started by John Yellott in the U.S. in 1955, generated international interest in solar energy.

Roger Morse, head of the Mechanical Engineering division of the CSIRO, was the champion in Australia and was a catalyst in applying solar energy in a focused scientific way. A longstanding interest in solar energy utilization, including the development of a flat-plate solar water heater, led Mr. Roger Morse to take control of the mandate. The international symposia in Phoenix, Arizona, from the mid-'50s through to 1967 had a great influence on establishment of the society in Australia and became a great focus for authentication of the practical pioneers of the industry.

Innovation in this period was particularly focused in Western Australia, led by people such as Ron Brown, Clarry Small, Dr. R. Lawrance, Dr. John Barker, Peter Little, and Arthur Meredith. There were many others during this period throughout the country. At this time the innovators were active in solar water heating and solar housing. Scientists with commitment to solar energy, such as Dr. Bill Charters, plus later Dr. Steve Szokolay and John Ballinger, began emerging as world leaders/educators in their fields, making significant national and international contributions and helping to establish solid grounds for technological development. They were also active in establishing the Society as a solid cornerstone organization with high-ground objectives. Thus they continued the mandate and vision set for the Society in America after the Second World War.

ISES Sources: ISES Records, supplied by Cesare Silvi, Italy,
                Sunworld; 1979; Vol. 3, no.2.

5.2 The First Steps of the ANZ-Section of ISES

5.2.1   1963 – 73 Emergence of Australia (Early Beginnings)

In 1960 the American-based Association for Applied Solar Energy, the precursor of ISES, passed a resolution that national and regional branches were to be fostered. Australians took up the challenge.

5.2.1.1   Establishment of the ANZ Branch

In 1961 a meeting in Brisbane resulted in the formation of a national branch with local branches in most states and New Zealand. The committee in charge of implementation was:

R. N. Morse	(Victoria)
Prof. D. Allen-Williams	(Western Australia)
R. F. Benseman	(New Zealand)
T. E. Bowden	(New South Wales)
R. V. Dunkle	(Victoria)
Prof. C. F. Kettleborough & C. J. Milner	(New South Wales)
N. R. Sheridan	(Queensland)

The United Nations held a conference on "New Sources of Energy" in Rome in 1961, where Norm Sheridan (of the University of Queensland) presented a paper on the Brisbane solar air-conditioned house.

The inaugural meeting of the ANZ branch was on 22 August 1962. Encouragement came from the American president of AFASE (Association for Applied Solar Energy), retired Brigadier General Harold Walmsley. Office bearers were elected:

- R. N. Morse (chairman)
- F. Hogg (honorary. treasurer and unofficial secretary)
- C. F. Kettleborough (editor)

The first decision of significance was the establishment of a society journal, because of the large distance separation between states. So was born the "News Sheet of the Australia and New Zealand Branch, AFASE." It reported on activities in research and manufacturing and was produced at the University of New South Wales.

In 1963 the chairman reported in the newsletter that there were 40 members and by the annual general meeting that year the membership stood at 81. In 1962 the newssheet started and in 1964 it became known as "Solar Energy Progress in Australia and New Zealand," an annual publication.

The organization had a low-key existence throughout most of the '60s, as the branch became a section and state branches evolved in:

- New South Wales (NSW)
- Victoria (Vic)
- Queensland (Qld)
- Western Australia (WA)
- South Australia (SA)

(There were no branches in the Northern Territory (NT), Australian Capital Territory (ACT), Tasmania (Tas) or New Zealand (NZ) at this time.)

Another key player in the evolution and management of the Australian Section was Dr. Bill Charters (Fig. 3). He arrived in Australia in 1965, joined ISES in 1966, and became heavily involved in the preparation for and aftermath of the ISES Melbourne congress in 1970. Serving as ISES president in 1980-81, he gained the high regard of the international community.

He became chairman of ANZSES in 1982. His contribution to the scientific progress of solar energy and the administration of ANZSES was very valuable, his influence ranging over many decades. He was a very active scientist in the early days, working with internationally recognized scientists like Felix Trombe, and delivering many papers at ISES conferences. Charters also was very active at the Paris conference.

Fig. 3: Bill Charters, Professor and Researcher, Melbourne University, 1965-1997

5.2.1.2   Difficult Time for ISES

In 1965 with a membership numbering 100, Mr. J G. Baker was elected vice Chairman and in 1966 *Solar Energy Progress* was transferred to Highett (suburban Melbourne), Victoria, with R. V. Dunkle as editor.

After a number of difficult years (1964-68) and burdensome debts in America, changes were made that were to have an impact on the history of ISES and on Australia as a contributor to the field of solar energy. Dr. Farrington Daniels had to step back in as international president, and many debts had to be waived by creditors to save the Society from extinction. Somehow the Society's journal continued.

Australian interest in the international body was spearheaded by Roger Morse of the CSIRO, and due to the financial support in "cash and kind" from the CSIRO, it became obvious to the Americans that Australia should be the headquarters of the solar energy society. Morse became vice president to the president Peter Glaser in 1967. An international conference in Melbourne was promoted and eventuated in 1970. The dominant agenda item was the future of the Society.

5.2.1.3   ISES Is Born

The Melbourne Congress highlighted that the finances of ISES were in such bad shape that urgent action was needed, and Australia via the CSIRO came to the rescue. The ISES headquarters was transferred to Australia and was to remain there for the next two decades. In 1970 Roger Morse became president of SES, the office in the USA was closed, and all records and documents were shipped to Australia. A name change in August 1971 to ISES, established the organization, as it exists today, as an "International Solar Energy Society."

During this era ISES owed a great debt to the voluntary services of:

* Frank Hogg (secretary/treasurer), Australia
* George Löf, USA
* William Klein (president after Roger Morse), USA
* Peter Glaser (editor of Solar Energy), USA

In the early '70s, John Yellott, professional engineer and professor in architecture, Tempe, Arizona, USA wrote: "Without their work and without the dedicated services of unpaid officers and underpaid staff, ISES could not have survived." (Source: *1979 International Congress Historical Notes*, ISES Silver Jubilee).

5.2.1.4   Coming of Age

The ANZ Section continued to have steady membership growth in the early 1970s, but global events in 1973 changed everything.

Solar energy was at that time considered by OPEC (Organization of Petroleum Exporting Countries) a serious option for future energy supply. Not only was solar energy seen as a desirable long-term prospect with distinct environmental benefits, it was beginning to be seen as an economic prospect. The cost of fossil fuel was predicted to rise meteorically. Defense strategy as well as economic security was placing conventional energy supplies in a less solid political position.

Scientific interest was always developing in photovoltaics, solar thermal, and wind power forms of power generation. Advancements were largely quarantined to university laboratories, with the exception of wind, where many small 32 volt wind generators were sold in Australia and overseas for use in remote areas. However, the mainstream activity in using solar energy during this era was the development and use of solar water heaters.

5.2.1.5   Solar Water Heater Focus

The original CSIRO patents for solar water heaters were taken up by some solar energy pioneers who had come from the plumbing trade and industrial hot water engineering disciplines. Two notable people from Western Australia, Ron Brown and Clarry Small, led the way early, Ron Brown developing the first low-pressure thermosiphon unit in Australia and Clarry Small concentrating on a separated tank/collector system made out of copper alloys.

Ron Brown was a key figure and enthusiast in the early days of the establishment of ISES in Australia. He was an original member of the WA branch set up by Professor David Allen Williams and was a committee member until the late 1980s when his health declined, which prevented his participation in his beloved trade and quest, the use of solar energy.

Clarry Small, a friendly competitor with Ron Brown's Sola-ray company, is remembered as a well-respected plumber and innovator. A returned prisoner of war, having spent most of the Second World War on Cyprus, became a very well-respected and revered personality. Apart from his genius as an innovator it is the opinion of all who knew him that he was a "salt of the earth,""honest personality.

Along with the Beasely Company in South Australia, Small's "Sola-heeta" developed credibility for solar water heaters in Australia, helping to place Australia as one of the major manufacturers of solar water heaters in the world. Small's generosity of spirit and willingness to share information and expertise helped set up Western Australia to lead the way and allow larger corporate entities such as Solahart to seize the business opportunity. Their eventual dominance in the Australasian and Southeast Asian region over the next 30 years was due to the solid control of product quality by award-winning engineer, John Riley (refer to ANZSES Branch History for WA).

Fig. 4: Solar water heater testing at the State Energy Commission of Western Australia's East Perth Gas Depot

5.2.1.6   Progress in Solar Energy Research

In the research sphere of activity a system of leadership evolved. The universities developed a type of revolving chain of command with successive universities taking the lead in turn. Early, R&D involvement at an institutional level started with the CSIRO as we have seen. Then the University of Queensland took the lead and became critical in the evolution of roof integrated storage tanks for solar water heaters. Norm Sheridan was at the helm, later followed by the remarkable Steve Szokolay.

Subsequently, Melbourne University began to become a significant participant in research and development, particularly the Department of Mechanical Engineering. At that stage there was no interest or activity in the architectural applications. After 1975 the UNSW (University of New South Wales) took great interest in the development of solar energy, with its Department of Mechanical Engineering, Physics. Later the architecture school took serious interest.

From this period onwards for the next decade or more it was the UNSW that showed the way through its ability to coordinate and initiate significant solar research and development as well as demonstration programs in Australia. The "energy crisis" was about to become the driving force for change at this time.

5.3   The Growth of the ANZ Section

From the early 1970s, interest in the applications of solar energy grew dramatically.

5.3.1   1973 – 1979 Energy Crisis

In 1979 R. L. Datta, president of ISES at the time said:

> It has taken millions of years for these fossil fuels to be formed and they will be spent in a few hundred years. Man has started recovering from the shock of emotional dynamism and has been discovering gaps.

What he was referring to was the 1973 oil crisis. Interest in ISES was rising sharply during this period, with international membership rising to 10,000 and to 707 in Australia and New Zealand in 1978. The regulation of oil supply and pricing in the Middle East threw the Western economic world into panic.

Australian scientists were becoming focused about this growing realization, and research was given a boost by the perceived pressing need at the time. The Australian Academy of Science published their Report #17, titled "Solar Energy Research in Australia" in September 1973.

An interesting coincidence happened in 1974. The USA/Australia Solar Energy Research Cooperation Agreement (1974) was signed by Prof. F. H. Morse and our R. N. (Roger) Morse. This event also illustrated how Australia was becoming a more recognized player in the field of solar energy research.

With the recognition that energy supply was going to be a possible short-term problem as well as a long-term challenge, solar and renewable energy became an important focus for research and development of new technological solutions. In Western Australia the Court government set up the Solar Energy Research Institute of Western Australia (SERIWA), modeled on the American initiative, SERI.

Fig. 5: Solar Thermal Plant built at Meekatharra by SECWA. Started in the late 1970s and built in the early '80s

5.3.1.1   Technological Exploration

In Western Australia it was a particularly active period in the mid-to-late 1970s. Scientists like Dr. Trevor Pryor, Wal James, Tom Crawford, and Sue Saunders were working with a number of scientists and innovators at the universities and through industries. David Langridge and Prof. Paul McCormick of the UWA were developing parabolic tracking collectors to produce medium- temperature hot water for industrial purposes including solar air conditioning.

SERIWA, in conjunction with the state energy commission, set up solar thermal plants at Meekatharra and Ballajura to investigate the potential for power generation. Steve Phillips, under the supervision of Prof. Phil Jennings, was investigating PV systems. Wal James was active in the field of heat pipes at this time, and John Riley, through his R&D work with Solahart, was making quantum leaps in the flat-plate collectors for mains pressure solar water heaters. There was a lot of activity in WA during this period.

Also, there was diverse activity on the east coast. In the late 1970s and early 1980s David Mills (Fig. 6) of Sydney University was starting his exciting R&D into evacuated tube solar collectors for the generation of high-temperature applications for industry and power generation. Prof. Martin Green at the UNSW was beginning to make tangible advances in the field of photovoltaic efficiency of Si solar cells and the development of viable power systems. Prof. Steve Kaneff and his colleagues were conducting world class research into dish collectors in the Australian Capitol Territory and Prof. Bill Charters in Melbourne was continuing his solar thermal R&D in tandem with the CSIRO.

Fig. 6: David Mills with his solar cooker (developed in the late 1980s) and standing in front of an array over evacuated tube collectors he had been working on since the late 1970s.

Fig. 7: The early evacuated tube collectors with Wes Stein (left), Ian Olney (centre) and David Mills (right)

ANZSES meetings in all states were well attended at this time. A growing area of interest was solar water pumping and remote area power systems. These were becoming a targeted commercial project for R&D and demonstration. But with the dissipation of the focus from the Energy Crisis by the end of the 1970s, it became clear that solar housing and energy efficiency could be a more economically viable focus for government money and public attention. Much of the technological solar research was proving uneconomic at this time.

Funding of solar energy research was starting to become very difficult until the realization that use of fossil fuels producing carbon dioxide was causing a large component of the Greenhouse Effect. However, it was to take a substantial effort by the prominent scientists in the country as well as key ANZSES office bearers to shift government and public opinion. In the meantime a group of committed solar architects took up the challenge and became involved in ANZSES and ISES and started to influence the building industry and their fellow architects. This profession was largely disinterested in or ignorant of what could be achieved in the built environment. Creative climatic design in architectural solutions needed to be taught. This professional involvement by solar architects eventually led on to significant building industry changes. Manufacturers shifted their focus to developing improved insulation, glazing, ventilation systems, solar control pergolas, and shading devices. Integrated roofing systems, more economical systems providing thermal mass walls and floors (both in-situ or precast), and low-energy air-conditioning systems became a new focus, as the idea captured the imagination of industrialists.

5.3.1.2   Birth of Solar Housing

The early 1970s onwards saw a rapid response to dissemination of the developing knowledge about solar housing. It was seen as immediately applicable and a precursor to a more economic implementation of renewable power systems. The general public in Australia and the media showed great interest, as "energy" became topical. ISES and the ANZ Section developed rapidly, and it was not uncommon to have rooms full of visitors as well as members at monthly technical talks around the country.

Each state branch flourished as the baby boomer generation made links with the older pioneering generation from the immediate post-war era, and a vision for the future was formulated and strengthened. There was a consensus of what needed to be done by governments. There was a sense of urgency!

It was indeed an exciting era when architects and "early adopters" of technology in society joined the scientific community and key industry leaders in advocating the development and application of solar energy in all fields. Many industrial and environmental groups owed their origins and successes to the Solar Energy Societies in each state. Proactive political activity created a need for specialized organizations to solve problems defined by enthusiastic members of the Society.

By the end of the 1970s there was serious interest and commitment, but oil prices were beginning to fall and the economic driver was dissipating enthusiasm quickly. Philosophical, environmental, social conscience, and anti-nuclear arguments continued. The momentum, kick started by the oil crisis, was waning. New thinking was needed. This all served to motivate people involved in solar energy to seek new information, solutions, and applications for the next decade. Solar housing became the first target of public attention.

From the mid-to-late 1970s, advancements were evolving steadily in the field of passive solar housing and buildings. John Ballinger of UNSW (Fig. 8) was leading the research into the thermal efficiency of housing. He joined the society in 1979 and was to become a significant force in research and teaching of passive solar design and planning of the built environment, not only in NSW, but throughout the whole country.

Fig. 8: John Ballinger, solar housing pioneer, pictured in his Kangaroo Valley retreat, 2003

John Ballinger became prominent in the field and worked collaboratively with specialists all over the ANZ region.

Dr. Steve Szokolay was also an early pioneer in the east coast of the country at that time. In Western Australia there were concurrent developments in the area due to the work of Dr. Bob Lawrance and Peter Little of Curtin University. Their research work led to very early examples of solar houses in Australia (more detail of this era in Western Australia can be accessed off the ANZSES web site). The most significant of their early work was the Solar Q1 house at Greenmount, WA, which was on display to the public in 1978 after a couple of years of research and development (Fig. 9).

The significant features of this house were the development of a day-night heating and cooling system, using hot and cold air collected in roof panels; heat and "coolth" storage rock beds for comfort distribution; and energy monitor incorporated into the home. It was the first example in Australia for wall insulation in cavity brick construction. Of international significance was the method used to monitor heat flows through construction materials, and temperature heat exchange down to a depth of three meters for ground temperature effects. The project brought together research, the building industry, and product manufacturers. More importantly, it brought together Clarry Small and Ron Brown and united many ISES members in WA.

Fig. 9: The solar Q1 house under construction at Greenmount, Western Australia, 1976-78

In NSW John Ballinger was not only producing excellent research data but also demonstrating principles architecturally (Fig. 10).

Fig. 10:. Bonnyrigg Solar Houses—John Ballinger (early 1980's)

Eventually the research work of the early pioneers flowed to influence younger solar architects such as Garry Baverstock in WA, Gareth Cole and David Baggs in NSW, John Held in SA, Geoff Barker in the NT, Trevor Lee in the ACT, Richard Sale in Qld., and David Oppenheim in Victoria. They were all making a mark in their profession and the building industry. Through being members of the ANZ Section of ISES these architects formed a fraternity with a purpose, which was to last for the next 30 years! In 2004, David Oppenheim, a recognized leading solar architect in Melbourne, aptly described the most successful function of ANZSES from this period as being the formation and operation of the "Buildings Group" as a subcommittee of ANZSES. This group brought the "fraternity" into a close cooperative team with a common interest in changing the public interest in solar and energy efficient architecture. It established a credible base for professional development.

The "Buildings Group" of architects was well supported by scientific colleagues in each state. These scientists made sure that the concepts being developed were sound and viable. Dr Steve Szokolay stands out as a scientist who was very dynamic. After arriving from Hungary after a period of political persecution from the communist regime and then a period of study in the UK, he became the most prolific researcher and producer of design data for architects in Australia. He was active during the 1970s through to the 1990s. Most architects of this era would have a number of Szokolay's books and manuals on their library shelves. The ANZ Solar Home Book by Steve Szokolay and Ric Sale was published in 1979 and had a seminal influence.

Dr. Bob Lawrance, a physicist specializing in solar energy, became a driving force in WA and became an invaluable mentor and advisor to Garry Baverstock, as did John Ballinger, Steve Szokolay, and Dr. John Barker. Angelo Delsante provided great scientific support to the architects on the eastern seaboard as well as did Szokolay. Early solar designed houses began in Western Australia with Peter Little and Bob Lawrance designing about 30 homes between 1976 to 1981 Their expertise was combined with Baverstock's firm in 1982.

At this time Gareth Cole in NSW was leading the way in the practice of solar design principles. He, through his publications and seminars, was inspiring and adding credibility to the cause during this period. He was prolific in the design and construction of numerous solar houses throughout NSW and together with David Baggs was an inspiration to many other architects in that state. Bob Sutton assisted architects like Michael Leach in Tasmania, and Terry Williamson's team in South Australia was doing fine research on a state and national basis. It was an exciting era, with professional cooperation at its maximum, with positive ramifications persisting for the next two decades.

Steve Szokolay (Fig. 11) was chairman of the ANZ Section of ISES from 1978 to 1980 and replaced the annual publication "Solar Energy Progress in Australia and New Zealand" with the quarterly journal Solar Progress,, of which he was foundation editor. He edited this journal until the end of 1983, when it was handed over to a Melbourne group. Szokolay built his solar air conditioned house in 1978 (at Mt. Cotton). John Ballinger built his Solarch Mk.1 at Fowler's Gap, also in 1978, and the Bonnyrigg solar village in 1981. The research from these projects was invaluable to all the emerging solar architects in Australasia (more information about the innovative architects in the period can be accessed off the ANZSES on their web site).

Fig. 11: Dr. Steve Szokolay, prolific scientific and ANZSES contributor, pictured at the 2001 Solar World Congress, Adelaide

ANZSES owes a debt of gratitude to Norm Sheridan, a very active member in the early days of ISES, for introducing Dr. Steve Szokolay to the society, whose contribution as a scientist as well as his service was prolific and legendary in this era. The cause of solar housing was dependent on the analysis work of Szokolay, as his research at this time and his publications inspired the younger breed of solar architects throughout the country.

During this period, Joan Hamilton became the guardian of ANZ Section activities. She gave great service to the Society and her administrative support was highly valued by all office bearers and overseas colleagues.

5.3.1.3   Emergence of New Zealand

New Zealand was involved in the ANZ Section of ISES via a number of dedicated individuals on an informal basis. Although New Zealanders attended Solar Congress and Australasian meetings and conferences in Australia, the formal structuring of a NZ branch did not occur until 1990. Solar Action, now the New Zealand branch of ANZSES, started life following the Fourth NZ Energy Conference held in Auckland in May 1979. The chairman was Robert Raine, the treasurer was Graeme Jessup, publicity was provided by Nigel Isaacs, and the newsletter editors were Karel Lieffering and Craig Blackwood. Regular meetings were held on the second Tuesday of each month, with a picnic in January. From the 1980s onwards New Zealand was to become a country of significance in the ANZ Section (this is covered in the second volume of this history).

5.3.1.4   ANZ Section Activity

The ANZ Section of ISES held the following meetings:

1975   (November 11) at the ANU (Canberra), on "Solar Energy Resources"

1976   (August 27) at the University of NSW, on "Architecture, Energy and the Sun", and (November 10) at the National Science Centre, Melbourne, on "Industrial applications of solar energy"

1978   The ANZ Section meeting was held at the University of NSW (November 15) on "Thermal Conversion."

1979   The annual conference was held in Perth, at The University of WA on "Solar Realities in WA in the '80s."

1980   (August 29) a symposium was held at the University of NSW, on "Progress in SolarThermal Applications."

1980   The annual conference was held in Melbourne in November with the title "A Place in the Sun."

5.3.1.5   State Branch Activity

Each state in Australia had its champions and motivators as the ANZ section of ISES moved closer and closer to corporate maturity. State branches were most active during this era and it is worth visiting the local history on a state-by-state basis:

NSW, Vic, Qld, WA, SA, NT all were established branches active in local meetings and national events.

ACT, Tas and NZ were not in existence at this time. (Refer to ANZSES web site for complete histories on each state)

5.4   The Impact of the ANZ Section

On a global scale Australians were making a large impact at the International level. Apart from the contributions of John Ballinger, Steve Szokolay, and Bill Charters, many others were making a mark in the many, diverse applications of solar energy. These people were to carry the baton from the Australian originators of ISES and ANZSES. The first twenty-six years placed Australia and New Zealand in a prominent position with researchers, developers, professionals, and entrepreneurs to assist the development of solar energy as a more mainstream energy source for the twenty-first century.

The recognition of the high level of expertise of ANZSES by governments, through the work of its members as well as the high ethical standards of the organization, is due in no small way to the efforts of the Founders of the organization and the mandate that they set out for it. The advances made and the continued ethical stance taken beyond the 1980s to the present day has created the opportunity for ANZSES to play an even greater part in the sustainable development of our world. The second volume of the ISES history will show how these early beginnings set the foundation to a solid future for our scientists, industrialists, and professionals.

How was this opportunity to be brought to reality? Since 1980, people like Trevor Lee (Fig. 12) took the initiative. Over the next twenty-four years Trevor has been the archetypal ISES/ANZSES professional. The impact of the ANZ section on the progress in solar energy of Australia and New Zealand was to blossom. It was mainly due to the support of genuine selfless efforts by many dedicated scientists and professionals. There were many who carried the baton but none so consistent and committed as Trevor. It seemed like no matter who was taking steps forward for solar energy and the Society, Trevor Lee was always there. We all owe Trevor appreciation for his staying power over the next twenty-four years and beyond.

Fig. 12: Trevor Lee, inaugural president of the Northern Territory Branch, dispensing tea and coffee from his linear-concentrating solar boiler in downtown Darwin in 1979

5.5   The Emerging Focus for the Next Decade

The building blocks set in place by the early pioneers opened the scope for the development and applications of solar energy. The emergence of solar housing as a scientific endeavour was gaining momentum, with a wave of enthusiasm about to sweep the country. A new generation of architects and engineers was taking the concept to an "early adopters" stage in the marketplace. The early solar water heater innovators had inspired a new breed of engineers who took great interest in higher temperature solar thermal applications. Photovoltaic systems were considered an important focus for research, as the cost of the systems was still two to three times more expensive than conventional energy generation for remote areas.

But great excitement was brewing for industrial uses of solar thermal systems and their potential to run solar air conditioning systems in commercial buildings. The next decade was to stimulate a number of demonstration projects all over Australia in the early 1980s.

Quiet achievers like John McNab from South Australia were taking another path using more "low-tech" approaches exploring the use of indirect evaporative cooling systems, which led on to the "Dricon" system being commercialized in the mid-1980s.

The use of evacuated tube collectors was an exciting focus at this time. Research into this technology began in the late 1970s and took a boost in progress when David Mills joined the team and eventually became the leader of it. This led on to some early applications such as the Campbell Town Hospital array (Fig. 13) used to produce steam at 200° C, using panel arrays in conjunction with parabolic dish reflectors (seasonally adjusted).

Mills was obviously inspired by the efforts of Professor Steve Kaneff of the ANU and the White Cliffs Power Station in the ACT (Fig. 14).

Fig. 13: Solar Thermal System developed in the early 1980s and installed in 1987/88 at Campbell Town Hospital (photo courtesy of David Mills)

Fig. 14:. White Cliffs Power Station, ACT (early 1980s)

5.5.1   ANZ Section/ANZSES Chairs

The following is a list of Chairs of the ANZ Section, as well as a list of AGMs. These people created a platform for solid progress during the next twenty-four years.

1969/70	F. G. (Frank) Hogg
1970/71	C. D. Campbell
1971/72	- " -
1972/73	N. R. (Norm) Sheridan
1973/74	- " -
1974/75	C. M. (Charles) Sapsford
1975/76	- " -
1976/77	W. R. (Wal) Read
1977/78	- " -
1978/79	S. V. (Steve) Szokolay
1979/80	- " -

AGMs

1969	Melbourne (with ISES)	7th
1970	Sydney, U of NSW	8th
1971	Highett	9th
1972	Adelaide	10th
1973	Melbourne, Nat. Sc. Centre	11th
1974	Sydney, U of NSW	12th
1975	Canberra, ANU	13th
1976	Melbourne, Nat. Sc. Centre	14th
1977	Brisbane, U of Qld	15th
1978	Melbourne, Nat. Sc. Centre	16th
1979	Sydney, U of NSW	17th
1980	Melbourne, U of Melbourne	18th

5.5.2   Acknowledgements from the Author

In writing the history of the ANZ Section of ISES, I must acknowledge great assistance by a number of people. This chapter has been made possible by the previous work committed on behalf of ANZSES to a history for the ANZSES web site. Each branch in Australia plus New Zealand, has supplied information, text, and editing assistance. I am grateful for the interest and contributions. It would have been impossible to attempt the overall history task without it.

This first twenty-five years of history was possible to compile due to the past efforts of Frank Hogg and the records kept by ISES. I am indebted to Cesare Silvi of Italy and David Mills of Australia, both past presidents of ISES; to George Hardy, our ANZSES secretary, for the supply of records and prior work; and to Steve Szokolay for his numerous contributions to enable this first period of the history to be more comprehensively and accurately covered.

Interviews with John Ballinger, Trevor Lee, and Bill Charters were very useful in putting together this first part of the history as well as to set the structure for the second part (1980 onwards). It enabled the research information to be put into a context that reflected what was happening in the world in general and in the Australasian region in particular. Assistance with proof-reading and editing from Trevor Lee and Steve Szokolay, in particular, was invaluable in completing this chapter of the early history.

Chapter 6

China Section of the International Solar Energy Society

by
Li Zhongming
Beijing Solar Energy Research Institute
3 Huayuan Road, Haidian District
Beijing, China 100083
Lizhongming001@hotmail.com

Abstract

The Chinese Solar Energy Society (CSES) was founded in 1979 and registered with the International Solar Energy Society in 1980. With a population approaching 1.3 billion and a rapidly growing economy, China is among the largest energy producers and consumers in the world. The dominant energy source is coal. It accounts for over 70% of the total energy supply; therefore, coal combustion is the major contributor to China's environmental pollution. Clearly, there are economic and social benefits from the increasing use of environment friendly solar energy in China. CSES is a national organization committed to promoting the awareness, understanding, and utilization of solar energy in China. CSES actively organizes academic exchanges, publishes professional periodicals, and provides consulting services etc. In the past twenty-five years, CSES made great effort in promoting solar energy production and application in China and in striving for national and international supports. In the solar thermal aspect, the technology and process of solar water heaters (SWH) have made substantial progress; production capacity and utilization of SWH takes up the first place in the world. In the solar PV field, R&D activities, utilization, and production have achieved great advancement. The progress of indirect solar energy application including wind power generation and hydrogen energy is also prodigious. Biomass is the most basic energy resource in rural areas.

Beijing, China, was awarded the right to host the 2008 Olympic Games;

CSES was awarded the right to host the ISES Solar World Congress in 2007. CSES believes that these two important events in Beijing will greatly speed up the development of solar energy applications in China.

6.1   Establishment of the Chinese Solar Energy Society

The petroleum resources crisis which occurred in the 1970s, made people realize that the fossil fuel reserves would be depleted sooner or later; therefore we have to explore sustainable energy resources. In the 1980s, the rate of energy consumption growth accelerated as the economy developed rapidly in China. The situation caused serious environmental pollution and ecological imbalance. It compelled people to explore clean energy. In fact, with its vast landmass, there are abundant solar energy resources in China. Sixty-six percent of the national geographical area has more than 2,200 solar hour equivalents per year. With its massive population and fast-growing economy, China has enormous energy needs; however, conventional energy resources use per capita in China is lower than the average level in the world. Using coal burning as the main method of power generation and heating has caused serious pollution and ecology problems in China. People aspire to utilize solar energy to conserve the limited and costly fossil fuels, reduce the emission of carbon dioxide, and avoid the greenhouse effect.

Just so, in this kind of situation, Chinese Premier Zhou Enlai asked his secretary to call the Scientific and Technological Office of the Chinese Academy of Science in 1974. He was concerned with the development of solar energy application in China, though Premier Zhou was in the hospital at that time. Almost at the same time, students coming home from abroad wrote a letter to the leader of the State Council; they hoped the leader would support their proposal of developing solar energy applications in China. Soon the State Council leader approved and transferred the proposal to the Scientific and Technological Office of the Chinese Academy of Science. The office paid high attention to this issue and decided to set up an investigating group to find out more about the international and domestic development of solar energy applications. In 1975 the State Development Planning Commission and Chinese Academy of Science drafted a ten-year (1975-1985) development program of solar energy application. In the same year, the First Experience-Exchanging Conference of Solar Energy Application was held in Anyang City, Henan Province, in the summer, and the Solar Photovoltaic Conference was held in Shanghai in December. Various research and development activities of solar energy application spread out gradually in China. The scientists and engineers working in the solar energy field felt strongly that they needed a national organization to organize various activities effectively and speed up the development of solar energy application in China. In 1978, representatives from twelve institutions including Beijing New-Technology Institute, Tsinghua University, Zhengzhou College of Technology, etc., met in Beijing. During the meeting they discussed how to develop solar energy applications in China and put forward the idea of setting up a relevant organization. After active preparation, Chinese Solar Energy Society came into existence in 1979. CSES registered at the International Solar Energy Society in 1980. At present, CSES has 4,000 individual members and twenty-seven institution members. There are seven subfields in CSES including photochemistry, solar thermal, solar photovoltaic, wind energy, biomass, hydrogen energy, and solar building. The supporting unit of CSES is Beijing Solar Energy Research Institute.

6.2   The Function of CSES

6.2.1

The Chinese Solar Energy Society is an academic organization of scientists and engineers in the solar energy field. It is a constituent member of the China Association for Science and Technology.

6.2.2.

CSES organizes activities such as academic exchange, editing and publishing, scientific and technological popularization, consulting services, etc. It also promotes the scientific development and technological innovation of solar energy application and transformation of advanced high-tech into the market economy. In the recent four years, CSES has organized fourteen national academic exchanges in China, 2,243 people participated in the meetings, and 1,415 articles were presented in these events. The journal of *Acta Energiae Solaris Sinica* and the intermediate popular magazine, *Solar Energy* are the professional publications of CSES, which have done a lot of work popularizing solar energy applications.

6.2.3

As a nongovernmental organization, CSES has strengthened international exchange and cooperation. Several international conferences and exhibitions were held in the last four years, including The 13th World Hydrogen Energy Congress and the International Hydrogen Energy Engineering and Utilization Technology Exhibition. There are more international conferences scheduled to be held in China, such as The 2nd International Hydrogen Energy Forum in 2004, The Third World Wind Energy Convention in 2004, The 15th International Photovoltaic Science and Engineering Conference in 2005, and the ISES Solar World Congress in 2007.

6.2.4

CSES also serves as the decision-making body on solar energy applications policy for the Chinese Government. CSES wrote letters to national leaders many times to suggest that the government has to pay more attention to the development of new and renewable energy utilization. As a result, the new energy utilization project was placed into Scientific and Technological Key Projects in the national "The Eighth Five-Year Plan" and "The Ninth Five-Year Plan."

6.2.5

CSES offers service to a vast number of members and scientific and technical workers in the solar energy field to achieve sustainable development of energy and to protect the environment.

Since the establishment of CSES, the national congresses (Fig. 1) and expositions (Fig. 2) have been being held biyearly to exchange information in the areas of research, development, production, and utilization of solar energy. National conferences in various subfields (Fig. 4) have been being held regularly to promote the progress of special subjects of solar energy application. The latest National Congress of CSES was held ceremoniously in Shanghai in October, 2003, where the Seventh Council of CSES (Fig. 3) was elected. We believe the new council will be able to fully develop its skills in solar energy, wind energy, hydrogen energy, and other renewable energy areas. The endeavors made by CSES and its branches at different levels have made the officers of the central government and local authorities realize increasingly the importance of solar energy and renewable energy applications.

Fig. 1: National Congress of CSES

Fig. 2: Exposition of solar energy application

Fig. 3: Prof. Shi Dinghuan, The President of CSES, Counsellor of the State Council

Fig. 4: Sunshine Forum on PV power Generation

China is the largest coal producer and consumer in the world. Its coal consumption accounts for 70% of the total consumption and constitutes the major source of pollution. And according to the goals of the Ministry of Science and Technology (MOST), the normal mode of development by the year of 2050, of the energy mix readjustment structure should be 42.7% of coal, 25.2% of petroleum, 18.9% of renewable energy sources, 8.0% of natural gas and 5.2% of nuclear. If China's development is driven by ecological considerations, by the year 2050 the energy mix readjustment structure should be aimed at 26.9% of coal, 20.0% of petroleum, 30.7% of renewable energy sources, 10.8% of natural gas and 11.6% of nuclear. In order to coordinate with the energy policy of the Chinese government, CSES has actively organized academic exchanges, published professional periodicals, and provided consulting services to promote the production and application of solar energy products. In the past twenty-five years, the endeavor made by CSES has played an active role in promoting solar energy applications in China, and especially played an important role in striving for national and international support.

6.3   The Development of Solar Energy Applications in China

6.3.1   Solar Thermal Utilization

China now has a well-established commercial solar thermal industry. Solar thermal utilization in China came during the 1970s. Solar water heaters began to be put into the market in the 1980s as China recognized the potential energy shortage crisis. Because of the rapid and stable development of the Chinese economy, the living conditions of the Chinese people have improved significantly. The demand for habitat hot water with hygienic and healthy quality is increasing. Because the domestic hot water supply infrastructure in most cities was not well developed, there was a good opportunity for the development of solar water heaters. At the same time, the technology of solar water heaters made substantial progress, almost equally sharing the water heater market with electrical water heaters and gas water heaters. The annual production quantity of solar water heaters in China reached 12 million square meters and the output reached 12 billion Yuan RMB in 2003 (Fig. 5), making China truly the largest SWH production and supply country in the world, 80 percent of the SWHs distributed in cities and towns. In coming years, the amount of sales in the city will still take up a larger ratio but, according to the situation in China, the giant market will be in rural areas. Since the economic reform, the economy has been developing very fast in rural areas. Large numbers of new farmhouses in rural areas, as well as houses in towns, have been built, so the demand for hot water has increased greatly. The total architecture area of houses in villages and towns in China is about 17.5 billions m², and 8.5 billions m² of houses will be added in the next 15 years. If the popularization ratio reaches up to 25% in these areas, the potential market for SWH, will reach up to 65 million sets, which is equal to 130 millions m². Expanding the scope of utilization in rural areas is very much needed. There are three types of solar collectors produced in China: evacuated tube collectors, flat-plate collectors and smolder collectors. About 66% of total output is for evacuated tube collector, 25% for the flat-plate type, and 9% for the smolder type. Generally speaking, the quality of solar collectors is fine, but up to now, it is still very difficult to integrate collectors with the existing multistory architectures.

Fig. 5: The utilization of SWH

Fig. 6: Solar air-conditioning&heating system

Traditionally, manufacturers of solar collectors in China were mainly satisfying local markets, so the regional distribution of manufacturers was quite common. However, the quick expansion of the solar water heater market and tough competition led to the formation of multi-regional management and several large solar water heater enterprises.

Other utilizations of solar thermal applications including solar ovens, passive solar houses, and solar greenhouses have been applied widely in China, and especially, active building-integrated solar houses with air-conditioning and heating functions came into use (Fig. 6).

6.3.2   Solar PV Utilization

In the solar PV field, there are over thirty institutes and universities involved in solar PV R&D activities. The areas of R&D cover the high-efficiency mono-crystalline silicon solar cells, polycrystalline silicon solar cells, polycrystalline silicon thin-film solar cells, amorphous silicon solar cells, GaAs solar cells, CuInSe2 and CdTe thin-film cells, concentration cells, space solar cells, and solar PV systems, etc. The main R&D results are shown in the following table.

Table: The Maximum Conversion Efficiencies of Various Solar Cells Developed in China

Solar Cell Type	Technology	Eff. (%)	Area (cm^2)
Mono-	Passivated Emitter Solar Cells	20.4	2x2
crystalline (IPSE)	Inverted Pyramids texturing & Selective Emitter Cells	19.79	2x2
silicon (MGBC)	Machine Grooving Buried Contact Solar Cells	18.47	2x2
solar (LGBC)	Laser Grooving Buried Contact Solar Cells	18.6	5x5
cell	Conventional	16.5	10x10
GaAs solar cell	LPE	20.1	1x1
	MOCVD	24	2x2
Polycrystalline silicon solar cell	Conventional	14.5	10x10
P-Si thin film cell	RTCVD on inactive Si substrate	15.12	1x1
Concentrator cell		17.0	2x2
a-Si cell(s-junction)	PECVD	11.2	
a-Si cell(d-junction)		11.4	
a-Si module		8.6	10x10
		6.2	30x30
CuInSe$_2$ solar cell	Co-evaporation	12.1	1x1
CdTe solar cell	Close Space Sub	13.38	1x1

There is a huge potential market for photovoltaics in China; there are about 60 million people who have no access to electricity in China. If the cost of solar cells could drop dramatically, one tenth of the households without electricity will be able to use solar PV power generation. Assuming each household consumes 150 watts of electricity, the quantity will reach up to 300 megawatts. The utilization of solar photovoltaic power generation in China has developed very fast; the annual average growing rate of solar cell and PV module production exceeds 25%. The larger PV market is in the communication sector, whose market share is about 30%. Its business range includes microwave relay stations, satellite TV stations, countryside telephone exchangers, army communication systems, etc. Through the actions of national R&D programs and government projects and international cooperation, the PV market for rural electrification has been enlarged to some extent, from 20% to over 30%. PV power generation systems with twelve megawatts were just installed in the northwest area in 2002 (Fig. 7). These PV systems of the "Brightness Project," implemented by the National Planning Commission, satisfied the power requirement of those northwest off-grid towns. Large amounts of solar garden lights and solar lawn lamps with solar cells have been exported to North America, Europe, Japan, and Southeast Asian countries. The annual sales reached up to 500 million Yuan RMB. Because of the quickly increasing demand for photovoltaics, besides existing PV manufacturers such as Qinhuangdao Huamei Photovoltaic Electronics Co. Ltd., Yunnan Semiconductor Devices Factory, Ningpo Electronics Information Holding Ltd., and The Shanghai Solar Energy Science & Technology Co. Ltd., several new PV manufacturers went into production, such as Wuxi Suntech Power Co. Ltd., Baoding Yingli New Energy Resources Co. Ltd., and Kyocera (Tianjin) Solar Energy Co. Ltd. Annual production capacity of each company will exceed 10 megawatts. Several more new PV companies are under way. In order to speed the development of PV technology and industry, the National Development and Reform Commission and National Economy and Trade Commission set goals for the development of photovoltaics in the next several years; the general installed quantity of PV power generation systems will reach up to 100 megawatts by 2005, and 450 megawatts by 2010.

In order to exploit the Chinese PV market, the World Bank initiated the Global Environment Facility (GEF) program. The first phase was started in 2001. The World Bank will give a subsidy of (U.S.) $25 million to install 10 megawatts of PV home systems in five years. The experts of the World Bank/GEF believe that the project will boost both Photovoltaic utilization and industry in China. With the promotion of photovoltaic projects in developed countries, more and more solar PV grid-connecting power generation systems have been installed in large cities in China for improving the energy environment and reducing pollution.

Fig. 7a & b: PV power generation systems at the town level were built with 12 MWp in 2002

The progress of indirect solar energy applications, including wind power generation and hydrogen energy is also prodigious. Biomass is the most basic energy resource in rural areas.

6.3.3   Wind Energy Utilization

China owns plentiful wind energy resources, and wind power farms experienced a rapid development period in the past six years. Wind energy technology has become mature and has met the requirement of large-scale development. By the end of 2003, the general installed capacity of wind power generation equipment reached up to 570 megawatts (Figs. 8 & 9). Because of the higher cost of wind power generation, in order to promote the development of wind power generation, the National Development and Reform Commission has carried out concession demonstration projects of wind power generation. The State Grid Corporation of China has purchased all electricity produced by wind power generation systems and formed a reasonable grid-electricity price for wind power generation. Putting forward these policies will encourage Chinese wind power farms to enter into a period of large-scale development. The accumulated installation capacity of wind power generation will reach up to 1 billion watts by 2005, 4 billion watts by 2010, 16 billion watts by 2020.

Fig. 8: The total wind installation in China was 570 MW

Fig. 9: 300 W wind turbine generator for home

6.3.4   Hydrogen Energy Utilization

In recent years, research and development of hydrogen energy has been on the ascendant. Chinese experts started to implement the High Tech Research and Development Programme on a fuel cell car, to facilitate the manufacture of a fuel cell car as a demonstration project. The Ministry of Science and Technology invested 380 million Yuan RMB in this project. According to an initial estimate, this project will be an economic success. The Ministry of Science and Technology assigned the R&D of hydrogen energy to The National Basic Research Priorities Programme to facilitate the basic research of manufacture, storage, and utilization of hydrogen energy. Up to now, some progress has been achieved, such as hydrogen produced on-board by organic fuel, multi-reaction coupling, and hydrogen production from biomass, etc. The development of hydrogen storage in metal alloy, in carbon nanotubes, or in organic hydrides slurry is under way. The effect of a running condition on the performance of the PEMFC engine is studied, too. China will participate in the United Nations Development Programme and Global Environment Facility to invite international bidding for a demonstration operation of fuel cell buses in Beijing and Shanghai. China is also making an arrangement for the manufacture and storage of hydrogen energy. There is some progress in hydrogen energy utilization in China. During The Third Beijing International PSE on Electric, Clean Car & Auto Environment Protection Technology, Beijing LN Power Sources Co. Ltd. and its partners demonstrated a fuel cell taxi, which can carry four passengers, with the maximum speed of 76 km/hr and a running distance of 150 km; a middle-FC bus for 12 passengers (Fig. 10), with the maximum speed of 90 km/hr and a running distance of 160 km; and the "Guiding car for Olympic Games" on fuel cell (Fig. 11), which can carry 4 passengers, with a speed of 24 km/hr and running distance of 50 km. The "Phoenix" demonstration vehicle on fuel cell power was shown in November 2001, and can carry 5 passengers, with the gross weight of 2,500 kg and maximum speed of 113 km/hr. Its accelerating time is only 13 seconds in 0-100 km/hr.

Fig. 10: LN-1 Zero-emission electrical vehicle

Fig. 11: LN-03B fuel cell (H2, air)

6.3.5   Biomass Energy Utilization

Basically, China is still an agricultural country. The population in the rural areas makes up over 70% of the general population. Biomass energy is one of the primary energy resources in rural areas; it also has an important position in the national energy structure. The Ministry of Agriculture has paid much attention to biomass energy utilization. Its efforts are focused on stalk biomass energy conversion. The Ministry of Science and Technology listed biomass energy research and development as priorities in several Five Year Plans. Practical R&D activities have been launched successfully in producing liquid or gaseous fuels through biological or thermal chemical reaction. In order to solve the problem of energy shortages in rural areas, China has exploited and vigorously popularized biogas technology for homes. The energy saved is equivalent to 200 million tons of standard coal use in the 1970s. In the 1990s China popularized modern biomass energy technology, such as a centralized supply of biogas, biogas power generation, and manufacturing ethanol fuels, etc., in order to reach the goals of assuring the energy safety of the country, realizing the reduction of carbon dioxide emission, and maintaining the sustainable development of China's economy. At present, centralized gasification supply systems have been installed in almost 300 villages, supplying gas to over 30,000 homes (Fig. 13). More than twenty sets of mega-watt-level power generation systems by biomass gasification were popular-ized and applied.

Fig. 12: Heating system with biomass gasification

Fig. 13: Using biogas for cooking

6.4   Further work

In 2001 Beijing, China, was awarded the right to host the 2008 Olympic Games. The Beijing Municipal Government announced the motto "New Beijing, Great Olympics," and set the goal to host a "Green Olympics, Hi-tech Olympics and People's Olympics." The Chinese Solar Energy Society has long advocated these concepts for successfully hosting the Olympic Games. The Chinese government has promised that large amounts of solar hot water systems and solar photovoltaic power generation systems will be installed in the Olympic stadiums and gymnasiums and in the Olympic Village.

Fortunately, the Chinese Solar Energy Society was awarded the right to host the ISES Solar World Congress in 2007. CSES believes that the congress will greatly speed up the development of solar energy application in China, especially since the congress will be held in the year before the 2008 Beijing Olympic Games. In order to achieve the goal of a Green Olympics, priority will be given to environmental protection in the planning, designing, and construction of Olympic venues and facilities. Strict ecological environment standards and systematic supporting systems will be established. Environmental protection technologies and means will be used extensively in promoting, on a large scale and in various aspects, environmental treatment, afforestation, and beautification of urban and rural areas. We will raise the environmental awareness of the whole society and encourage the public to consciously opt for green consumption and actively join in activities aimed at improving the ecological environment in an effort to drastically improve the environmental quality of the capital and build it into an ecological city. We can imagine that exploiting renewable energy and preventing environmental pollution are the necessary trends of human development, by expanding organic integration of light, heat, and electricity conversion of solar energy with architecture thereby supplying heating, cooling, electricity, and hot water to inhabitants; alleviating the depletion of fossil fuel; reducing the emission of carbon dioxide and other poisonous gases; improving the people's quality of life, and ensuring the present and future quality of the environment for China and the world. From every step, and every little progress made in the solar energy field in our country in the past 25 years, we can see the effort from the CSES. We proudly contributed enormous effort, talent, time, and energy in the past, and we are determined to continue to do the same to achieve the full potential for a bright future.

Fig. 14: Demonstration architecture with solar PV grid-connecting power generation system and solar air-conditioning and heating system

References

[1] A Proposal for ISES World Congress 2007
[2] 1999 White Book on New & New & Renewable Sources of Energy in China
[3] Zhao Yuwen, Cui Rongqinag, Proceeding of the 2003 Anniversary Solar Energy Conference of CSES, Shanghai, 2003, p. 9
[4] Mao Zongqiang, as above, p. 662
[5] Shi Pengfei, as above, p. 834
[6] Zhu Junsheng et. al., New & Renewable Sources of Energy in China

Acknowledgement

During the writing of this paper, I got support from the Secretary General of CSES, Mr. Meng Xiangan and the Canadian Chinese, Ms. Mona Shi. I want to thank them here for their help.

Chapter 7

German Section of the International Solar Energy Society History of Solar Energy and ISES in Germany

by
Adolf Goetzberger
Retired, Professor, former Director of the Fraunhofer Institute for Solar Energy Systems e-mail: Adolf.Goetzberger@ise.fraunhofer.de
and Sigrid Jannsen
Professor, President, Deutsche Gesellschaft fur Sonnenenergie, e.V., e-mail: JAnnsen@ise.fhg.de

Abstract

In this chapter we report about the history of solar energy in Germany, which was strongly influenced by ISES, but also by other factors. Occupation with solar energy started quite early in Germany, in the second half of the nineteenth century. These early theoretical studies were not further pursued because of the preeminence of fossil energy fuels. Solar societies played an important part in preparing the ground for the successful development of solar energy. The history of societies at the national level consists of two lines, DGS and ISES, which after some time combined into one. At a much later point a third very influential society was founded in Germany: Eurosolar. The DGS (Deutsche Gesellschaft für Sonnenenergie) was founded on October 17. 1975 in Munich. A solar energy journal (*SONNENENERGIE*) was initiated and still exists today. In 1977 the first International Solar Forum was held. The German section of ISES was founded in 1976, one year after the DGS. The major historic event was the ISES Solar World Congress in Hamburg in September 1987, organized by Dr. Horst Hörster. The ISES Section in Germany united with the much larger DGS in 1989. The first EuroSun conference, combined with the 10th International Solar Forum of DGS, took place in 1996 in

Freiburg. Germany has built a large R&D capacity in solar energy. All large solar centers are members of Forschungsverbund Sonnenenergie. Many innovations were developed by German solar industries. Germany also developed the most effective market introduction scheme for renewable energy, the feed-in tariff, and is today the second-largest market for PV after Japan.

7.1   Early History of Solar Energy in Germany[1]

The scientific discussion about the limitation of fossil energy resources and their possible replacement started in Germany after the second law of thermodynamics had been formulated by Clausius, Rankine, and Thomson in the early 1850s. Franz Grashof, president of the German engineering Society (VDI), demanded in 1877 the enhanced use of renewable energy, in particular hydropower. He was joined in 1885 by Rudolf Clausius himself, who was the rector of the University of Bonn. The physical chemist Wilhelm Ostwald who had a deep understanding of thermodynamics developed a concept of energetics which he published in 1906. In this concept efficient use of energy and widespread use of solar energy played a major role. On the experimental side Wilhelm Maier and Adolf Remshardt built, in 1906, the first solar trough concentrator, for which they filed a patent application the following year. All these activities of visionaries, however, had very little practical consequences. Coal continued to dominate for many more decades, but solar energy continued to fascinate those who occupied themselves with the future of mankind.

7.2   History of Societies

7.2.1   The Role of Solar Societies

Solar energy is just becoming an accepted energy source. To arrive at this point took a hard struggle against technological obstacles, preconceived public opinions, massive resistance by vested economic interests, and the immobility of political decision makers. Very early, the proponents of solar energy formed more or less organized associations, which later coalesced into bigger units. Solar societies played an important part in preparing the ground for the successful development of solar energy. They established networks for the

[1] Many of the historic facts in this article are excerpted from the doctoral thesis of G. Mener, "Geschichte der Solarenergienutzung in Deutschland und den USA," L. K. Verlag Ludwig Klehr, Baldham, 2001

exchange of technical and scientific information, for contacts between enterprises, for informing public media, and for lobbying political decision makers. The history of societies at the national level consists of two lines, DGS and ISES, which after some time combined into one. At a much later point a third very influential society was founded in Germany: Eurosolar. Besides these groups, many more local activities were started which existed for limited times before they disappeared or were absorbed by DGS/ISES.

The development in Germany was strongly influenced by two events, the oil shock in 1973 and the nuclear accident at Chernobyl in 1986. The oil shock brought home the dependence on potentially unstable sources of supply; the reactor accident, the fall-out from which also affected large parts of Germany, made clear that nuclear energy was a very dangerous energy option. Particularly Chernobyl mobilized large parts of the German population and considerably improved acceptance of solar energy. At the same time it fortified the resistance of utilities against solar energy because they perceived every supporter of solar energy to be an opponent of nuclear energy. This was indeed the case for a large part of the solar community.

Finally in later years the effects of CO_2 emissions on climate dominated the energy debate. Again in Germany the concern about the environment was very pronounced, which gave additional push to the development of renewable energy.

The foundation of the two national societies was preceded by industrial activity, research work at universities, and some support by Government. Industries interested in solar energy were on one hand producers of solar cells for space applications and on the other hand were large firms who were attracted by government grants for R&D work and demonstration projects. In 1975, the same year in which DGS was founded, an industrial association, ASE (Arbeitsgemeinschaft Solarenergie) was founded. Because Germany's largest utility participated in this grouping, solar proponents outside of industry regarded it with some suspicion. This was one of the reasons for the establishment of a public society, DGS.

7.2.2   DGS[2]

The DGS (Deutsche Gesellschaft für Sonnenenergie) was founded on October 17, 1975 in Munich. The founding assembly took place in the Hofbräuhaus, a historic beer hall and tourist attraction, normally not the place

---

2 The history of the DGS was also described by G. Mener in: 20th anniversary of DGS, Köln, 1995, pp.53 – 61

for serious business. Some fifty persons participated in this event and thirty signed up for membership immediately. They worked out the by-laws and goals of the new society. It is not known how much beer was consumed after signing of the papers.

The founding members represented a broad spectrum of persons interested in solar energy. They included scientists involved in developing solar power plants, journalists, business people, craftsmen, architects, and private persons interested in building their own collector systems. The stated goal was advancement of solar energy in the broadest sense, including all renewable energies and even rational use of energy. The society was not conceived as a professional or scientific association, but rather the main goal was transfer of knowledge from the laboratory into practical application.

The founding assembly was chaired by Dr. Ulf Bossel, a physicist from Göttingen working at DFVLR, the German aerospace institution, who became president the following year. The first president was Dr. Pitter Gräff. The new society developed many activities and grew very rapidly. The structure of the DGS consisted of a board of five members headed by the president (Präsidium) and local groups (Sections) represented by delegates. Very soon a solar energy journal (*SONNENENERGIE*) was initiated and found wide circulation. This journal is on one hand the most important link of the board to the members and on the other hand an excellent journal about scientific, technical, and political aspects of renewable energies, with the main emphasis on solar energy. It comes out six times a year. The journal is given free of charge to the members but it is also sold to nonmembers. Since 2002 a special edition on Solar Building is published once a year.

From the beginning the DGS organized important seminars and congresses. Membership grew rapidly from the initial 30 to 3,000 in 1977 and more than 6,000 in 1980 (Fig. 1).

Members

Fig 1: Development of DGS membership

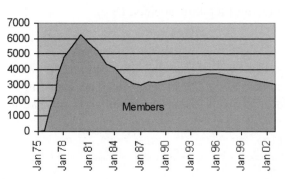

In the initial years DGS concentrated on solar collector systems for water and space heating. The first large congress, "Heizen mit Sonne" (solar heating), generated considerable interest and participation. DGS also appreciated the importance of standardization and quality control and organized a working group on this subject. The early occupation with thermal conversion caused a certain neglect of photovoltaics which received more attention from other sides, mainly the European Community.

In 1977 the first International Solar Forum was held. This biennial series of conferences continues until today. Several times the International Solar Forum was combined with scientific events organized by the DGS together with other solar organizations, such as the first EuroSun in 1996 together with ISES Europe, the millennium conference "Solarimpulse" in 2000 together with the German Research Alliance Solar Energy (Forschungsverbund Sonnenenergie). In 2004 the 14th International Solar Forum will again be part of a EuroSun conference: the EuroSun 2004 in Freiburg, which is organized by DGS.

DGS is politically neutral but consistently used whichever means were available to influence political decision making as was laid out in the by-laws. The success of this activity depended on the political constellation. During the entire history of solar energy in Germany it can be observed that solar energy always received stronger support when the political pendulum swung to the left at the federal level. This does not apply at the state (Länder) level. Bavaria, which is conservatively governed, has the highest density of solar systems on a per capita basis.

The rapid growth of the society led in the early years of DGS to a crisis because all actors were rather inexperienced and lost control over finances, membership, and other activities. The society ran into financial problems and its existence could only be saved by personal loans by some leading members. Ulf Bossel had to turn over the presidency in 1978 to Dr. Albert Derichsweiler, who started the consolidation of the society.

At about the same time a technological and market crisis developed in the early '80s. Many of the newly marketed collectors and systems did not stand the test of practical application. They showed materials and lifetime problems. This in turn affected the confidence of the customers and consequently the market took a downturn. Oil was again plentiful and cheap, which also reduced interest in solar energy. These effects can clearly be seen in the development of DGS membership.

Fig 2: Fifth International Solar Forum. Former DGS presidents Selzer (left) and Goetzberger (right) with government representative

In the early years of DGS there was also a controversy about the founda-tion of the German section of ISES between DGS and the established techni-cal network in Germany (VDI), in which DGS lost the first round. This will be described in more detail in the following subsection. Briefly, what appeared at the surface to be personality clashes was based on deeper funda-mental differences of opinion. The majority of DGS members and its man-agement were not only passionate proponents of solar energy but were also opponents of nuclear energy. The fight against nuclear energy was never an acknowledged goal of DGS, but many members were also active in antinu-clear groupings. In contrast, the industrial and engineering establishment was at that time pro nuclear.

The consolidation of DGS continued under the next president, Dr. Horst Selzer, who stayed in office from1981 until 1993.

In 1989 finally the unification with the German section of ISES was accomplished. A new generation of leading persons in both societies was able to surmount the old lines of divisions. This was facilitated by the fact that many individuals were members of both societies. Now DGS had better con-tacts to the global solar community. Another positive effect of this fusion was that the scientific and technological side of DGS was strengthened. Technical working groups on subjects like thermal conversion, photovoltaics, solar architecture were established. In 2001 a working group "biomass" was initi-ated. These working groups are involved in very different activities: They organize meetings with specific themes, they work out information about their specific field, and they participate in the perfection of official regulations, etc. Together with the Section Berlin-Brandenburg of the DGS, a handbook on photovoltaics and second one on solar thermal systems for tradesmen, planners, and architects was published in the year 2000. The success of these handbooks was enormous. They are now translated into English, Spanish, Italian, and Portuguese. The translation and publication of a handbook on biomass is supported by the EU.

Prof. Adolf Goetzberger was the next president for four years until 1997. Many new activities were started. The Solar Forum conferences continued to attract large audiences, and slowly the solar market recovered. On the political side, already in 1982 an electricity feed in law was proposed to the then ministry of research and technology. This law was realized very successfully much later during the '90s.

Fig. 3: At the first Eurosolar Conference 1996: Angela Merkel, then federal minister for the environment and now leader of the opposition party CDU flanked by Freiburg Lord Mayor Böhme (left) and conference chairman Prof. Luther

The German ISES Section contributed to the establishment of new sections in Eastern Europe. The newly emerging states of the former Soviet block had great difficulties in paying ISES dues in hard currencies. The German section helped the Russian and Polish sections in getting started and supported them for many years.

DGS also participated in the foundation of ISES Europe. The first EuroSun conference combined with the 10th International Solar Forum of DGS took place in 1996 in Freiburg. It attracted 1,100 attendees, a number that was never reached in subsequent conferences in this series. From 1997 – 1999, Thomas Schmalschläger was the president of DGS.

His successor in 1999 was Prof. Sigrid Jannsen. For the first time DGS was led and represented by a woman.

In 1998 the political situation in Germany changed and the left wing party together with the green party took over power, with the consequence that renewable energies became an important part of the government agenda. The new government supported a campaign, "Solar—na klar!" (Solar—of course!).

The subject of this campaign was solar thermal with the intention to convince craftsmen to offer solar thermal collectors to consumers who should install them on their roofs. DGS was part of the organizing committee, particularly in regional activities. This fit very well with the decentralized structure of the DGS. DGS will be a member of a new campaign of the Ministry of Environment in 2004. The new campaign will be an image campaign including all the renewables.

Fig. 4: Opening ceremony of EuroSun '96. At the podium from left to right: EU representative Tent, Program Chair Prof. Goetzberger, Lord Mayor Böhme, ISES Europe President Dr. Leslie Jesch, Angela Merkel, Economics Undersecretary Mehrländer, conference Chair Prof. Luther, ISES President Dr. David Mills

Fig. 5: DGS President Prof. Sigrid Jannsen opening School competition

Since the very beginning DGS was very active in demonstrating the technical standard of PV and solar thermal collectors. After very humble beginnings at local fairs the devices are high technology nowadays. Especially a small local fair in southern Germany (Pforzheim) grew with help of DGS and became the largest European solar trade fair, the Intersolar, since 2000, taking place in Freiburg im Breisgau. DGS is still a partner of the trade fair.

Fig 6: A winning team at the school competition

One of the main activities of DGS is education. There is a working group discussing and organizing programs of further education for craftsmen. DGS also runs solar schools for these clients.

Another field where DGS and the local sections are very active is collaboration with schools. Every year there are competitions for schools. The pupils demonstrate their activities in solar energy. Not only technical demonstrations are shown but also musical and art contributions are presented. The winners get nice prizes which are donated by German manufacturers of solar equipment. Several hundred schools and thousands of pupils and teachers participated in the past in these competitions.

7.2.3   German Section of ISES

The German section of ISES was founded in 1976, one year after the DGS. Its history started before that because many solar scientists and engineers had become members of international ISES. As mentioned above, there was a controversy who should organize ISES in Germany. On the one hand DGS had offered to become the German section of ISES, but on the other side, there was a strong grouping which wanted to host ISES and which eventually won out. These were the industrial association ASE—many of their academic employees were ISES members—and the German engineering association VDI (Verein Deutscher Ingenieure) which already had a solar energy section. DGS had many reservations about VDI because the latter was a strong supporter of nuclear energy. No agreement could be reached, so VDI simply took the initiative and called a meeting of German ISES members for the founding of the section. DGS was not involved in this event. The membership of the ISES Section consisted mainly of professional people employed in industries and universities. Therefore the ISES Section was always much smaller than DGS.

Fig. 7: Conference Chairman Dr. Horst Hörster opening Hamburg Solar World Congress

Fig. 8: ISES President pointing the way at opening ceremony

ISES in Germany also developed important activities. Special meetings and seminars were organized, but the major historic event was the ISES Solar World Congress in Hamburg in September 1987. With 1,700 participants, it was one of the largest congresses in the history of ISES. Its organization was excellent, and many memories of this congress still exist all over the world. Organization of this large congress was a challenging task for the relatively small section. The biggest merit for this success belongs to Dr. Horst Hörster, the conference chairman, who was responsible for the entire organization, and to Prof. Werner Bloss who chaired the scientific committee.

As was mentioned above, the separate ISES Section in Germany united with the much larger DGS in 1989. Prof. Goetzberger served as ISES chairman during this period.

Fig. 9: Program Chairman Prof. W. Bloss at get-together

Fig.10: Prof. Jack Duffie receiving the Farrington Daniels Award from ISES President Prof. W. Beckman

7.2.4   Other Societies

Besides the public society DGS/ISES, an industrial association played an important role in the early history of solar energy in Germany. In 1975, the same year in which the DGS was founded, several large companies, mainly aerospace firms, formed a solar working group, ASE (Arbeitsgemeinschaft Solarenergie). The intention was to coordinate the activities of the companies and also to serve as a counterpart to the federal Government, which supported development and pilot projects with increasing budgets. In 1978 its name was changed to BSE (Bundesverband Solarenergie).

Fig.11: Prof. A. Goetzberger with solar pioneer Ludwig Bölkow at Hamburg Congress

Since many smaller companies, particularly those in the collector branch, did not feel adequately represented by BSE, they formed a separate organization, Deutscher Fachverband Solarenergie. It took until 2003 before these organizations became united. Many other, more local, societies became active over the years. They are too many to list. However, one local grouping deserves special mention, the Solarverein Förderverein Aachen which was founded in 1986 by Wolf. von Fabeck. In 1989 they developed the model of rate-based incentives on which the present grid feedback law is based and which serves as a model for many other countries.

Fig. 12: Dr. Hermann Scheer, President of Eurosolar and Member of German Parliament

A newer and very influential society is Eurosolar, which was founded in 1989 at the initiative of Dr. Hermann Scheer. Eurosolar is very active in the political and public arena. Among its members are many parliamentarians and other influential persons. Hermann Scheer and Eurosolar were very instrumental in changing the political climate in Germany. Especially the favorable feed-in law and other market-support measures are due to the work of Scheer and his colleagues from the governing coalition.

7.3   History of Technology and Institutions

7.3.1   Development of the R&D Infrastructure

Germany has built a large R&D capacity in solar energy during the period considered here. This was only possible because of a strong commitment and support by federal and state governments. Solar R&D projects are carried out at many universities today. We can only refer to major institutions in this contribution.

In the mid '70s in Stuttgart several university institutes combined their efforts and formed Insolar. Participants were professors Lehner, Bloss, and Hahne and the Stuttgart unit of DLR (DFVLR at that time, the German aerospace research institution). In 1988 a foundation ZSW (Zentrum für

Sonnenenergie- und Wasserstoff-Forschung) was founded in which all institutions participate.

In 1981 the Fraunhofer Institute for Solar Energy Systems (ISE) was founded by A. Goetzberger. It developed into Europe's largest solar institute and has today, under the direction of J. Luther, approximately 400 employees. The ISE main business fields are solar buildings, solar cells, photovoltaic systems, and hydrogen technology.

In 1987 the Institut für Solarenergieforschung in Hameln (ISFH) was founded. Under the direction of R. Hezel it carries out research in photovoltaics and solar thermal systems.

In 1988 Prof. Kleinkauf founded the ISET (Institut für Solare Energieversorgungstechnik). It is connected to the University of Kassel and concentrates on solar electric systems.

The state of Bavaria combined its solar research, in 1991, under the roof of ZAE (Zentrum für Angewandte Energieforschung). It has departments in Munich, Erlangen and Würzburg.

A strong research activity in photovoltaics has developed at the University of Konstanz under Prof. Bucher.

All large solar centers are organized under the roof of Forschungsverbund Sonnenenergie, which serves as a focal point for coordination and joint activities. The large research institutions FZJ (research center Jülich) and HMI (Hahn-Meitner Institut) participate with their photovoltaic groups.

7.3.2   Major Technological Developments in Germany

Solar technologies were developed in Germany continuously during the second half of the nineteenth century. Only a very brief summary can be given here.

Thermal collector systems: Starting from early do-it-yourself systems the performance and quality of collector systems was continually improved until today. They are efficient, reliable, and easy to install and cost has come down due to mass production.

Photovoltaics: Development of solar cells for terrestrial application started very early in Germany. The most remarkable innovation was the casting technique for multicrystalline silicon developed at the Wacker company by Bernhard Authier starting in 1972. This type of material has surpassed the market share of crystalline silicon in recent years. Today a number of companies are producing silicon solar cells and modules with modern manufacturing methods.

Thin film solar cells have been under development at several institutions. Most remarkable are the record efficiencies obtained by the University of Stuttgart with CIS (copper indium diselenide) cells. These cells have now entered the first stages of production.

Solar architecture: In this field enormous progress was made. It can best be expressed by the following figures. The old building stock consumes 250 KWh per year and m^2 on the average. With modern active and passive technologies less than 20 can be reached within economic boundary conditions. With more advanced technology even complete energy independence can be reached as was shown by ISE in 1992 with the self-sufficient solar house (Fig.13). The large potential of solar and passive architecture can only slowly be exploited because renovating the large building stock will take considerable time.

Fig. 13: The self-sufficient solar house, Freiburg, 1992. This house was powered only by solar energy. Long-term storage was realized by hydrogen technology

In the German climate with very little sunshine in winter, long-term storage is an important issue. During the last decade a number of demonstration projects, for example, by the university of Stuttgart with district heating systems and large volume storage, have shown the feasibility of this concept.

7.3.3   Development of the Solar Industry

The solar industry in Germany has experienced ups and downs. Factors influencing growth of this industry were shifting political boundary conditions and global availability of fossil fuels.

Collector systems: After an early phase of rapid growth the collector market faced a sharp downturn. Not only the technical problems of the early collector systems were behind this decline but also a large marketing campaign by RWE, the biggest German utility. They tried to push electric heat pumps and in this process disparaged solar collectors. Many companies had to close their doors or move their production to cheaper locations. Recovery occurred in 1987 as is seen in the graphic (Fig.14). The collector market is still dominated by relatively small companies. Only now the larger players are beginning to enter the collector market.

Photovoltaics: The photovoltaic market started very slowly (Fig. 15). In the early years the market consisted almost entirely of demonstration projects and some consumer and industrial applications. The major producer in Germany was AEG, which had developed the multicrystalline cells together with Wacker. Siemens also started a small production of solar cells. Later, AEG was broken up and the solar factory had several different owners until it ended up with RWE. Both Siemens and RWE phased out production in Germany because they had large American subsidiaries, Siemens had acquired ARCO Solar and RWE Mobil Solar. Only in recent years has solar cell production returned to Germany. The largest producers are RWE, which is now co-owned by Schott, and Shell, which took over the solar cell capacity of Siemens. Production of silicon wafers for solar cells continues in Germany. Wacker sold the technology to Bayer, which in turn transferred it Deutsche Solar.

7.4   Development of Markets and Support Programs

7.4.1   Development of Solar Markets

The long-term development of the solar collector market is shown in Fig 14.

The photovoltaic market in Germany has shown a strong growth in recent years (Fig.15). This is a result of the very efficient support policy of the German government, which will be detailed in the next subsection.

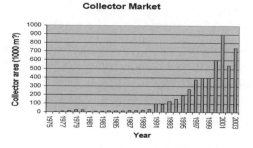

Collector Market

Fig. 14: Yearly installed collector area in Germany

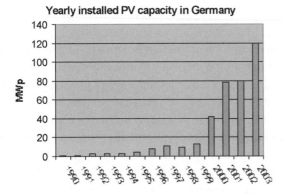

Fig. 15: Development of PV market in Germany

7.4.2   Development of Support Programs

Just as is the case with every other new energy technology, solar energy cannot compete economically with established energy sources and therefore requires subsidies. Historic experience shows that R&D without markets does not bring about efficient progress. Large cost reductions only occur through interaction of the two. Many different types of support of solar markets are possible and have been tried in the past by different countries. In Germany, also, different support schemes have been introduced. Their effect can clearly be seen in the solar market development. This search process has finally led to the most efficient support mechanism which is now in place, namely the cost-covering feed-in tariff. This concept was first proposed by Solarverein Aachen, a local association. Before its institution in Germany it was tested in some Swiss communities. Realization of this concept required an all-out effort by the entire solar community. Most crucial was the process of political decision making. Here two prime movers should be mentioned, Dr. Hermann Scheer and Hans-Josef Fell, who maneuvered the law through parliament. The present law states that utilities have to pay each producer a feed-in rate which is fixed for 20 years after start of operation of the system. The rate differs for each source of renewable energy. It is lower for wind and bioenergy and highest for PV. It is further stipulated that each year the rate for newly erected photovoltaic systems drops by 5% in order to follow the learning curve. Although the present rate is not fully cost-covering the impact on the market was tremendous. Germany is now the second largest market for PV after Japan and ahead of the U.S.

Unfortunately a similar rule cannot be applied to thermal energy because it is not fed into a grid but is consumed directly and is therefore hard to measure. Here direct subsidies are still the best approach. These subsidies are also working well in Germany, where we now have the largest market in Europe.

7.5   Conclusions and Outlook

Although Germany is not as blessed with the sun as some other countries, solar energy has always had an enormous appeal for scientists, technologists, and even the general public. After a long period of only theoretical occupation with the potentials of the different kinds of solar energy utilization large strides were made during the last decade toward practical realization of solar energy. The market in Germany for photovoltaics and thermal systems is one of the largest in the world. How ISES in collaboration with other societies and individuals has contributed to this development is described here. Because support for solar energy was strong in Germany and Europe in general, ISES decided to move its international headquarters to Freiburg in 1995. This event is described in more detail in another chapter.

The outlook for solar energy in Germany remains bright. Renewable energies already now employ more persons than the declining coal industry. This means its further development cannot be stopped any more. The use of solar energy together with other renewable energies will help to make the world more sustainable in the decades to come.

Chapter 8

UK Section of the International Solar Energy Society

by
Bernard McNelis
Managing Director
IT Power
The Manor House, Lutyens Close
Chineham, Hampshire
RG24 8AG UK
bernard.mcnelis@itpower.co.uk

Abstract

In this part I attempt to summarize the past thirty years of the UK Section. In the early years of ISES, before our Section was formed, we had two solar pioneers, but both passed away before our launch in 1974. The Section was formed at the initiative of Mary Archer, with John Page as first chairman, and with David Hall providing boundless energy. The chronological development of the Section is described, with a peak of membership in 1981 when we hosted the International Congress, followed by a decline, and a renaissance. Conference publications and influencing government policy are mentioned. Finally, I conclude that the future looks bright.

8.1   Introduction

In the years much before the formation of the Section, there was very little solar research or other activity in Britain, with the most notable exception the work of Harold Haywood. He conducted extensive work, demonstrated his domestic solar water heater in 1947, and had numerous publications in the 1950s and '60s. Harold and his wife Frances were friends of Farrington Daniels and his wife Olive, since they travelled together to the 1955 Conference at Tucson and Phoenix. His last published paper was at the 1st ISES Congress in Melbourne in 1970, and sadly he passed away before the UK Section was formed. But he did inspire many of the leaders of our Section. Britain also had an early and outstanding example of passive solar architecture. St. George's School in Wallasey (near my home town of Liverpool) was designed by architect Emslie Morgan and was opened in 1962. The building was designed without any conventional heating system. However, the local Education Authority insisted that a heating system be included, but this was never required. Morgan never made public his design calculations (as he had applied for a patent) and he died in 1964.

By the late '60s, interest in solar energy was significantly increased. In 1969 Brian Brinkworth at University College Cardiff completed the work for his book Solar Energy for Man, which was published in 1972. Sales boomed in 1973 and helped lay the foundations for the launch of the Section.

8.1.1   First Steps in the Establishment of the Section, 1973 – 74

Prior to July 1973, there were eight individual members of ISES in the UK. At the UNESCO "Sun in the Service of Mankind" Conference in Paris in 1973 there were over forty UK delegates, including Mary Archer and John Page. Mary Archer noted that they were struck by the fact that nobody knew each other. So at a business meeting of ISES one evening, she got the go-ahead from the board to try and form a UK Section. At the time, Mary Archer was doing research in photoelectrochemistry at the Royal Institution. She made time to deal with forming the Section and corresponding with a rapidly growing number of enthusiasts (I was one of them!). The Preparatory Committee was comprised of John Page (chairman), Derek Bryce-Smith (vice chairman), Mary Archer (Hon. secretary), Ted Jefferies (hon. treasurer), Harry Brown, David Hall, Cleland McVeigh, Dickie Richards, and Steve Szokolay. The team planned an Inaugural Meeting, to formally establish the Section, followed by a public meeting, set for January 1974. Three further technical meetings for 1974 on water heating, a general forum, and on photovoltaics, were also planned even before the inauguration. The Section was well organized even before it was launched!

The Inaugural Meeting was on the evening of 24 January 1974. By this time there were about 100 UK members of ISES, and the Royal Institution's historic lecture theatre was packed to capacity. I had had great difficulty in persuading the research center, where I worked in Manchester, to join ISES and allow me to travel to London to attend the meeting. We heard Mary Archer, David Hall, John Page, and Sir George Porter (Director of the Royal Institution, and winner of the Nobel Prize for Chemistry in 1967) give reviews of the current actions in the UK, in photobiological conversion, solar in architecture, and photochemical conversion. I can trace the start of my absolute obsession with solar to this meeting, and in particular to the energy, dedication, and charisma of David Hall.

The UK Section started in the Royal Institution, principally because Mary Archer worked there, and always stressed that there was no formal link between ISES and the RI. But I would like to imagine that there was more than just coincidence. Everyone knows of Michael Faraday, "the father of electricity," who directed the RI until 1861. Few people, even in Britain, have looked closely at the £20 note to see Faraday and, most importantly, the sun on the wall (Fig. 1). Faraday started the Friday Evening Discourses (and Christmas lectures) in 1826. Britain's first solar pioneer, Harold Haywood, gave his Discourse on solar energy in 1957.

Fig. 1: British £20 note. Michael Faraday gives a discourse at the Royal Institution.

1974 was an exciting year. As well as the further conferences, John Page started efforts to influence government and led a UK-ISES delegation to meet Energy Minister Eric Varley in April. Shortly after, the Minister announced the establishment of the Energy Technology Support Unit (ETSU). The second conference in April on solar water heating at the Polytechnic of Central London (now Westminster University) was also a sell-out. Organizer Steve Szokolay (having seen successful completion of his active solar heated house in Milton Keynes) had already announced his plans to move to Australia, and he was replaced on the committee by Dominic Michaelis. The third sell-out meeting in July, in Brighton, organized by Cleland McVeigh, included developing country applications and was the occasion when it became clear that the UK was serious and should take a part in international activities.

The fourth conference of the first year was on photovoltaics, held at Imperial College in November, with the first paper by Peter Landsberg. Despite the 27 pages of differential equations, the audience was able to wait for Roger Mytton on cadmium sulphide cells, Phil Woodcock of Ferranti on terrestrial silicon modules (Ferranti's business was space cells, but they had a 2Wp prototype module), Fred Treble of the Royal Aircraft Establishment on space cells, and Dickie Richards on marine applications. Trinity House had been experimenting with photovoltaic cells since 1961 and had a trial installation at Crossness, with four further installations planned. PV was shown to be a serious topic for this country.

UK-ISES was also represented at the ISES Congress in Los Angeles in July 1975. Cleland McVeigh presented a paper on the UK scene; and Roy Swayne, Toby Harrison, Ken Page and I were there to support him (among the 4,000 delegates). Roy Swayne was a continuous supporter of the Section and also became executive secretary of the Solar Trade Association, a position which he held for more than 10 years. Roy, sadly, died in 2003.

The Solar Trade Association (STA) was launched in February 1975, almost exactly a year after UK-ISES was formed. The aim was, and still is, to promote use of solar in the UK (particularly use of thermal collectors) and establishing and maintaining high professional standards. The founding Chairman was David Gerassi, also a founding member of UK-ISES. (He had planned to organize a UK group trip to the 1999 Congress in his native Israel. Sadly, David died before this could come about.)

8.1.2   Growth of the Society, 1975-1981

By the end of 1974 there were 300 members and growth continued. June Morton (Fig. 2) was recruited as administrator and worked in an attic in the

Royal Institution (actually the historic Lawrence Bragg room), and so a period of expansion ensued, with four high-profile conferences per year, visitors
from all over the world, and UK-ISES impacting on other ISES Sections and
programs.

In 1975, a grant from the Wolfson Foundation enabled the Section to
undertake a major assessment of the potential for solar energy. John Page and
David Hall worked with seven groups and thirty-nine specialists to produce
the mammoth study. The 375-page report was published in May 1976, and the
first print run of 2,000 copies sold out quickly. The report was used by the
European Commission in the formulation of its Renewable Energy R&D
Program. The Director, Albert Strub, made a presentation on the program to
UK-ISES in November 1976. The European program was the "saviour" for
the UK solar energy community in the absence of any serious UK program.

Solar energy and the Section gained wide exposure at the Energy Show
at Olympia in 1977. The Society organized and manned a stand on solar energy for the eleven days, which was one of the biggest attractions due to the
photovoltaic-powered model railway, built by Bill Coates of the Royal
Institution.

By 1978 the Section and its members were busy and confident. On 3 May
enthusiasts of the newly launched *SunDay* gathered for sunrise outside the
House of Commons. Contributions were made to international conferences
including the 7th ISES Congress in Delhi (postponed from 1977), and the
IEEE PV Conference in Washington, and David Hall and June Morton organized the first Middle East Solar Energy Technology Exhibition and
Conference (SOLTECH), held in Bahrain in April. The exhibition attracted
1,500 visitors from thirty countries. The proceedings were also published by
ISES-UK. A well-attended Conference at the Royal Institution on Solar
Thermal Power Generation, which I organized, heard eleven presentations,
nine of which were from abroad. Even though this technology is inappropri-
ate for this country there was a lot of interest and a lot of expertise on offer.

1979 brought with it a new editor to *Sun at Work*, who did not waste time
in criticizing the government for the inadequacy of its solar program, and the
lack of information, indeed the secrecy, about it. (This was presumably the
start of my demise in official circles, as I still present the same arguments!).
The program of four conferences per year continued. A Midlands branch was
formed by Leslie Jesch and was very active. In September its conference on
practical applications had Bill Beckman as special guest speaker and attracted 250 delegates. There was a large British contingent at the ISES Silver
Jubilee Congress in Atlanta, where President Jimmy Carter sent a representa-

tive to do the opening (few of the Brits could understand her), the Cloggies provided entertainment, and there was outrage at the very negative official (ETSU) British presentation. But the members were very active in promoting the next Congress scheduled for Brighton in 1981.

Fig. 2: 1981, Brighton; Harry Tabor and June Morton in jovial spirits at the Congress dinner

8.1.3   The High Point, 1981

In 1978 the UK's bid to host the 9th ISES Congress was successful. David Hall and June Morton worked tirelessly to realize their ambition. They even managed to persuade HRH Prince Philip, Duke of Edinburgh, to be patron (one worrying moment though was when David drove his very old, recycled Post Office van into Buckingham Palace and told the military guard "we've come to see the Duke"). Eight hundred abstracts were submitted, and the technical program committee met over a weekend to select about 550 for presentation.

In summer 1981, Brighton became the "Solar Centre of the World," to quote several press articles. The Solar World Forum included over 550 papers and attracted more than 1,600 participants from seventy-six countries. The exhibition had 114 stands from companies in fourteen countries. The exhibition included the Solar Challenger, the photovoltaic aircraft that had just earlier flown from France to England. Congress Chairman David Hall (Fig. 3) correctly pointed out that solar energy was not seen as a panacea for the world's energy problems, but he called for decisions to be made that would enable renewable energy to be a serious contribution to the future energy mix.

Unfortunately the Minister responsible for New & Renewable Energy, John Moore, did not show up to open the Congress, but he was not missed, and the event was a huge success.

For me, the most moving part of the Congress was Harry Tabor (Fig. 2) receiving the Farrington Daniels Award, from ISES President Bill Charters. In his acceptance speech he talked about his love affair with solar energy, and stressed how we must learn to live with the limitations of solar energy (low density, intermittency) while training solar engineers, so that solar can play a vital part in the world's energy supply, especially in the developing world. His opening words were: "I am very moved by the recipient of the Farrington Daniels Award—especially with the ceremony taking place here in England. "Harry was born in London but moved to Israel before embarking on his remarkable solar career.

Fig. 3: 1981, Brighton; David Hall addresses the Congress press conference. On his immediate left is Bill Charters, ISES President, and to his right Barry Justin, UK-ISES Chairman.

8.1.4   Declining Fortunes, 1981 – 1992

In the build-up to the 1980s there had been a lot of well-reasoned arguments for increasing government support for renewable energy research, development and demonstration. But what was made available was always "too little, too late."

By the time UK-ISES was approaching ten years old, it appeared that the Department of Energy support had "peaked, declined and was close to death," according to my *Sun at Work* editorial. There was a sizeable UK contingent at the 1983 ISES Congress in Perth, Australia, which included two Brits among the keynote speakers; John Page and Peter Musgrove. The Society continued to hold four conferences per year, but attendance dropped, as did membership numbers. There were healthy financial reserves, thanks to the 1981 Congress and publication of *Solar Energy: A UK Assessment*, but the conference program, a full-time administrator, and an office in a prestigious address (the Royal Institution) was not sustainable. Operating costs were reduced by firstly moving the office to a subsidised location, namely London University King's College, thanks to David Hall. June Morton left UK ISES in 1989. In 1990 there was only one conference, and only two in 1991. The Society moved to a school location with a telephone answering machine and a very part-time secretary. By 1994 no accounts had been published for three years or subscription payments passed on to ISES headquarters, and the Society looked to be insolvent.

The high-point of this period was John Page receiving the Farrington Daniels Award at the Kobe Congress in 1989. But following the excitement of the 1970s and the euphoria of the Solar World Forum, the end looked to be in sight.

8.1.5   Renaissance, 1993 – 1998

The demise of UK-ISES by the early '90s—no administrator, no office, no accounts, few conferences, membership below 100 and falling—led some of the old-timers as well as some youngsters to try to revive the fortunes of the Section in time for its twentieth anniversary. The annual election of committee (board) members, as required by the by-laws, seemed to have been dispensed with, or forgotten. But having "demanded" an election, I became chairman in 1993. Leslie Jesch was elected Vice chairman, and we worked very closely together. The headquarters function was taken on by the Franklin Company in Birmingham, thanks to the dedication and generosity of Leslie and Alison Patterson. A large proportion of the operating costs was borne by Franklin, which also published conference proceedings. I negotiated with Wal

Read, and the debt arising from unremitted subscriptions to ISES Headquarters was converted to a loan, and further loan facilities were made available by committed members, most notably Jean Rosenfeld.

We put a huge effort into preparing for and organising the twentieth Anniversary Conference. I was helped particularly by Jenniy Gregory. The Conference was held at the Royal Institution on 20 January 1994. The four speakers (Sir George had been "promoted" to Lord Porter in 1990, and had retired as director of the RI in 1985. He died in 2002 aged 81) from the Inaugural Meeting took part and were joined by other old-timers as well as newer-generation solar enthusiasts. Special guest speakers included ISES luminaries Jack Duffie and Adolf Goetzberger. Wolfgang Palz, Director of the European Commission Renewable Energy R&D Program, presented his "Power for the World" initiative and commented that UK-ISES had been an inspiration for, and helped with, the formulation of the EC Program. As part of the occasion, Mary Archer also gave a Friday Evening Discourse, "Hello Sunshine." Like Harry Tabor's in Brighton in 1981, hers was about a love affair with the Sun (Fig. 4).

Fig. 4: 1994, London; ISES-UK 20th Anniversary Conference. A special edition of the popular (tabloid) newspaper, The Sun, was printed for the occasion.

UK-ISES returned to the custom of organizing conferences. There were further small but successful conferences on environmental aspects of renewable energy, passive solar, and renewable energy for social development in 1994 and 1995. The improving situation led to the decision to hold longer, two-day conferences, perhaps once per year in conjunction with the AGM. In February 1996, the Society held "Opportunities for Renewable Energy in

Europe," organized by Jenniy Gregory, over two days at the Institution of Civil Engineers in London. The conference was also supported by the British Photovoltaic Association (PV-UK), British Biogen, the British Wind Energy Association (BWEA), Solar Trade Association (STA), the Association of Electricity Producers (AEP), and Friends of the Earth (FoE). This was a huge success and produced the first significant financial surplus for the Section for many years.

Also in 1996, I initiated the Special Service Award to be made, periodically, to individuals who had made an outstanding contribution to the advancement of renewable energy, through the channels of the ISES-UK. In September a second two-day conference, linked to the PV-UK Annual General Meeting, was held at the University of Northumbria in Newcastle, hosted by Bob Hill. This allowed participants to visit the photovoltaic façade opened the previous year. At the conference banquet the first Special Service Award was presented to Fred Treble. The presentation was made by Frank Cook, M.P., Chairman of the Parliamentary Renewable and Sustainable Energy Group (PRASEG), with the laudation by Wolfgang Palz. Fred was the natural candidate to receive the award. He had served the Section in various capacities, including vice chairman and secretary, attended and contributed to all the conferences, and could be relied on to give his time and energy to SunDay events. Fig. 5 shows him on SunDay duty (Fred was also awarded the European Commissions Becquerel Prize at the seventeenth European Photovoltaic Solar Energy Conference in Glasgow in May 2000).

Fig. 5: 2002, Hampshire. Fred Treble inspires young James Plastow (IT Power) as they wait for SunDay customers.

Successful conferences in 1997 on advanced glazing and low-head hydropower led to the two-day conference "Solar Water Heating: A Hands-on Approach" and AGM in Cardiff in May 1998. The second Special Service Award was awarded to David Hall.

After the UK-ISES secretariat had been "rescued" by Franklin and the Society re-established on a firm footing, the office was moved to the Centre for Alternative Technology at Machynlleth, before moving to its present home at Oxford Brookes University. The move to Oxford was thanks to Mick Hutchins, working with our able administrator Christiane Buckle.

The new event of a Christmas lecture followed by a social event was started in 1996. In 1998 the Society was honoured to have Energy Minister John Battle as speaker in the Kings College Great Hall. A packed room listened to the Minister, and then tackled him with questions, to which he responded enthusiastically (without the aid of officials). It appeared that the Society was now back on track for capacity conferences, and was recognized by the government.

8.1.6   Firmly Re-established and with a Bright Future 1999 –

The Section moved toward its Silver Jubilee, led by Jenniy Gregory. The Silver Jubilee Conference was held over three days in Brighton in May 1999. It was a tremendous success. A total of forty-five papers were presented and the Proceedings ran to 300 pages. Special ISES guest speakers included Anne Grete Hestnes, Jack Duffie, and Erik Lysen (Fig. 6 shows some of the delegates relaxing). The SSA was awarded to Leslie Jesch for his outstanding work for the Section (Fig. 7). Cleland McVeigh, had been the organizer of the Section's 3rd Conference in 1974, was instrumental in selecting his hometown of Brighton as the venue for the 1981 Congress, and, after the Silver Jubilee Conference, entertained guests in his home (Fig. 8).

Fig. 6: Relaxing Jack and Pat Duffie with Coti and Leslie Jesch

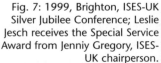

Fig. 7: 1999, Brighton, ISES-UK Silver Jubilee Conference; Leslie Jesch receives the Special Service Award from Jenniy Gregory, ISES-UK chairperson.

Fig. 8: 1999, Brighton; Following the conference, Cleland McVeigh entertained us in his home. Leslie Jesch is sleeping, but Jack Duffie appreciates the music.

Following the conference, we decided to appoint a president. Mary Archer was the obvious candidate and we were very pleased that she accepted. Jenniy was succeeded as chairperson by Jean Rosenfold, who had previously held several positions in the Section. He continued improving the services and financials of the Section, working closely with Mick Hutchins, who was kindly providing the Secretariat at his university. When Jean decided to accept a position in Denmark, Mick was an obvious candidate to become the next chairman.

8.2   ISES-UK Committee and By-laws

Being British and old-fashioned, we have a Committee, not a Board of Directors. Our constitution and by-laws are an adaptation of the ISES by-laws (but we have never devoted the same level of (wasted?) energy as the ISES board to changing the membership rules or election procedures!).

The eleven chairpersons over the past 30 years are listed in Table 1. Most have been described in the previous section. Two of these leaders spoke at our Silver Jubilee Conference, but sadly passed away not long after. They deserve special mention.

Table 1: Chairpersons of the last 30 years.

	UK-ISES Chairpersons 1974 – 2004	
1	1974 – 76	John Page
2	1977 – 79	David Hall
3	1980 – 82	Barry Justin
4	1983 – 85	Julian Keable
5	1986 – 88	Bob Hill
6	1989 – 91	Peter Dunn
7	1992	Ali Sayigh
8	1993 – 95	Bernard McNelis
9	1996 – 98	Jenniy Gregory
10	1999 – 2000	Jean Rosenfold
11	2001 –	Mick Hutchins

David Hall (1935–1999, Fig. 9), was our second chairperson. I have already described him as having inspired me at the UK-ISES inaugural meeting. His vision and enthusiasm for photosynthesis as a source of energy for the world, particularly the 2 billion people in the rural areas of developing countries, made him the world's star of biomass. He was editor of Biomass and Bioenergy, did fundamental research, and published papers, but still found time for teaching across the globe including in Africa, India, and South America. The Section decided that he should be remembered through the annual David Hall Memorial Lecture given each December. The first of these was by David Bellamy, a well-known environmentalist and broadcaster, in December 1999. The title of his topical talk was "How to Unscrew a Sunburnt World." David's wife Peta was present, and she has been at all subsequent memorial lectures. David was also especially recognized when the World Conference in Biomass launched the David Hall World Prize for Bioenergy in his memory, which was awarded for the first time in 2000 in Sevilla to Hermann Scheer.

Bob Hill (1937–1999, Fig. 10) was my closest friend throughout my career. He had a lot in common with David Hall, in that he did fundamental research in photovoltaics, but he also believed fervently in PV's contribution to making the world a better place. Like David, he also worked in the developing countries of Africa, Asia, and South America. Bob was the undoubted pioneer of PV in Britain. He persevered against brain-dead bureaucrats and against-the-odds he led the project to install a large PV façade at his University. Giving a eulogy at Bob's funeral in Newcastle, I called on the university Vice-Chancellor to re-name the building after him; but a small plaque is all we could manage. At the time of his death, Bob was co-editing, with Mary Archer, a major textbook, *Clean Energy from Photovoltaics*. Mary had to complete the work without him, but the book, published in 2001, is dedicated to his memory. The sixteenth European Photovoltaic Solar Energy Conference, held in Glasgow in 2000 (for which I was vice chairman), was also dedicated to Bob's memory.

Fig. 9: 1999, Brighton, ISES-UK Silver Jubilee Conference; David Hall, as always, promoting biomass (David passed away shortly afterwards).

Fig. 10: 1997, Newcastle; Bob Hill and wife Ana introduce young Chloë McNelis to the 40kW PV façade on the Northumbria Building.

8.3   Conferences and Outreach

I have described many of the conferences in this chronology, and so I will not use much more space here. The Section has organized a total of eighty conferences over its thirty years. The eightieth Conference, in September 2003, was titled "Towards Zero Carbon—renewables, fuel-cells and embedded generation." This was a successful joint exercise with the Energy Institute, organized by Tony Day. Increasingly, our Section looks beyond the limitations of "traditional solar topics" and is engaged across the spectrum of renewable energy technologies, climate change, and other policy issues.

Historically, the scientific and technical conferences have been the bread-and-butter of ISES, and the Section. But increasingly we look more to information dissemination (I prefer a single word, insemination) to the nonconverted, from high-level policy makers to the general public. The SunDay events are crucially important in this matter. These are growing in size and scope, but are still just scratching the surface. Alison Patterson initiated extensive European co-ordination and exchange on SunDays. In 2000 the Section received the ISES-Europe Award for the most interesting national section activity—more than half of all the European SunDay events were held in the UK. (Fig. 11).

Fig. 11: 2000, Eversley; Representatives from local councils and housing associations attended IT Power's Solar SunDay event, held at the PV Test and Training Centre in Eversley.

8.4   Publications

In 1974 the Founding Committee decided to launch a magazine/journal. With permission from ISES, whose original journal was called *Sun at Work*, UK-ISES launched *Sun at Work in Britain* (SAWIB). Alan Pulford of Pilkingtons was first editor, and Pilkingtons became the first industrial sponsor of UK-ISES by printing the magazine. The first issue was published in July 1974 and contained the presentations from the inaugural meeting.

Following this two-year sponsorship, efforts were made to find further support, and in 1978 Pergamon Press (publishers of *Solar Energy*, which has been a major source of income for ISES), took over publication, with myself as editor. This was not a commercial success for the publisher and the arrangement ended in 1983. After one interim issue, Leslie Jesch took over as editor and an arrangement was made with the Institute of Energy to publish *Sun at Work* as a supplement to their own publication, *Energy World*. This lasted for only three issues, and in 1985 the two issues were prepared in-house. Table 2 lists the editors of *Sun at Work in Britain* during its lifetime. But despite the decline of Sun at Work in Britain, this was also the origin of *Sun at Work in Europe*, which was launched in 1986 as a private venture by the Franklin Company, with Leslie Jesch as editor.

Table 2: Editors of Sun at Work in Britain

	Sun at Work in Britain Editors 1974-1985	
1	1974 – 75	Alan Pulford
2	1976	Cleland McVeigh
3	1977 – 78	Toby Harrison
4	1979 – 83	Bernard McNelis
5	1983 – 85	Leslie Jesch

The major stand-alone publication of UK-ISES was *Solar Energy: A UK Assessment*. There are also the proceedings of eighty Conferences (which must be a record) and three books. I have described this elsewhere. *Heating Water by the Sun* and *Solar Electricity* have been revised and reprinted numerous times.

8.5   Awards

In 1985 the Solar Energy Unit at University College Cardiff, led by Brian Brinkworth, won the Achievement Through Action Award. This was a real encouragement to the Section.

In 1989 John Page received the Farrington Daniels Award at the Congress in Kobe. John, as professor of building science at Sheffield University, had a strong interest in solar energy for twenty years before the launch of ISES-UK. As well as his work in buildings, planning, solar radiation, etc., he had always had an intense concern for the world's climate and energy resources. At our inaugural meeting he suggested we would exhaust our natural gas supplies in thirty years (oil in forty, coal in sixty years), and although these predictions have proved wrong, we still need to take the action he advocates. In his Farrington Daniels Address, he made much reference to the Bruntland Report and the need to look at energy on a global basis. His closing comment was: "If one is wise, and one's dreams are sound, one knows their achievements rest safely in the hands of the young." I was deeply impressed when John came to our IT Power 21st Anniversary Summer Party and made an impromptu speech of congratulations to the founders, which really encouraged our young scientists and engineers (our successors) (Fig. 12).

The Achievement Through Action Award has mostly been given to Laboratories and Institutions, but I was honored to receive this personally in 2001, at the Congress in Adelaide. The certificate is beautifully framed and on the wall of my office (although some have noticed it is stained with red wine!).

Fig. 12: 2002, Chineham; John Page chats to (old) Fred Treble and inspires (young) Paul Cowley at IT Power 21st Birthday Summer Party.

8.6   Relationship with ISES

When we started, all our members were, naturally, members of ISES. But there were arguments right from the beginning that most of the subscription monies collected were passed on to HQ in Australia. Additionally, many members did not have any use for the journal *Solar Energy*. It would be too boring to report on the evolution of our membership grades, but suffice it that we now have two basic grades of membership of the Solar Energy Society, and membership of ISES.

I believe that the UK Section has contributed a lot to ISES, and this can be attributed largely to the seemingly limitless energy of Leslie Jesch. As Director, vice president, and editor of *Sunworld*, ISES was his life. The Brits are known to be somewhat Euro-sceptic; we still do not use the Euro as currency and measure in pre-historic imperial units, but in terms of ISES, the UK led in the development of the European Regional Grouping. When Leslie Jesch took over from me as Editor of SAWIB in 1984, links with other sections in Europe were few, but there was a growing importance of the European dimension to energy issues. He developed the concept of a pan-European publication *Sun at Work in Europe* (SAWIE), which was launched in 1986 with the full support of ISES Sections in Belgium, Denmark, Ireland, the Netherlands, and Norway, as well as the UK. By the end of the 1980s the SAWIE network extended to most countries in Europe and the groundwork had been established for the creation of ISES-Europe, the European regional secretariat of ISES. ISES Europe is described in Volume II of this book.

8.7   Influencing Government Policy

At the inaugural meeting all the speakers called for government support for solar energy research. In April 1974 the Secretary of State for Energy received a UK-ISES delegation. Shortly afterwards he announced the setting up of the Energy Technology Support Unit (ETSU) at the Atomic Energy Research Establishment (AERE), Harwell. Many UK-ISES members claimed that recycled nuclear scientists at Harwell might not be big supporters of solar power!

UK-ISES published *Solar Energy—A UK Assessment* in July 1976, a report which analyzed all aspects of solar energy and assessed the potential for solar in the UK. The report recommended R&D needs for solar systems for the UK and for export. In 1976 UK-ISES also gave evidence to the Energy Resources Sub-Committee on Science & Technology. By 1976 solar energy was being treated with a little more respect, and the Department of Energy had instructed ETSU to make an "official" assessment of solar energy. But "Solar Energy—its potential contribution within the UK"— Energy Paper Number 16 was not published until 1977.

The Government launched a renewable energy R&D program, which supported a variety of projects. But this was very modest compared to funding in other advanced countries, and then it was cut smaller. We made representations to Energy Minister David Mellor in 1982, arguing that simple economics and accountants' mentality should not be the basis for deciding on long-term and important energy options.

At the same time UK-ISES proposed and initiated the formation of the British Renewable Energy Forum (BREF) together with the other renewable energy associations, to try to influence government policy. This was led by our Chairman Julian Keable but was probably "before its time" to be very effective.

During the 1960s and early 1970s the British government funded R&D into PV cells and arrays for space applications. Around the world the "oil crises" spurred interest in PV technology as a significant energy producer. Almost all the major industrial countries initiated ambitious PV R&D programs, and new companies were formed or evolved from the space PV manufacturers, to develop and market terrestrial PV systems. The UK government was notable for its lack of support for research into PV for electricity supply or for exports.

In the 1976 assessment of solar energy for the UK, we concluded that the UK was well placed to become a major international supplier of PV systems, and we recommended that the government should support PV development.

The 1977 government review of solar energy for the UK did not consider PV because of the high cost. A review of the publication, which I wrote, for Sun at Work in Britain concluded with a comment that it was disappointing that PV had been "disqualified" for consideration, given the enormous global and export potential. But this passage was deleted by the editor! (Toby Harrison who worked for ETSU).

During the 1980s, the Newcastle Photovoltaic Applications Centre (NPAC) was established by Bob Hill. NPAC, as well as conducting research, led efforts to secure support from the Department of Trade and Industry (into which the Department of Energy was eventually absorbed) and proposed the establishment of a National PV Centre, as a means of supporting development of the industry, but this was rejected by the government. In 1988 the government again reviewed renewable energy technologies and up-graded PV to a "long-shot," but not appropriate for government support. But in 1990 a review concluded that PV had the potential for some niches to make a cost-effective contribution to UK electricity generation, and that in particular, distributed, grid-connected PV systems integrated into buildings could be classified as "promising but uncertain." At the same time Bob and I worked together to launch an industry group, the British Photovoltaic Association (PV-UK). We lobbied hard, and I especially used the occasion of Minister John Battle's UK-ISES Christmas lecture. Today we have a (relatively) generous PV support-program, including 50% grants, which Bob could only have dreamed of.

The Section maintains a close watch on policy developments and actions (or inaction). The latest Energy White Paper, Our Energy Future – Creating a Low-Carbon Economy, was published in 2003. John Page was very quick to study the report and to mote the lack of scientific and engineering analysis, as regards "climate-based" energy resources. With the brain, energy, and dedication of our founding chairman still available as a resource, UK-ISES will continue to press our government to act on renewable energy and global climate issues.

8.8   The Future

The past thirty years has seen growth to a large peak, decline into a trough, and now we are on to a second period of growth, with membership now over 300 and growing. A lot has been achieved. At the peak it was not possible to persuade a government Minister to open the World Congress, but since then we have had an Energy Minister present our Christmas Lecture, so we must be doing something correctly!

The Section held its 80th Conference in London in November 2003. After 30 years we have a Section which has a firm membership and financial base. We are doing project work, such as Solar Schools, supported by the European Commission and co-ordinated by the ISES HQ in Germany. I believe the future is bright (Fig. 13).

Fig. 13: December 2003, London; David Hall Memorial Lecture Reception. Bernard McNelis wishes Chairman Mick Hutchins well as we embark on the next 30 years.

Chapter 9

Israeli Section of the International Solar Energy Society

by
Gershon Grossman
Faculty of Mechanical Engineering
Technion – Israel Institute of Technology
Haifa 32000, Israel
Tel: ++972-4-8292074 Fax: ++972-4-8295711
e-mail: mergr01@techunix.technion.ac.il

Abstract

This chapter describes the history of the Israeli Section of ISES, formed in 1979. The information in this chapter is based on contributions from many of the Section's members, to whom we would like to express our sincere appreciation. We are describing a rather long period of solar energy activity that has led to the formation of the Section. The most important events including national conferences, and the landmark event—the Solar World Congress held in Jerusalem in 1999—are described. A chronological listing of the Chairmen of the Section is provided. Major solar developments in our country that received international recognition are presented, as well as international awards that some of the members of our solar community have received.

9.1   Introduction: Solar History in Israel— Leading to the Formation of our National Section

9.1.1   The Early Years

Interest in solar energy in Israel preceded the State. In the 1930s and 1940s Dov Ashbell, professor of meteorology in the Hebrew University of Jerusalem (HUJ) and Nathan Robinson, professor of physics at the Technion—Israel Institute of Technology in Haifa, published works related to solar energy, but it is doubtful if they were thinking of solar hardware. Professor Robinson concentrated his efforts on solar passive design of buildings, and several of his reports with co-workers from the Civil Engineering Department, on "thermal protection of concrete roofs," "response of walls to outside thermal influences" and the like are still found at the Technion's library.

With the establishment of the State in 1948, one of the first acts of Prime Minister, David Ben Gurion was to set up the Research Council of Israel (RCI) within his office, to promote R&D that could harness science to help a new country having virtually no natural resources. Less than a year later, a new immigrant from the UK arrived in Israel—Harry Tabor, an applied physicist with industrial experience. He was given the "physics and engineering" desk of the RCI, which included the task of setting up a national physical laboratory (NPLI)—on the British model—to put some order into the measurement units (British, metric and Ottoman) in use in the country. And here, from an unexpected source, he got involved in solar energy.

His desk received many suggestions from the public on how to develop the country (understandable in a new country), including proposals on harnessing the sun, and he had to examine these proposals to see if they had any value. He received reports and proposals on how to exploit solar energy from very persistent people (though with no knowledge of physics or solar geometry!). Tabor had discovered that he could only deal with enthusiasts like these by knowing the subject better than they did. So he read whatever literature there was on the subject, and this caused him to think about a subject with which he had had no previous contact.

There were at the time a few domestic solar water heating installations in the country, rather poor copies of such installations elsewhere, and Tabor asked himself why their efficiency was so poor. This led him to the concept of black surfaces that were not black bodies in the thermodynamic sense, which he called "selective black surfaces" and his industrial experience brought him and his team in the NPLI quick answers to finding an industrial process (a modification of the known nickel and chrome processes for blackening metals) for producing selective surfaces on the large areas of solar collectors. Here he was triply lucky: (i) this development occurred in 1955, just prior to the first World Congress on Applied Solar Energy held in Arizona (Phoenix and Tucson); (ii) his "boss" (the director of the RCI, Dr. Shmuel Sambursky), was a professor of physics at HUJ who particularly appreciated a black surface that was not "black" and what this could do to improving solar energy collection; (iii) he, in turn, excited *his* boss—the prime minister who decided to send Tabor with an exhibit to Arizona, which required finding a cargo plane able to take a full-size flat-plate collector (FPC) in its "belly" (remember, this was 1955!). The exhibit (Fig. 1) was a great success, with steam emerging from an FPC that had no concentrating mirrors, and put Tabor and Israel on the world map as solar pioneers.

Fig. 1: Harry Tabor exhibits the new collector and applications at the First World Symposium on Applied Solar Energy, Arizona (1955)

Tabor, as director of the NPLI, had good relations with the director of the Standards Institute of Israel (SII), Dr. Arnon, and this led to the SII establishing test procedures and the issuing of official performance certificates (possibly the first country in the world to do so) so that no one would buy a solar collector that did not carry SII certification. An extremely valuable follow-up to this was that, in 1980, the government made solar water heaters, obligatory on all new dwellings up to eight stories high. Today, there are about 1 million domestic installations in Israel, which the Ministry of National Infrastructures (MNI) estimates save the country 2 million barrels of oil a year.

Other developments at the NPLI included small power units. Like their colleagues in other parts of the developed world in the early 1950s, the NPLI team considered solar energy as a help to developing countries that did not have energy grids. So, it would be good to develop a small solar power unit for these countries (these would be thermal units since PV was not an option at that time). To minimize the maintenance problems of reciprocating engines, Tabor proposed a turbine operating on organic fluids (since the low temperature from simple FPCs would not provide a decent steam temperature). Here, he was again lucky: a new immigrant from France, Lucien Bronicki, had just completed his "practical training" on turbine design, so he and Tabor made a marvelous team. The result was a small organic Rankine cycle (ORC) turbine—with only one moving part, the rotor. A 3 kWe unit was exhibited at the UN Conference on New Sources of Energy, Rome, 1961. It used a novel inflated plastic solar collector invented by a team member, Ing. Zeimer, and the plant was erected on a farm some 30 km outside Rome, and interested congress delegates were ferried by bus to see it in operation. A little later, a similar unit—but using FPCs with side-mirror boosters—(Fig. 2) was erected in a developing country in Africa (but was withdrawn following a change in the country's regime).

Fig. 2: ORMAT solar-powered ORC employing FPCs with booster mirrors for water pumping, Mali, Africa (1966)

The NPLI looked for a company to commercialize the product but there were no takers. With faith in their son, the Bronicki family offered to set up a factory in Yavne (where they had set up a leather recycling plant) and they received the license on the turbine from the Israel government. The new company was named ORMAT. After a good deal of additional development, they had a product ready for the market but here they suffered a severe disappointment. Despite the need, there were no buyers in the developing countries because they simply did not have the money. ORMAT found another market for the turbine: reliable, maintenance-free power supply for remote microwave repeaters (using, however, fuel rather than solar energy…).

Attempts were made at the NPLI to produce inexpensive PV cells based on CdS, produced by a spray process. Efficiency was low but the power cost was lower than from silicon cells then available. Some panels were erected including a traffic signal on the Jerusalem-Tel Aviv road, and one at the straits of Tiran in the Red Sea. The program was terminated when the cost of silicon cell power dropped, and there were some doubts about the long-term stability of the CdS cells.

Solar ponds were proposed in 1948 by Dr. Rudolph Bloch, research director of the Dead Sea Works, who had observed the absence of convection in some natural saline ponds and had realized the possibilities. He was a member of the board of the RCI but could not get anyone interested till he met Tabor in 1958. Tabor at once saw the potential and organized a solar pond R&D team. This triggered solar pond R&D in several other countries.

9.1.2   The 1970s

The oil crisis in the wake of the 1973 Yom Kippur war sparked renewed interest in solar energy in Israel, as it did in the rest of the world. Research on a variety of solar projects began at academic institutions. At the Technion—Israel's oldest and premier institute of technology—a new solar energy laboratory was established in 1974 by three (then young) faculty members—Gershon Grossman, Avraham Shitzer, and Yoram Zvirin. Initial support for this effort was provided by the Institute, and additional grants followed, from government ministries and from abroad. Students were very excited about this research area and worked on a variety of solar thermal subjects – flat-plate and concentrating solar collectors, space heating and cooling systems, air heaters, heat storage, and more. A solar heating system was installed in the library of the Mechanical Engineering Faculty. Cooperation with industry had begun. One distinctive project involved a concentrating collector based on a stationary spherical mirror with a tracking absorber. The spherical geometry makes it possible to build very large mirrors and even incorporate them in a building structure, since they do not move; all tracking is done with a rather small moving absorber, placed parallel to the solar rays. Several versions of this collector were built, and there were contacts with industry to develop the concept for process steam generation, but this never materialized. The largest model had a 10-meter diameter dish that generated steam at 300°C (Fig. 3). It was installed in the parking lot of the Mechanical Engineering building, and looked like a giant radar antenna; several colleagues expressed concern that it could be mistaken for a military target and, in case of war, would be bombed from the air, taking with it their cars parked nearby.

The group's work soon gained recognition and many visitors – engineers, architects as well as nonprofessionals—came to look into the projects in the laboratory. Among them was a fact-finding committee from the U.S. Congress who came in 1979 to check for areas of possible cooperation between Egypt and Israel, following the historic Camp David peace agreement. Solar energy seemed like a good subject, where both countries could make a contribution. The committee's visit was kept confidential, in order not to jeopardize this delicate mission. Nevertheless, the Technion's public relations people got wind of it and showed up with their cameras, only to be told politely but firmly to leave and keep quiet.

Fig. 3: Ten-meter diameter stationary spherical solar concentrator with tracking absorber at the Faculty of Mechanical Engineering, Technion – Israel Institute of Technology, Haifa (1979)

In 1974, Israel Dostrovsky, then president of the Weizmann Institute of Science (WIS), together with David Wolf, decided to establish a Solar Energy Laboratory at the Institute. The first efforts concentrated on improving the performance of the existing FPC. A new selective surface was invented, based on electrochemical anodization of a copper surface. Its aim was to replace the "nickel black" developed previously at the NPLI that suffered from poor resistance to outdoor humid conditions. This development was adopted by MIROMIT, a pioneer Israeli manufacturer of FPCs at that time, who built a production plant based on this process. Another development was an anti-reflective coating to reduce the reflection losses from the glass pane, especially when higher temperatures were needed, e.g. for air conditioning. Special laboratory equipment was built for measuring the spectral absorbance and emittance of this coating at different temperatures. David Wolf, together with Avraham Kudish and Michael Epstein, built a laboratory aimed at measuring the performance of full-scale FPCs under controlled conditions using a sun simulator. This laboratory became a center for measuring the performance of commercial FPCs, until the SII established a standard rating procedure and took over this national mission. A pioneer, large, forced-circulation solar central water heating system was built to supply hot water to the Animal Breeding Center at WIS. This system was used later by the Ministry of Housing as a model for its first demonstration project in a multistory building in Ashdod.

Ben-Gurion University (BGU) of the Negev was established in 1970 in Beer-Sheva, the capital city of the Negev region covering the greater part of Israel. The Negev is half-desert, sparse in population but rich in sunshine. The declared vision of the new university was to help bring new life to this vast, barren land. Among the first University faculty to pioneer solar energy for the Negev were David Wolf and Aharon Roy. They brought with them former experience in energy technologies, desalination, electrochemistry, and techno-economics. Aharon Roy initiated the solar power laboratory with several projects, including a 10 m^2 polar-mounted linear-focusing tracking solar concentrator; innovative PCM-salts energy-storage systems with Eli Korin and Emanuel Menczel, who pioneered the full Dead Sea salt phase-diagram; and a 10 amp. hydrogen-oxygen fuel-cell. He also established a techno-economics team.

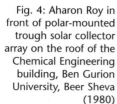

Fig. 4: Aharon Roy in front of polar-mounted trough solar collector array on the roof of the Chemical Engineering building, Ben Gurion University, Beer Sheva (1980)

David Wolf and Abraham Kudish established a Solar Energy Laboratory and Center at BGU. One of the first projects was to set up a meteorological station to measure solar radiation. With Abraham Tamir, they designed and installed one of the first solar central domestic hot water (DHW) systems in Israel, on the roof of one of the BGU dormitory complexes. A solar system for heating the BGU swimming pool was also designed and installed in the early 1980s. They also began investigating solar collectors constructed from polymeric materials. Roy and Korin joined Wolf and Kudish in a project on the application of PCMs in solar greenhouses. Along with Dov Pasternak they developed a solar heated greenhouse using special transparent panels filled with PCMs.

In 1975, Aharon Roy initiated and directed a new solar energy laboratory at the Institute for Desert Research, a branch of BGU located at the new Sede Boker campus. A large-scale project involving the study of shallow solar ponds was undertaken. Abraham Kudish joined in to work on solar distillation in conjunction with controlled environment system, viz., a greenhouse. This laboratory served as the nucleus for the National Solar Laboratory, which established several years later by the Israeli government. Several solar systems were procured and installed by the Ministry of Energy for demonstrating and testing industrial units. The site was then taken over by the Solar Calculation Group, who further developed and augmented the laboratory.

The Solar Calculation Group was started by David Faiman in 1976, assisted initially by David Govaer, Jeffrey Gordon, and Yair Zarmi. They were later joined by Daniel Feuermann, Amos Zemel, and others. Initially, the group worked as a kind of "think tank" in attempts to solve a number of immediate problems associated with the recent oil crisis. They were the first to validate the well-known University of Wisconsin's F-chart method, using real data, from a large central solar water heating system they designed for a neighboring kibbutz. Together with Ari Rabl, one of several frequent visitors at that time, they developed and optimized a low-cost, high-efficiency method for designing solar industrial process heat systems without storage. They developed the Gordon-Zarmi method for the optimal design of passive solar buildings and invented a number of devices such as the rotating prism wall, an 'invisible' thermosiphon solar water heater, and the multipyranometer—a method for monitoring direct beam insolation with no moving parts.

In parallel with academic research, there was considerable industrial activity. Manufacturers of solar collectors and water heating systems continued to improve their products both for the local market and for export. The increased energy awareness, brought about by the oil crisis, seemed to help their business. Alongside the common individual family thermosiphon-type water heater, central systems for large buildings started to emerge.

The government of Israel did its share to promote activity in the solar area. In 1975, the newly formed Ministry of Energy and Infrastructure (currently the Ministry of National Infrastructures) announced the launch of a National Project to develop and commercialize solar products. Led by one of Israel's major corporations—TADIRAN Electronics Industries—and co-funded by the government, this national priority project concentrated on building applications, both residential and commercial. Solar collectors, and heating and cooling systems were the subjects of development. The TADIRAN team, headed by Yehuda Landau, included Yeshayahu Vardi, Joseph Bourne, Yigal Kimchi, Jonathan Ben-Dror, Moshe Hirsch, and a Technion consultant – Gershon Grossman. The main product was a lithium bromide-water absorption chiller especially designed for solar applications. It had several unique features including a solution preheater and an auxiliary generator for maximum utilization of the available solar heat. Several units of this type were built and some exported to the Caribbean islands. A 700 kW (200 TR) solar-powered air conditioning system, one of the largest ever built anywhere in the world, was inaugurated in 1980 at the Tel Hashomer hospital near Tel Aviv, where it functioned year-round to air condition the surgical facilities (Fig. 5). This application involving year-round operation was carefully selected, as it improved the economics of the solar system considerably. Unfortunately, the technological success did not materialize into a thriving business, as was originally hoped. The high cost of the solar part of the system—collectors and storage—made it hard to compete with alternative primary energies. Shortly after the completion of the Tel Hashomer project,

TADIRAN decided to abandon this business and the ASD (Applied Solar Devices) division was closed. The solar air conditioning systems at the various installations continued to work, however, for many more years.

Fig. 5a, b: Solar collector field and storage tank (above) serving 700 kW LiBr-water absorption chiller (right) at Tel –Hashomer Hospital near Tel Aviv (1980)

Solar pond research continued. The Israel government decided to sponsor the building of a 5 MWe plant, with a 1 square kilometer of pond area, and a company, SOLMAT, under Lucien Bronicki's direction, was established for this purpose. Actually, one pond was built of 40,000 m² and one of 250,000 m², and both operated exactly as planned. There were also plans to bring Mediterranean water to be floated on the surface of the Dead Sea and turn it into a one huge solar pond. The efficiency from solar to heat was about 16%

but the overall efficiency (solar to electricity) was lower than 1%. The investment per m² of pond area was not high, but the fresh water for surface leaching of the pond and the operation and maintenance nearly tripled the cost. After a long-term demonstration of the operation of a 5 MWe turbine by the 250,000 m² pond, the government stopped the funding in 1991 ("as the point had been proven") and the program collapsed, as private investors were not yet ready to take it over.

Fig. 6: 5 MWe solar pond and power plant at the Dead Sea, Israel (1982)

9.2   The Israeli Section of ISES is Formed

Academic and industrial activities have led to an ever-expanding group of people engaged in solar R&D in Israel, who met from time to time for symposia. Ironically, the formation of the Israeli Section of ISES was prompted not by lack of local organization (the solar community was functioning quite well in an ad-hoc manner), but by the wish to host the ISES World Congress in Israel. At the 1979 ISES Silver Jubilee Congress in Atlanta, Georgia, an ad-hoc Israeli delegation consisting of Harry Tabor and Gershon Grossman presented to the ISES Board a proposal to hold one of the next ISES congresses in Israel. The presenters were greeted warmly, but were told that only countries with an ISES section could be hosts to an ISES

Congress. This information was passed on to the solar community in Israel and, following organizational efforts, the Israeli Section of ISES came to be. The inaugural meeting was held at the Petroleum Institute building in Tel Aviv on December 17, 1979, attended by over 50 solar energy devotees. Harry Tabor was elected chairman and Gershon Grossman as the first secretary of the Section. The Technion—Israel Institute of Technology volunteered to host the Section's headquarters, which has remained there ever since. The Technion also generously allocated some resources for the Section's logistics. With changes of chairpersons and secretaries, the Section has functioned effectively over the years, due in large part to the efforts of Mrs. Ariela Rozen, who continues to do a marvelous job looking after the Section's affairs.

The Israel Section of ISES had 30 members at its inception. Membership peaked in 1997 to 63 (most of whom were full members of ISES) and is currently at 71 paid-up members (31 full members, 40 local members). For a country of six million inhabitants, this makes for one of the highest per capita memberships in the world.

So the Israel Section was officially set up but had to wait till 1999 before the World Congress was held in Israel. An application was submitted to the board during the Hamburg meeting in 1987, but lost in the competition. One reason was the desire of ISES to hold a Congress in an ex-Soviet-block country, and the 1993 Congress was held in Budapest. There, the ISES Board decided to hold the ISES Congress in Israel in 1999.

Over the years, members of the Israeli Section have been quite active in ISES and have accrued a remarkable record of service to ISES, considering the Section's size within the Society. First and foremost is Harry Tabor, having served on the ISES Board for many years and having been president of ISES during 1981 – 1983. Harry received major prestigious awards from ISES and the book of his reprints was issued at the 1999 ISES World Congress. Other Israeli members who have served on the ISES Board over the years include Gershon Grossman, Dubi Dvorjetski, and presently, Abraham Arbib. Amos Zemel and Jeff Gordon were chosen as associate editors for the journal *Solar Energy*—the flagship of ISES—and were among the individuals who have helped shape the journal and how solar energy research is perceived. The recent ISES-sponsored book on the state-of-the-art in solar and a review of all major progress ("Solar Energy—The State Of The Art- ISES Position Papers") was edited and organized by Jeff Gordon, at the request of the ISES Board.

9.2.1   Our Board of Directors and the By-Laws of Our ISES Section

At the Section's inaugural meeting, election of the first board of directors was conducted. The seven-member Board consisted of Baruch Givoni, Gershon Grossman, Ami Katz, Joseph Nowarsky, Aharon Roy, Yeshayahu Segal, and Harry Tabor. The members of this preliminary board worked out the first version of our by-laws, which were soon adopted by the total membership.

The Section's by-laws state its main objective—to foster the science and application of solar energy utilization, with due consideration for the needs of the country. Rules of membership allow any individual or organization actively engaged in research, application, or implementation of solar energy utilization to become a member and describe the rights and responsibilities of Section members. The Institutes of the Section are its General Assembly and its Board of Directors, to consist of three to seven members, including the Chairperson and the Secretary. The by-laws further specify the rules for handling the Section's finances.

A chronological list of the Section Chairpersons, since its formation, is given below:

1979 – 1990	Harry Tabor
1991 – 1992	Israel Dostrovsky
1993 – 1995	Gershon Grossman
1996 – 2000	Harry Tabor
2001 – present	Gershon Grossman

9.2.2   Our Conferences

The first National Symposium on Solar Energy Utilization in Israel was held at the Weizmann Institute, Rehovot, in June 1975, and the second followed at Ben Gurion University, Beer Sheva, in November 1976. Technion researchers organized the first International Conference on the Application of Solar Energy, held at the Technion, Haifa, in September 1978. Further national symposia, about once a year, were organized.

Two types of national meetings are held regularly in our country. One is the ISES Section annual meeting, where members present the results of their research and other activities; we often invite representatives of the government and/or industry to discuss policy and plans. Part of the meeting is dedicated to the Section's business. The other type of meeting is the Sede Boker

Symposia on Solar Electricity Production, which have become a regular event since 1985.

9.2.3   The Relation of Our Section to ISES

Formally we are a Section of ISES and as such our members are encouraged to become full members of ISES. We also offer a local membership at a reduced fee, which some of our members prefer. Student and corporate memberships are also available. At the beginning, we collected the dues and transmitted its part to ISES. Automatically, ISES offered the *Solar Energy Journal* as part of the benefits, but our members could opt out for a reduction in dues. At present, members can pay their dues directly to ISES, or continue to do so through our Section's office. During the first few years almost 80% of our members were also members of ISES. There were also substantial discounts for members of ISES to participate in ISES conferences.

9.3   The 1980s and Beyond ...

After the second energy crisis of 1979 (the Khomeini revolution in Iran) oil prices dropped again and interest in solar seemed to decline worldwide. The Reagan administration in the USA cut many of the incentives to solar research offered during the time of President Jimmy Carter. Nevertheless, activity in Israel kept pace.

9.3.1   Academic Activities

Academic research has continued at Ben-Gurion University, the Technion, Tel Aviv University, and the Weizmann Institute. These are the centers of solar energy research among Israel's seven research universities.

David Faiman's group at Ben Gurion University (BGU) constructed "PETAL," a 400 m² multi-purpose parabolic dish reflector with adjustable concentration up to 10,000X (Fig. 7). It also established an ultrahigh-accuracy PV test facility thanks to the almost perfect AM1.5G spectrum presented by the Sede Boker sky. It has pioneered research into the possible use of Fullerenes for PV cells and has performed extensive research into a number of practical uses for highly concentrating mini-dishes.

Fig. 7: "PETAL"—a 400 m² parabolic dish reflector with adjustable concentration up to 10,000X, at Ben Gurion University, Sede Boker (2003)

Important work is also conducted at BGU by Yair Etzion and his colleagues, Evyatar Erell, Isaac Meir and David Pearlmutter, at the Desert Architecture and Urban Planning Unit of the Institute for Desert Research. The work combines academic research with applied architectural design and is focused on passive cooling systems (radiative and down draft evaporative), passive heating, microclimate of open spaces and urban microclimate. One innovative project, conducted by Etzion and Erell, was the development of a reversible glazing system, allowing winter solar heating while neutralizing glare and fading of space content—and also helping in reducing summer heat gain—while maintaining the option of daylighting in the space behind it. In the 1980s Meir, Etzion, and Faiman published the design manual "Energy Aspects of Design in Arid Zones," which has become an important design tool and gained popularity among design firms, practitioners and students. Research by Pearlmutter has shown how outdoor thermal comfort for inhabitants of desert cities may be enhanced through urban design at the scale of streets and neighborhoods. Among the applied projects carried out by the unit are the building of the International Center for Desert Studies, which combines earth sheltering, down-draft evaporative cooling, passive and hybrid solar heating, and an atrium with selective glazing. Another project is the Neve-Zin neighborhood, the first bio-climatic neighborhood in the country. In this project designers and house builders were given the opportunity, through the design of the neighborhood, to use passive techniques for maintaining thermal comfort in the houses, thus significantly reducing energy consumption.

In 1983, David Wolf and Abraham Kudish of BGU initiated a study on solar collector aging, installation, and material problems together with Avraham Rudnick and Yeshayahu Kaplan of the Standards Institute of Israel. Panels and systems operating up to 15 years and more were tested and analyzed. They were the recipients of the 1986 Löf-Duffie Best Paper Award by ISES for the manuscript detailing the results of this study. In 1993 Kudish joined the late Avraham Kushelevsky in an investigation of the ultraviolet (UV) radiation at the Dead Sea. The purpose of this work was to develop a protocol for the treatment of skin diseases, e.g., psoriasis and atopic dermatitis, by natural solar radiation, viz., photoclimatherapy. They have shown that the Dead Sea has a unique UV spectrum as a result of its location at the lowest point on earth, i.e., the attenuation by scattering phenomena is a function of optical path length and is an inverse function of wavelength.

Aharon Roy of BGU has continued to study solar energy systems, both concentrating and PV panel systems, with the emphasis on the analysis of system performance and cost. He is especially involved in the development of analysis techniques that provide a fair and unbiased inter-comparison of such systems. He embarked on a mission to inform government officials on the latest advances and the practical viability of solar power. In the 1990s he was invited by the IEA (International Energy Agency) SolarPACES (Power & Chemical Energy Systems) to initiate, organize, lead, and chair the international techno-economic activity—Evaluation Standardization (Task 3.2.3) and Israel has become an IEA-SolarPACES member. There is continuing international activity in this developed discipline, which helps arrive at cost-benefit assessments of systems. Recent activities address the quantitative evaluation of environmental consequences of solar thermal hybrid systems, a must for enabling the design of better solar power plants.

The laboratory for solar energy at Tel-Aviv University, Faculty of Engineering, is headed by Joseph Appelbaum has and operated since the mid-'70s. Basic and applied research has been carried out on photovoltaic components and systems, from the characterization and modeling of the single solar cell to the performance analysis of complete PV systems. Special devices and algorithms have been developed to measure, model, and analyze the performance of PV components and systems. These include a solar cell simulator (Fig. 8), a special DC to AC inverter for solar cells, an I-V curve tracer, a solar radiation sensor, and a UV-B measuring and displaying instrument. Secondary reflectors for spherical and circular cylinder concentrators are under development in cooperation with Avi Kribus (Tel Aviv University) and a German partner. Joseph Appelbaum was one of the leading investigators on the project of modeling the available solar energy on the Martian surface and determining the performance of solar cells on Mars. This solar radiation model was provided to the Jet Propulsion Laboratory (NASA, USA) and was incorporated into the computer model and used for the design of the solar array for the mission of the Mars Pathfinder Spacecraft in 1997.

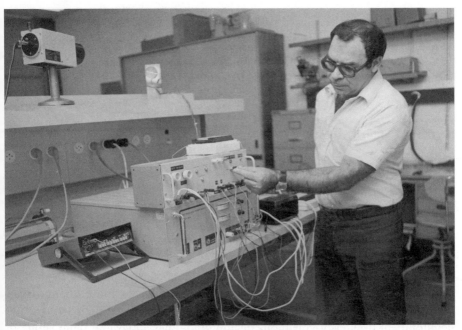

Fig. 8: Joseph Appelbaum with solar cell simulator developed at Tel Aviv University (1979)

Solar thermal energy research has continued at the Technion's Center for Energy Engineering headed by Gershon Grossman. Among the projects was a novel type of air heater, based on transparent insulation. The concept aims at reducing natural convection losses by pumping the air heated in the collector in a direction opposite to that of buoyancy. In the project, conducted by Gershon Grossman and Yoram Zvirin, a prototype collector was constructed that functioned well, and was made entirely of plastic materials, with significant cost reduction potential. A second project currently under way is a solar-powered liquid desiccant system for cooling and dehumidification, conducted by Grossman and Khaled Gommed in cooperation with several EU countries. Here, a hygroscopic salt solution is employed to extract humidity from the air, thus reducing its latent load; the solution is then regenerated with solar energy. The system is capable of using as its source of power low-grade solar heat, of the type obtainable from low-cost flat-plate collectors and has a potential to provide both cooling and dehumidification in variable ratios, as required by the load. A prototype system (Fig. 9) has been constructed, complete with a collector field, and serves to air-condition a group of offices on the top floor of the Energy Engineering Center building at the Technion. A third project involves solar water desalination by distillation, using low-grade heat in a multiple-effect system.

Fig. 9: Solar-powered liquid desiccant system for cooling and dehumidification (12 kWt) at the Technion, Haifa (2003). The solar collector field is visible in the back of the picture

Work in the area of passive solar and its assimilation in architectural practice is conducted by Edna Shaviv, Guedi Capeluto, and Abraham Yezioro at the Technion's Faculty of Architecture and Town Planning. This group has founded the national laboratory "Climate and Energy in Architecture," sponsored by the Ministry of National Infrastructures. Research at the laboratory covers topics from energy consumption in buildings to bio-climatic urban design. These include the development of CAD tools and their use for the development of energy-conscious design guidelines, solar and wind rights in the urban environment, and daylighting in buildings. Selected recent projects include: recommendations for a national policy on reducing greenhouse gas emissions under the Kyoto Protocol; thermal performance of buildings and the development of guidelines for energy-conscious design, including the development of a new energy code for buildings in Israel; climatic and energy aspects of urban design in hot-humid and temperate-cool regions of Israel - principles for climatic and energy design, determination of design strategies; bio-climatic and energy aspects in the construction of tall buildings in Israel; solar rights in high-density urban design, including the development of criteria and a simple design tool.

Dan Zaslavsky of the Technion, while working on cost reduction in the aforementioned SOLMAT solar pond project, came to an interesting conclusion: the only chance to realize economically reasonable renewable energy would be from wind, bio-mass, hydro, or from other products of solar energy, but with no need for a solar collector of any kind. This belief gave birth to the project of "Energy Towers." The idea was first patented by Philip Carlson in 1975; Zaslavsky was not aware of this at the early stages, and started working on it independently in late 1982, supported by the Israel Ministry of National Infrastructures and by the Israel Electric Corporation. The principle is to build a very tall and large diameter chimney in arid zones; water is sprayed from the top, partially evaporates and cools the air, which in turn flows down and exits through openings at the chimney's bottom. Zaslavsky and his team have in effect produced a 24 hours wind machine with improved cost effectiveness by about 7:1 compared with Carlson's idea. The cost of electricity production for the south part of Israel has been estimated to be below that of conventional methods, with potential to produce well over all of Israel's electricity demand. The global potential has been estimated to be 30 times the whole world electricity production at a cost of 2 – 6 cents per kWh. At the moment efforts are under way to erect the first 50 MW average power station with built-in pumped storage and sea water desalination at nearly half the conventional cost.

In the early 1980s, following Prof. Israel Dostrovsky's vision, the management of the Weizmann Institute of Science (WIS) decided to develop high-temperature technologies in order to increase substantially the contribution of solar energy on a national scale. Two large-scale research facilities involving high concentration of solar radiation have been constructed. The first was the solar furnace, built in 1983, capable of providing 25 kW of solar power at average concentration of 7,500. Some of the pioneering work at WIS - solar pumped solid state lasers, solar chemical heat pipe based on CO_2 reforming of methane, high temperature chemical reactors, secondary optical concentrating devices—was conducted at this facility during 1983 – 1988 by groups headed by Amnon Yogev, Moshe Levy, Michael Epstein, and others. The second facility was a solar tower (Fig. 10), inaugurated in November 1988, capable of collecting 3 megawatts of solar power using a field of 64 tracking heliostats, 55 m^2 of reflecting area each. The tower itself is 58 meters high and contains four experimental levels, where several tests can be performed in parallel. This is a unique research facility with only two similar ones worldwide, one in the USA (Sandia National Lab, Albuquerque, New Mexico) and the other in Spain (near Almeria). The rationale behind its construction was the assessment that any development in the area of concentrated solar energy would require demonstration on a preindustrial scale of about one megawatt. WIS undertook this national mission and built it as part of its long-term vision to introduce solar energy as a substantial component of the energy market. Several pioneering projects have been performed since, using this facility: A 2 ton/hour high-pressure steam production system; demonstration of a closed-loop chemical heat pipe, capable of conversion of 450 kW solar energy into chemical form for storage and transportation (Epstein); development of a high-temperature air receiver for solarized Brayton cycle (gas-turbine) and its demonstration on a 500 kW scale (Jacob Karni); and solar pumped lasers (Yogev).

Fig. 10: Solar Tower at the Weizmann Institute of
Science, Rehovot (1988)

A major activity at WIS during the last decade was related to the production of hydrogen using solar energy. Different routes and processes have been studied and examined thoroughly, including steam reforming of methane (Epstein), cracking of methane (Abraham Kogan), direct splitting of water (Kogan), metal oxide thermochemical splitting of water (Epstein), and gasification of low-grade solids, such as biomass (Epstein and Karni). The most advanced project is the solar reduction of zinc oxide to the zinc metal that can be stored, used in a zinc/air battery, or react with water to generate hydrogen and recycled zinc oxide. This project is now demonstrated on a few hundreds kW scale by a European consortium and supported by the EC under the fifth program framework (FP5). Another EU-supported project, SOLASYS, incorporated a few European institutions and WIS and ORMAT from the Israeli side to demonstrate steam reforming of methane for the production of syngas for operation of a gas turbine by ORMAT (Uri Fisher and Chemi Sugarmen).

9.3.2   Industrial and Commercial Activities

The solar collector and water heating industry continued to improve its products, with the export market in mind, while maintaining its domestic business. With approximately 1 million systems installed in Israeli homes, the domestic replacement market alone accounts for about 100,000 systems per year. This makes Israel (present population 6 million) the world leader in per capita use of solar energy.

Practicing architects have contributed to the advancement of passive architecture in Israel. Principal among them are Ruth Lahav and Tonny Rigg, Arie Rahamimov, and Matti Konnes.

Several commercial companies (apart from collector manufacturers) entered the solar field. Tabor had been interested in transparent honeycombs, as insulation for conserving energy in buildings. But there was no real activity in Israel and very little elsewhere, as the honeycombs available were found to be unstable. Some years later, in 1983, an ex-member of Tabor's team, Ofer Novick, had an idea of a new method for producing plastic honeycombs. He succeeded in interesting a local industrialist, Shimon Klier, who set up a company, AREL, for this purpose. A number of panels were produced using the new method and some were shipped to Germany for testing. But architects then were very slow in appreciating the potential value of transparent honey-combs (saving energy was not an issue as it has since become): there were no buyers and the project died in 1989.

ORMAT continued to develop new applications for its organic Rankine cycle (ORC) turbines. Since 1986, a 70 kW turbine is operating in the El-Paso solar pond in Texas to produce electricity. Lucien Bronicki noticed that there were geothermal sources in the world that were unexploited because the temperature was too low for steam engines; but the low-temperature ORC turbine could be used. Today, ORMAT is a multi-million dollar business supplying power units to low-temperature geothermal sources all over the world. Beginning in 1989, ORMAT together with the Israel Electric Company (IEC) and WIS, set out to prove the concept of operating a Brayton cycle gas turbine with solar energy only. Operation succeeded in 1991 at the Weizmann solar tower facility, but in solar-only mode the turbine proved difficult to start and to control.

In 1996, an Israeli industrial consortium named CONSOLAR was established under the auspices of the Ministry of Trade and Industry, initiated by Amnon Yogev of WIS. Its goal was to demonstrate and implement several of the aforementioned high-temperature technologies. Member industries set out to develop solarized gas turbines (ORMAT), concentrated PV with the option for beam spectral splitting (MALAM-IAI), volumetric receiver (ROTEM), and micro-turbines (EDIG). Under this project, a new optical approach to the solar tower was developed and implemented. This unique optical concept is known as "beam-down" or "reflective tower," which affords the possibility to place the solar receiver and its associated equipment on the ground. The government-supported development program was terminated in 2001 and the industries are presently struggling with demonstration and market penetration of some of these technologies.

Another Solar consortium was established under the umbrella of the United States-Israel Science and Technology Foundation (USISTF). ORMAT and ROTEM joined with McDonnell Douglass (today Boeing) and developed the know-how and tools for design and construction of small high-concentration solar systems for the operation of a 250 kW gas turbine by solar energy, utilizing the beam-down optical technology. ROTEM developed the high-temperature volumetric receiver, ORMAT dealt with all power block aspects including gas turbine modifications in the control and fuel systems and high temperature ducting (Fisher, Sugarmen and Sinai). Design and evaluation of large systems (above 50 MW) were conducted by the partners along with a market study.

The European 2001–2003 SOLGATE project (partially funded by the EU) led by ORMAT, with partners including the German aerospace center DLR and Spanish government energy agency CIEMAT, has the target of operating a small gas turbine in hybrid solar mode at the solar demonstration platform in Almeria, Spain. The project has already achieved most of its goals with the ORMAT Solar Turbine OST3 achieving ~240kW at ~20% thermal-to-electricity efficiency at the design point of 800°C at the combustor inlet. Testing is continuing, with a target of 1,000°C at the receiver outlet. This technology has the potential to be the most efficient and cost effective, achieving at least 40% efficiency in a full-scale base-load power plant with high solar contribution

One of Israel's landmarks in the solar field is the story of the LUZ Company. In 1979, a local entrepreneur, Arnold Goldman, a man with much vision and enormous energy, decided to go into the solar power business in a large way even though the general opinion at that time was that solar could not compete with power produced from fuel (or nuclear). To generate solar thermal power, he chose the tracking horizontal trough technology—à la Boys-Shuman of 1913—but employing improved absorbers with selective surfaces and mounting them in evacuated glass tubes. The collectors heated thermal oil that transferred the heat to a steam power plant (The next generation collectors were to generate steam directly). Goldman established his factory in Jerusalem, though the LUZ plants were erected in the Mojave Desert in Southern California. Goldman took advantage of a system of incentives provided by the State of California and the U.S. government that made the whole project viable. LUZ constructed nine plants totaling 354 MWe generating capacity, unbelievable to most solar buffs, and these plants are still operating (under separate operating companies established after the collapse of LUZ). LUZ collapsed due to a complex coincidence of circumstances, including the loss of incentives under a new U.S. administration that stopped the company's funding at a critical point, when LUZ was building a very large unit, its tenth, 80 MWe plant. LUZ was caught short of cash and folded in 1992.

SOLEL Solar Systems Ltd., founded in 1992 following the demise of LUZ Industries, purchased LUZ's intellectual property rights and manufacturing facilities. Former employees of LUZ wanted to ensure that the technology that had been developed would continue to be advanced both technologically and commercially. Headquartered in Beit Shemesh, near Jerusalem, SOLEL continues to supply expertise and spare parts to the solar plants in

Southern California. The company has dramatically increased the thermal efficiency of the collecting tubes and yearly output of the solar fields there, by up to 20% since LUZ. In addition, SOLEL has developed an innovative range of solar energy applications in the areas of central power, distributed power up to 10MW, water and space heating, and solar cooling solutions for the industry/commerce, as well as solar desalination. In 2000 SOLEL launched an innovative distributed solar thermal cogeneration power plant at its own facilities. With assistance from the EU, the company built a plant to meet 30% of its own energy demands, reduce the cost of electricity, and demonstrate its capabilities. The plant comprises 48 m long solar collectors installed 10 meters above the company's parking lot and produces 450 kWt at 300°C, used to generate 50 kW of electricity, 30 TR of air conditioning, and water and space heating for the offices and factory.

The landmark event of recent years was the Solar World Congress held in Jerusalem in July 1999, on the 45th anniversary of the International Solar Energy Society. The Congress was held under the theme "Solar is Renewable," adequately representing a meeting on the threshold of the twenty-first century. The event also marked the twentieth anniversary of the Israeli Section. With Yoram Zvirin as Congress chair, Gershon Grossman as scientific committee chair, and Dubi Dvorjetski as Congress secretary, the Congress was a successful event—attended by over 520 participants representing 47 countries. The Program included 207 oral presentations that ran in six parallel sessions during the five days of the Congress, and 149 poster presentations in three main sessions. In addition, 10 plenary lectures and 14 keynote lectures were presented. A business track under the title "Solar Means Business" included presentations and discussions on market implementation of solar technology. The Congress further included two panel discussions and two workshops. An exhibition presented the latest in solar products.

Fig. 11: Welcome reception at the July 1999 Solar World Congress, Jerusalem. Left to right: Dubi Dvorjetski (Israel), Congress Secretary; David Mills (Australia), ISES President; Cesare Silvi (Italy), ISES President-elect; Yoram Zvirin (Israel), Congress Chair; Gershon Grossman (Israel), Congress Scientific Committee Chair

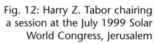

Fig. 12: Harry Z. Tabor chairing a session at the July 1999 Solar World Congress, Jerusalem

As we enter the year 2004, several promising developments are taking place in the area of solar energy in Israel. Public awareness of environmental issues is on the rise, along with explicit support for replacing polluting fossil fuels with renewable energy sources. Solel, the successor of LUZ Industries, is now closer than ever to building Israel's first solar thermal power plant, employing the LUZ technology of the SEGS plants in California. An area has now been selected for this purpose in the Negev. The Israeli Section of ISES has made it a goal for itself to help convince the government to take concrete steps in further increasing solar utilization in the country. Avraham Arbib, Section secretary, and Gershon Grossman, Chairman, met with the Minister of National Infrastructures on Arbib's initiative to offer the Section's support on professional issues and to point out possible governmental initiatives. A peculiar situation exists: While most Israeli homes use solar energy for water heating, making the country the largest per capita user of solar energy in the world, solar utilization for process heat in the industrial sector is close to nil. We proposed a set of government incentives, which were received favorably by the Minister, who instructed his aides to explore the issue further. The Minister also proposed a solar exhibition at the Knesset—Israel's parliament—on the longest day of the year, in which the Section will take an active role.

Acknowledgements

The assistance of members of the Israeli Section of ISES who provided information for this article is gratefully acknowledged. Particular recognition is due to Joseph Appelbaum, Avraham Arbib, Yehuda Bronicki, Dubi Dvorjetski, Michael Epstein, David Faiman, Uri Fisher, Yair Etzion, Jeff Gordon, Aharon Roy, Edna Shaviv, Barbara Shaw, Harry Tabor, David Wolf, and Dan Zaslavsky.

Chapter 10

ISES-ITALIA Section of the International Solar Energy Society (1964-1980)

by
Cesare Silvi
GSES (Gruppo per la Storia dell' Energia Solare)
Via Nemorense, 18
00199 Roma, Italy
e-mail: csilvi@gses.com

Abstract

This chapter reports the story of the Italian Section of ISES from 1964 to 1980. The first part outlines the history of solar energy in Italy from before the introduction of fossil fuels, to the 1950s, when the country launched its programs for the use of nuclear energy.

The second part describes:

- the creation of the Italian Section of ISES, in 1964, on the initiative of Vittorio Storelli, an industrial engineer interested in what he called "the science of the Sun;"
- the Section's activities before and after the 1973 oil shock, when growing interest in solar energy led to a rapid expansion of the Section's role;
- the legal adoption of the by-laws of the association in 1978 and—as major Italian energy companies and agencies (including ENI and ENEL) joined—its transformation at a time when large-scale solar projects were starting up in Italy (among them the 1 MW "Eurelios" solar thermoelectric plant built in the Sicilian town of Adrano, whose construction was completed in December of 1980).

10.1   History of Solar Energy in Italy, and Solar-related Activities Until the Early 1960s

10.1.1   Solar energy before fossil fuels

Many historical sources preserved in Italy testify to interest in solar energy from the earliest times. Archaeological evidence—unique in the world—is likewise invaluable. A good description of developments in solar architecture and technologies in antiquity and during the Renaissance is available in Butti and Perlin, *A Golden Thread* (1979).

Aside from the story of Archimedes (287-212 B.C.) using mirrors to burn the Roman ships besieging Syracuse, Italy is the land of Marcus Vitruvius (90-20 B.C.), author of *De Architectura*, one of the ancient texts most studied and cited in relation to solar architecture. The remains of Pompeii, Herculaneum, and the great baths in Rome and other cities of the empire provide evidence of the important developments produced by the Romans in this field. The Romans had learned to make transparent glass and use it to capture the sun's heat for their homes, baths, and greenhouses.

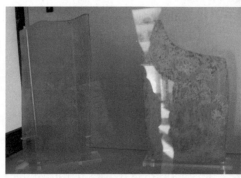

Fig. 1: Window panes from Pompei; first century A.D. (Photo Archaeological Museum, Naples)

For the first time in history, the Roman empire enacted laws regulating rights to sunlight and similar matters. In the first century A.D., for instance, the emperor Diocletian issued an edict setting prices for window glass (six or eight denarii per pound, depending on its quality).

The advances achieved by the Romans in the use of solar energy seem to have been put to fairly wide use throughout the empire from the first century A.D. on, though only among the wealthy classes. But after the fall of the empire, "for almost a thousand years, European architects virtually ignored the principles of solar orientation. Large panes of glass went out of fashion;

they were no longer available, affordable, or practical. The main urban centers were not planned for the Sun" (Butti and Perlin).

Studies and discoveries regarding the use of solar energy began again during the Renaissance, when scientific societies and academies flourished all over Italy. Descriptions of projects or experiments can be found in the writings of Leonardo da Vinci (1452–1519), who began in 1515 to build a huge mirror that would enable solar energy to be used for industrial applications; of Giovanni Magini, who used a spherical mirror to melt metals; and of the disputes among famous mathematicians and scholars, including Galileo (1564–1642), Jerome Cardano (1501–1576) and Giovanni Battista Della Porta (1540–1615), regarding the story of Archimedes and his burning mirrors.

In a treatise written in 1632, the mathematician Bonaventura Cavalieri (1598–1647), a pupil of Galileo's, devoted particular attention to the matter of burning mirrors. Like many of his contemporaries, Cavalieri tried to reconstruct Archimedes' mirror, but without success. He stressed the fact that his book, unlike Magini's, treated elliptic, hyperbolic, and parabolic mirrors as well as spherical ones (Bonetti E., 2000).

Cavalieri's successor at the University of Bologna in 1650, the astronomer, Gian Domenico Cassini (1625–1712), was the inventor of a high-quality burning mirror, one of the largest (2.7meters in diameter) ever built at the end of the seventeenth century in France, where Cassini had been living since 1668, invited by the French King Louis XIV, Le Roi Soleil, for the construction of the Paris observatory.

Fig. 2: Cover of Bonaventura Cavalieri's book The Burning Mirror: A Treatise on Conical Sections and Some of Their Wondrous Effects on Light, Heat, Cold, Sound and Much More (Bologna, Clemente Ferroni, 1632)

10.1.2   From Fossil Fuels to Nuclear Energy

More investigation needs to be done in identifying and resurfacing studies done on solar energy from the 1700s to the late 1800s, when the use of coal started to grow also in Italy. Even the important experimental work on the use of sun's light and heat by Antonio Pacinotti (1841–1912), who, at a

very young age, gained his reputation as a great physicist and experimental-
ist for having developed the ring armature of the dynamo in 1861, has today
been completely forgotten.

Pacinotti left notes, memoirs and letters about the results of his studies
and experiments on photoelectricity and on using the sun's heat to power
solar motors. His enthusiasm for solar energy is beautifully illustrated in several letters he wrote from 1863–7 to his father Luigi, also a physicist.
Pancinotti thought that even if some results could have been obtained by collecting the sun's energy using large concentrating mirrors, the best way to tap
the large solar energy potential of African deserts was to power a heat engine
by exploiting temperature differences between night and day.

News of the first solar motors developed in France by Augustine
Mouchot, starting in 1860, circulated in Italy but apparently stimulated no
similar projects. Italy, like France a coal-poor country, bent its efforts to
developing two other renewable energy sources, hydro and geothermal. In
1898, Europe's first and largest hydroelectric plant was built in Paderno
d'Adda, near Como. In 1904, the feasibility of using geothermal energy to
generate electricity was demonstrated for the first time ever at Lardarello, in
Tuscany.

In the late nineteenth and early twentieth century, one advocate of solar
energy in Italy was the world-famous chemist and physicist Giacomo
Ciamician (1857–1922), founder of Bologna University's chemistry department (which still bears his name). In September 1912, Ciamician attended the
eighth International Congress of Applied Chemistry, in Washington and New
York, and gave an impassioned lecture on the "Photochemistry of the Future"
and the benefits that humankind could gain through the use of solar energy.
In his paper, distributed in four languages, Ciamician asked, "Is fossil energy
the only one that may be used in modern life and civilization?" Appointed in
1910 to the Italian Senate, he argued for the use of solar energy during the
proceedings of the Luiggi Commission, a body set up at the end of World War
I to look into the country's energy problems.

During World War I, Italy had undergone a severe energy crisis, due to
the embargo on coal imports. The price of coal had risen from 28–35 lire per
ton before the war to 450 lire in 1917, with peaks at 925 lire, and the authorities hoped to find a way to avoid similar crises in the future. These same concerns led the Fascist regime to adopt policies intended to favor energy self-
sufficiency, in particular by exploiting the nation's hydroelectric resources,
which are plentiful in the Alpine and Apennine basins.

In 1938, on the occasion of the centennial of the first meeting of Italian scientists (in Pisa, 1838), the Italian Society for the Progress of Science (SIPS) reviewed a century of Italian scientific progress. Regarding solar energy, Giovanni Polvani described the Italian contribution to photoelectricity and cited the dozens of scientists who had studied this phenomenon, including A. Pacinotti (1863–64), A. Righi (1888–89), A. Pochettino (1906–34) and E. Fermi (1923). Another communication, only a few lines long, noted the contributions to the development of solar motors of Mario Dornig, Alessandro Amerio, Luigi D'Amelio, Tito Romagnoli and Giovanni Andri.

Fig. 3: From left, Mario Dornig with Daniel Benedict at AFASE Symposium in Arizona in 1955 (Photo provided by Jack Duffie from ISES Archive)

Since the early decades of the twentieth century, Dornig had stood out for his interest in solar energy; he had published a number of articles in which he underlined the importance of using it in a rational and integrated way.

He was also one of the few Italians who attended the first world conference on solar energy, organized in Phoenix, Arizona, in 1955 by AFASE (the Association for Applied Solar Energy). In a two-part article published in the journal *Rivista di ingegneria* (Engineering Review), Dornig reported extensively on "Solar Energy and the Arizona Symposium," describing all the solar technologies and devoting a great deal of space to the Bell Lab's discovery of the silicon cell in 1953.

According to Dornig, the Arizona Symposium was a milestone in the scientific and technical application of solar energy for the benefit of humankind. No new principles were announced at the event, but it achieved a "grand, organic association of all the different disciplines that the human spirit has worked out over so many centuries"—geography, astronomy, climatology, physics, thermodynamics, chemistry, agronomy, physiology, gastronomy, economics, the social sciences, and others. This combination was bound to lead, he thought, to the rational use of solar energy to farm marginal land, especially in hot and dry countries, thereby increasing food production.

Italy was also represented at the exhibition of solar machinery and products, though by only one company, Ferruccio Grassi's Somor, based in Lecco. Somor displayed a solar pump consisting essentially of a flat-plate collector fitted with side mirrors, which provided a degree of concentration, and utilizing sulfur dioxide rather than steam. Dornig reported that Grassi's pump kept on operating throughout the show and aroused wide interest.

Fig. 4: Ferruccio Grassi's solar pump, exhibited at the Phoenix show in 1955 (Photo provided by Jack Duffie from ISES Archive)

Unfortunately, Dornig's encouraging news from Arizona on solar energy developments came just at the time when interest was growing in the prospects opened by discoveries in the field of nuclear energy, to which Italy had made a significant contribution through the group of Via Panisperna's physicists, led by Enrico Fermi (Fermi had built the first atomic pile in Chicago in 1942).

When U.S. President Eisenhower announced the "Atoms for Peace" initiative in December 1953, the Italian government had already started a large-scale nuclear research program conducted by the CNRN (National Center for Nuclear Research) and funded with some 35 billion lire between 1952 and 1960. At a 1958 exhibition in Geneva, Italy showed the world a whole series of important achievements: three nuclear power plants under construction, the nearly-completed synchrotron, a research reactor ready to start operating in Ispra, and the start of construction of the nation's largest nuclear research center, located at Casaccia, near Rome.

Eisenhower's choice was certainly prompted by the speed with which the Soviet Union had equipped itself with nuclear weapons. To counter these developments, Eisenhower reversed his predecessor Harry Truman's policy of keeping all knowledge related to atomic energy under wraps, and made the part regarding its peaceful uses available to any country that would undertake to refrain from using it for military purposes. Many think that Eisenhower's policy on nuclear power resulted in forgetting the solar energy program outlined by the Paley Commission's report to President Truman (The Promise of Technology—The Possibilities of Solar Technology), published in 1952.

Because of the widespread enthusiasm for nuclear energy, in Italy the field of solar energy was relegated to the background, as it was in other countries. In 1960, Parliament transformed CNRN in the National Nuclear Energy Committee (CNEN) and gave it the mission of encouraging the development of peaceful uses of atomic energy. The CNEN was born under the most auspicious stars. International bodies considered that Italy and Japan, the only industrialized countries lacking fossil fuel resources, would be the first to go massively nuclear. The development of nuclear energy was seen as the means whereby a country without fossil fuel could hold its own against countries rich in coal and oil. Until then, Italy had relied mainly on its hydro resources; in 1955 they met more than 80% of the nation's electricity demand.

After World War II, however, the Marshall Plan gave strong impetus to the installation of new thermoelectric plants. Between 1956 and 1965, installed capacity at coal- and oil-fired power plants began for the first time to draw ahead of installed hydroelectric capacity.

The development of nuclear energy was also a key factor leading to the nationalization of about 1,000 electric companies and utilities and the creation of ENEL, the Italian public electricity utility, in 1962.

This was the context in which the handful of Italian solar energy pioneers had to operate at the beginning of the second half of the twentieth century.

Italy was industrializing rapidly, and energy demand was likewise growing apace. Government policies were directed at meeting it by importing fossil fuels and developing nuclear energy, rather than by achieving energy self-sufficiency. In the country where nuclear energy had taken its first fundamental steps with Enrico Fermi—a country that had firmly decided to travel the road toward the use of nuclear energy—solar energy was practically ignored as a possible alternative to fossil fuels.

10.1.3 The Early '60s and the U.N. Conference on New Sources of Energy (Rome, 1961)

An event that sparked new interest in solar energy in Italy, and in renewable sources in general, was the United Nations Conference on New Energy Sources (solar, wind, geothermal), held in Rome in August 1961 at the headquarters of the U.N. Food and Agriculture Organization (FAO). The decision to organize the conference had been made in May 1956, when the U.N. Economic and Social Council recommended that "the United Nations should display the same interest in all new sources as it had in the conventional sources of energy and in atomic energy."

The conference was attended by 447 people from 29 countries. The largest numbers came from Italy (87), the United States (63), and France (57). Two hundred and fifty papers were presented, 118 of them dealing with various aspects of solar energy. In terms of the number and quality of the participants, the Solar session was considered the most important international gathering in the field since the Arizona Symposium in 1955. The Italians presented 24 papers, including 19 on geothermal energy, a field in which Italy boasted world primacy because of its plants at Lardarello, which by then had reached a net generating capacity of 300 MW.

There were only four Italian papers on solar energy. Arnaldo Maria Angelini's was titled "Reflections on the Economic Value of Geothermal Energy, Wind Power and Solar Energy, Especially After Conversion to Electrical Energy." Giovanni Francia, a professor of analytic geometry at the University of Genoa, presented the anti-radiating honeycomb structures he had discovered in 1960, and that made it possible to retain heat in a sort of "black body"—an idea that is widely applied today in various solar technologies.

Fig. 5: Giovanni Francia behind a
honeycomb structure
(Photo Ansaldo Review N. 11/81)

Luigi D'Amelio, from the University of Naples, described a thermal solar motor coupled to a simple, flat, low-temperature thermal solar collector. Giorgio Nebbia, who had been doing research at Bari University since 1953 on solar stills that could be used to desalinate seawater, especially on islands and in arid areas, read a paper on the "Present Status and Future of Solar Stills."

An experimental solar heating system installed at the Swedish astrophysics station on the island of Capri was described by two participants from Sweden, Gunnar V. Pleijel and B. I. Lindström. The building had gone up the year before and the solar collectors were built right into its façade; this may have been the first system of its kind to be installed in Italy. In connection with the inauguration of the main building in 1961 a Swedish TV team visited the observatory to report about the solar energy installation.

Fig. 6: The main building of the Swedish Observatory on the Island of Capri in 1961 (Photo Y. Öhman's collection)

Somar, the Lecco company that had already exhibited at the Phoenix show in 1955, presented its solar pump once again; it was then on the market at $1,000 per kilowatt.

The 1961 conference in Rome not only enabled many Italians to share their ideas and meet colleagues from other countries; it was also an important occasion for getting to know AFASE. AFASE provided technical assistance to the U.N. on solar energy, and several of its leaders, including Farrington Daniels, were in Rome for the event.

Later that year, at a conference organized by NATO in Sounion, Greece, a group called COMPLES was formed on the initiative of a number of academics who had fled the war in Algeria, where they had worked at a solar energy research laboratory. COMPLES (Coopération méditerranéenne pour l'énergie solaire) was mainly oriented toward the French-speaking world, but representatives from Spain, Greece, Portugal, and Italy were among its founders.

After this conference, in 1962, Italy's National Research Council (CNR) set up an "Enterprise" operating under the chemistry committee and dedicated to encouraging cooperation among various institutes for studies on "Chemistry and Technology in the Field of Energy Sources."

One of the main groups working in the "Enterprise" framework on the use of solar energy was the Milan Polytechnic Institute's technical physics department. Under the leadership of Gino Bozza, it built in the Alpine town of Cortina d'Ampezzo what was perhaps the first experimental solar station in Italy. The station included a prefabricated lab equipped for making systematic measurements of solar radiation and testing solar heating systems, including a "solar chimney."

The Milan Polytech group also experimented with solar processes designed to produce ice, and built a solar absorption refrigerator based on the use of solid ammonia and vinyl chloride compounds.

Another "Enterprise" group, headed by Giorgio Nebbia of Bari University's commerce technology department, worked on solar desalination of saltwater. Nebbia reported on these activities in the SES's "*Sun at Work*" in 1964.

Other important activities were conducted in the early '60s at the University of Genoa, where Giovanni Francia did a number of experiments using the anti-radiating honeycomb structures he had described at the Rome conference in 1961.

In 1960–61, Francia built and tested the first high-temperature solar boiler at a facility in the town of Cesana Torinese. This device was based on an anti-radiating structure made up of 2,000 thin glass tubes, and with the sun overhead it generated steam at 100 atm and 500–600°C. In 1963, in collaboration with the French scientists from COMPLES, Francia built two linear solar boilers with anti-radiating cells for steam at 100 atm and 450°C with the sun at 1,000 W/m_, the first in Genoa and the second in Marseilles. In 1965 he built the first point-shaped solar boiler, for the generation of steam at 150 atm and 500°C, at the station operated by Genoa University in the town of Sant'Ilario di Nervi, on the Riviera. These plants functioned with mirror fields moved by ingenious mechanisms that Francia himself had invented. His work was financed by the CNRS, the CNR, and NATO, and he described it in an article published in the September 1968 issue of the *Solar Energy Journal*, "Pilot Plants of Solar Steam Generating Stations."

Fig. 7: The first point-shaped solar boiler, installed at
Sant'Ilario di Nervi in 1965
(Photo Ansaldo Review N. 11/81)

10.2   The Italian Section's Creation and Early Activities

10.2.1   Creation of the Section

The Italian Section was founded and promoted by Vittorio Storelli, an industrial engineer who had a strong interest in what he called "Sun Science" and was attentive to developments in the sector.

Fig. 8: Vittorio Storelli, founder of the Italian Section of ISES

His work in the aircraft industry had led him to study and teach space applications of solar energy at the University of Turin.

In 1963, during a study trip to the United States, he met with the SES and, pointing out that there was already a group working in Naples in the field of solar energy, and that a number of Italian scientists and engineers had taken part in one or another of the international conferences held in the past, decided to set up an Italian section of the organization.

In creating the Section, Storelli knew he could count also on the useful advice of Giorgio Nebbia who would become the first Italian member of the board of directors of ISES from 1967–70. The Section became operational as of January 1, 1964, and was based in Naples, at Via Crispi 72. Storelli became the secretary. The creation of the Section was announced later that year in the second quarterly issue of *Sun at Work*.

The Section's first project was to publish the first issue of what was to become the *Rassegna Italiana di Eliotecnica* (Italian Solar Technology Review).

Storelli himself did the work of starting up the Section and the *Rassegna* [review]; later on, too, he could rely only occasionally on some assistance. Today, at 90, he recalls with utmost clarity and irony that only a handful of people in Italy were interested in solar energy in the '60s, and that there was only one way to get the newborn Italian Section of ISES on its feet: roll up your sleeves and do it yourself!

Fig. 9: Giorgio Nebbia, second from left, with his collaborators testing a solar still at the University of Bari in the late 1950s

His determination in managing the Section (sometimes putting up money of his own) and editing the Rassegna provided an important means of information and linkage to the small and widely scattered community of Italian scientists and engineers interested in solar energy. In most cases, their work was little recognized and even unknown within the universities and research institutions where they were employed. Now the Italian Section gave them a point of reference; they could get to know each other through the pages of the Rassegna and keep up on what was being done abroad and report on activities in Italy through the *Solar Energy Journal* and *Sun at Work*.

10.2.2   Publications and Activities Prior to the Oil Shock of 1973

The cover of the first issue of the Italian Section's *Rassegna* is dated January 1964 and flourishes the slogan "The sun toward the world, the world toward the sun." In the foreword, Storelli underlines the journal's purposes, including "publicizing what has been done up to now in Italy and other countries in the field of solar energy, in terms of science, technology, experiments and applications." Next came a message from Hal Walmsley, president of the SES, in which he welcomed the Italian Section and noted that, "If bold advances are to be made in solar energy application, the concentration of much intellectual power must be brought to bear on the problem. These intellects must be brought together in close collaboration under a concept and system of free exchange of information."

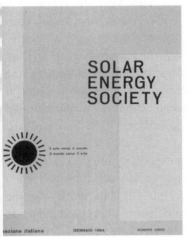

Fig. 10: The cover of the Italian Section's first publication in January 1964

The first pages of the journal also carried an article by Farrington Daniels (translated into Italian) on the state of the art in solar energy research, where the author reviewed nearly all the methods developed for its use. Then came contributions from two Italian academics. Vincenzo Caglioti, chairman of the National Research Council's chemistry committee, reports on studies on "Chemistry and Technology in the Field of Energy Sources" (cf., section 2.3 above), and Carlo d'Amelio, of the University of Naples, on thermal solar machines.

When the next issues of the *Rassegna* would come out often depended on the Section's finances and the need to report on projects of interest to the members. Some were published with aid from the National Research Council and Banco di Napoli. The second issue came out in December of 1964, the third in December 1965, and the fourth in November 1966.

The second issue reprints the speech delivered by the chairman of the SES at the first meeting of the organization's members, in March 1965 (with the announcement of the publication of the seventh volume of the Proceedings of the UN Conference held in Rome in 1961), and includes an article by Peter Glaser on solar energy. Other contributions came from Ambrogio Locatelli, of the Milan Polytechnic Institute, on the use of solar energy to heat water, and from Ferruccio Grassi, on solar pumps.

In 1965, the Italian Section took part in the conference on desalination in Palermo organized by the United States Information Service. In 1967, the interest aroused by its publications led the Section to organize a conference itself. It was held at the University of Naples, with Frank Edlin, secretary-general of the American SES, as the keynote speaker and a large audience of academics, engineers, entrepreneurs, and students. The event was reported in the fifth issue of the *Rassegna*, dated January 1967. Among the Italian contributions to the field, Tito Romagnoli's on the use of solar energy in agriculture (1923) received special mention for its historical importance.

Also in 1967, a meeting of specialists in solar radiation measurement was held on the island of Capri. Among the attendees was Guglielmo Righini of Florence, co-author, with Giorgio Nebbia, of a book titled *L'energia solare e le sue applicazioni* (Solar Energy and Its Applications) that Feltrinelli of Milan had brought out the year before.

The December '67 issue of the *Rassegna* is especially important because it contains a detailed description of Giovanni Francia's research at Genoa University's Sant'Ilario station (see section 1.3 above). His work was the basis for the design of the "Eurelios" solar thermoelectric plant built a decade later at Adrano in Sicily by ENEL, in collaboration with several European partners.

In 1968, Storelli took part in the annual SES meeting in Palo Alto, California, where he also met Peter Glaser. Storelli reported on research activities in Italy, including Francia's research on anti-radiating honeycomb structures in plastic and the photovoltaic cells for space utilization, manufactured by the Italian company Selenia. The results of the meeting were reported in the CNR journal *Ricerca Scientifica* of December 1968. The next year, the Italian Section took part in the SES conference in Melbourne—the first one held outside the United States—which gave Storelli an opportunity to meet Farrington Daniels and receive useful suggestions on how to organize the Italian Section.

The April 1970 issue of the *Rassegna* contained a report on other research projects of Francia's. In the *Rassegna*, Storelli dealt again the topic of how to power artificial satellites and spacecraft with solar photocells—the solution that came to be widely adopted and made it possible to build satellite-based telecommunications systems.

In 1970, the Solar Energy Society changed its name to the International

Solar Energy Society (ISES) and the Italian Section's name changed accordingly.

In 1971 Storelli attended the solar energy conference organized by NASA at the Goddard Space Flight Center, where he presented "The Solar City—Hypothesis for an Urban Structure," a project designed by Giovanni Francia and his collaborators.

Fig. 11: View of a solar city designed by Francia and collaborators (from the 1971 scale model). The apertures of two solar ducts to bring light to lower floors can be noted (Figure, Rassegna Italiana di Eliotecnica, 1972).

Fig. 12: Another view with a solar duct in the center (Figure, Rassegna Italiana di Eliotecnica, 1972)

In December of that year, Francia's project was presented at the Court Theater in Naples, in the presence of architect Paolo Soleri, who had immigrated to the United States and, now living in Arizona, was likewise designing a solar city. Francia's project was described in detail in the October 1972 issue of the *Rassegna*. He and his collaborators hoped to create an urban complex where a large group of people could live together without losing touch with nature, and where the essential services—lighting, heating and electricity—would be provided via solar.

Also in 1971, the Italian Section was present at the international solar energy conference in Paris, organized jointly by ISES, COMPLES, and AFEDES under the auspices of UNESCO. This was an interesting and unusual example of encounter and collaboration among specialists from different geographic and cultural areas.

In 1972–73, Mr. Storelli was invited to lecture on solar energy at the Pozzuoli Aeronautical Academy and at the American Studies Center in Naples.

10.2.3   The Italian Section after 1973

The great turning-point for solar energy around the world, and in Italy too, came in 1973, with the first oil crisis. Oil flows from Arab countries were curtailed for weeks, and from October 1973 to the end of 1974 the price of oil soared, increasing by 800%.

To save energy, the Italian government tried to cut consumption with measures such as a ban on vehicle circulation on Sundays.

The "great fear" of that year and the following ones drove scientists and engineers to look with new interest at alternative sources of energy whose supply would be less chancy than that of fossil fuels. The development of nuclear energy, at a standstill after its dazzling debut in the 60s, returned to the fore with the government's proposal, in the first national energy plan of 1974, to build 20 nuclear power plants. However, already at its launching, environmental movements started to oppose nuclear programs.

At the same time, solar energy started to be viewed with new interest. Just as the 1914–18 coal crisis had worried Italy and led people to consider alternative energy sources, so the 1973 oil crisis rekindled interest in them. And this time around, solar energy was not just the hobbyhorse of a single scientist, albeit a famous one like Ciamician; research centers and the great state-owned energy companies were pushing it too. The Italian government decided to offer incentives for the installation of solar systems, and the result was a growing commitment by researchers and private enterprise and a proliferation of manufacturers of solar panels (mainly water-heaters, the easiest technology).

This new departure confirmed the foresight of those who had laid the groundwork for it, in terms of knowledge and experimentation, and especially of ISES and its Italian Section.

The effects of the new political and economic situation soon became evident in the Italian Section's activities. The 1974 issue of the *Rassegna* opened with an article by Storelli, on "The Conquest of the Sun," that reverberated with the new technical and scientific situation, and also contained many items from new contributors. Among them was Vincenzo Balzani, from the University of Bologna, writing about the prospects of photochemistry, which had been anticipated in the early part of the century by Ciamician, his predecessor as head of Bologna's chemistry department.

That year the Italian Section was present at a number of solar-related meetings, which were starting to multiply. At the 14th International Conference on Space, held in Rome, Secretary Storelli spoke on "A New Industry of the Sun." He treated the same subject at Loyola University's Rome branch and at a round table organized in Milan by FAST (Federation of Scientific and Technical Associations), where he spoke on "The Prospects for Solar Energy."

The National Research Council (CNR) had just launched its first Targeted Energy Project, in which it was to invest nearly 50 billion lire from 1976 to 1979. The solar energy subproject had a budget of over 9 billion lire with which it funded a large number of academic and industrial research groups.

In 1975, a solar energy research group was set up at the University of Naples on the initiative of Vittorio Silvestrini, who organized a course on solar energy conversion (held on the island of Procida, just off Naples), and reported the results of the studies conducted in Naples in the September issue of the Rassegna. The Naples research on cooling by nighttime irradiation was particularly interesting. Two training courses were organized by the International College for Applied Physics, with the sponsorship of the Italian Section, the first in Nerano, in September 1975, and the second in the Sardinian city of Alghero, in 1976. In 1977 Silvestrini's group published a book titled *Il Clima quale elemento di progetto nell'edilizia* (Climate as a component in building design, published by Liguori Editore.

It should be noted that the Italian government organizations never once mentioned the existence of the Italian Section in their initiatives, for instance in the proceedings of the CNR's solar energy subproject. This goes to show that there was a disconnect between "voluntary" research and institutional projects, which in the second half of the '70s began to receive notable amounts of public funds.

In 1975 Storelli attended the ISES international congress in Los Angeles, where he reported on what was being done in Italy; and the meeting of the Italian Thermotechnics Association in Santa Margherita di Pula. In 1975–77, he lectured and gave courses at various meetings, some of them organized by the Italian Section. Through these activities, the Italian Section made it clear that the proper use of solar energy could provide opportunities for industry and employment in Italy too, and opportunities for exporting equipment and know-how, as was already happening in the United States.

In the meantime, an Italian branch of COMPLES had been formed under the direction of Roberto Visentin, of the University of Calabria. It must be said that relations between the Italian Section of ISES and COMPLES-Italy seem never to have been very lively.

Italian solar literature became richer with the publication in 1976 of a book by Aurelio Robotti, *Impieghi dell'energia solare* (Uses of Solar Energy). The book was written following the success of a previous booklet by Robotti about "The introduction of solar energy use in Italy," written in 1975 to let people know about the possibility offered by solar energy to overcome the Italian energy crisis.

In 1977, ten years after the Naples conference, the Italian Section, on the occasion of its national assembly, organized, again in Naples, a technical conference attended by some 300 people. Many Italian universities and CNR institutes participated, as well as manufacturing and energy companies, including Fiat, Montedison, and ENEL. The thirty-six papers presented at this event were enthusiastic about the growing interest in solar energy and testified to the wealth of new initiatives and projects for using solar energy in agriculture, architecture, and electricity generation. In the latter field Italy stood out for the solar thermoelectric plants designed with the consultancy of Francia and being built by ENEL, which was represented at the conference by Corrado Corvi. A paper on wind generators was also presented.

Amid the general enthusiasm there were also words of caution. Nebbia, in a paper titled "Lights and Traps in Solar Energy," warned that these forms of energy should be developed in an appropriate way, and that the great opportunities offered by solar energy should not be wasted.

The conference was followed by a round table on the Section's purposes and charter.

10.2.4   The End of the Italian Section's Pioneering Phase

The new interest in solar energy in Italy prompted changes in the organization of the Italian Section of ISES. People like Storelli and some other members who had labored for more than a decade amid the general indifference of the energy establishment thought the Section should have legal status and a charter so as to be able to respond better to the new growth prospects.

The Section's by-laws were established, and the Italian Section of ISES, as a nonprofit organization, was legally formed in April 1978, in Naples; Vittorio Storelli was named president and a board of directors was appointed. The major state-owned energy companies—ENI (oil and gas) and ENEL (electricity)—became charter members. In October, the first elections were held for the management positions; Storelli was confirmed as president, Corrado Corvi of ENEL was elected vice president.

This change was made at the time when solar-related initiatives were proliferating in Italy. ISES-Italy continued to disseminate knowledge of Italian activities, especially abroad, and to raise public awareness of the importance of solar energy, in part via TV and radio. Italian TV and radio played a role in diffusing information on the possibilities of solar energy to the general public by promoting talk shows with the participation of solar energy experts. In 1978 Storelli, still acting as secretary of the Italian Section, attended and spoke at the New Delhi conference on solar energy.

On May 3, 1978, Sun Day was celebrated in Italy too, the same day as in the United States. This event had been thought up and organized by Hayes as a way to get the message to the American people that a modern industrial society can run on solar energy. The White House's Council on Environmental Quality had stated that the goal of meeting much more than 50% of the nation's energy requirement with solar sources could be reached by 2020. This optimism reached Italy and could be found in the Italian Section of ISES, which undertook to print and distribute Sun Day pamphlets to schools of all kinds, and in June set up a stand of its own at a permanent exhibition of solar energy applications organized by the City of Rome.

The first major trade fair devoted to solar energy was held in Genoa that same year, and drew eleven government ministers from as many Mediterranean countries. Italy's industry minister pointed proudly to the results obtained by Giovanni Francia at the Sant'Ilario station. The Italian Section promoted a National Award for the best research project on solar energy.

In 1979 Storelli and Corvi attended the "jubilee" conference held in Atlanta on ISES's twenty-fifth birthday. Storelli reported on the activities of the Italian Section and the solar projects under way in Italy, including ENEL's "Eurelios" plant and the "Solar Building" designed by the Florence-based company Nuovo Pignone. Corvi spoke about research activities at ENEL. Contacts were established between Italian and American concerns.

In 1979 photovoltaic technology was used in Italy for a 1kW power plant installed at the Mandrione Pass through the Apennine mountains, between Tuscany and Romagna. This was Italy's first fully monitored photovoltaic plant coupled to a wind generator.

By this time, the Rassegna Italiana di Eliotecnica could not suffice to keep up with developments in the solar sector; in any case, financial difficulties had compelled its suspension. In May 1979, the new management of the Italian Section proposed to replace it with a bimonthly magazine that was already registered; the publisher, PEG, would handle the business end. Under the title Energie Alternative—Habitat, Territorio, Energia (shortened to HTE) and had the subtitle "Official organ of ISES—Italian Section," the first issue came out in September 1979. On the first page was a greeting to members and readers from Vittorio Storelli, president of the Section. The magazine was sponsored by the CNR, and representatives of the great research institutions and energy companies that are members of the Section sat on its scientific committee, among them Ugo Lucio Businaro, Giancarlo Chiesa, Mario Columba, Maurizio Cumo, Alvaro Donadio, Giacomo Elias, Giovanni Francia, Mario Pavese, Luigi Paris, Giuseppe M. Sfligiotti, Giancarlo Schileo, and Mario Silvestri. HTE still comes out regularly, and was not long in establishing itself as the place to publish technical articles, policy articles, and articles for the general reader on what is happening in Italy in the field of solar energy.

Fig. 13: Front cover of the first issue of HTE, the official bimonthly magazine of the Italian Section of ISES, September/October 1979

The late 70s were the years in which the views of the anti-nuclear movement were gaining ground and more and more Italians were becoming interested in solar energy. Other reasons for moving in this direction were the second energy crisis of 1978–79 and the accident at the Three Mile Island
nuclear power plant in 1979. The National Nuclear Energy Committee
(CNEN), whose original mission was limited to nuclear matters began to
change course, adding research, development and demonstration activities in
the field of renewable energies to its nuclear programs.

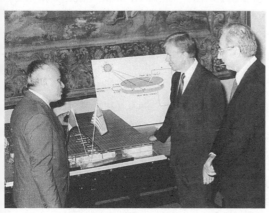

Fig. 14: Scale model of the Delphos
plant, shown by Cossiga and
Colombo to U.S. President Jimmy
Carter in the summer of 1980 (Photo
CNEN)

The change was due in good part to the influence of U.S. President
Carter's "soft energy" policy; his pro-solar message came through clearly in
Italy. Carter visited Italy in July 1980, and prime minister Cossiga thus had a
chance to illustrate—with the aid of CNEN's new president, Umberto
Colombo—Italy's commitment to the quest for clean energy sources by
showing him a scale model of the 600 kWp Delphos photovoltaic power
plant, which was to remain for more than a decade one of the largest pilot
photovoltaic plants designed in Europe.

CNEN also started the publication of many technical scientific papers,
broadening knowledge about solar energy and its applications.

1980 ended with ENEL's completing the construction of the 1 MW
Eurelios plant in Adrano, Sicily, the world's largest tower-type solar thermoelectric plant connected to the national grid.

For the Italian Section, 1980 ended with a satisfactory balance sheet: 250
individual members, 50 collective members, a bi-monthly magazine averag-
ing more than 50 pages per issue, and a board of directors on which major
government agencies and institutions were represented. However, this was
also the end of the pioneering activity that the Section had conducted up till
that time.

10.3   Conclusions

The period from 1964 to 1980 ended with the Italian Section of ISES operating in a context entirely different from that of 1964, when it was created. Italy was no longer focused on the nuclear option to free itself from reliance on fossil fuels. Our members, by their number and the associations they represent, had made the Section one of the country's principal and best-known reference points, where research, industry, and other interests could meet and exchange ideas and projects for the future of solar energy in Italy. Our leadership, with Storelli as president, count on further contributions from Corrado Corvi of ENEL, our vice president, and from the members of the board, who represented universities, research institutions, manufacturers, and major energy corporations.

Key Developments of the Italian Section of ISES 1964–1980

December 1963	H. Walmsley, President of SES (Solar Energy Society) approves the formation of the Italian Section of SES. Vittorio Storelli is the Secretary.
January 1964	The first issue of *Rassegna Italiana di Eliotecnica* is published. Storelli is the editor. The *Rassegna* will be published in 1965, 1966, 1967, 1970, 1972, 1974, 1976.
April 1964	Official announcement by Storelli of the start of Section's activities. Section's office is in Naples in Via Crispi 72
January 1967	National conference in Naples. Among the participants: Frank E. Edlin, E. Carlevaro, R. Preti, L. D'Amelio, G. Francia, G. Nebbia, L. M. Guarino.
February 1967	Giorgio Nebbia is elected board member of SES for term March 1967-70
June 1970	Solar World Congress of SES in Australia. SES becomes ISES. Participants from Italy include Vittorio Storelli and E. Pisani. The Italian Section of SES becomes the Italian Section of ISES.
February 1977	National Conference in Naples. 300 attendees. Storelli presents a paper in which the Section's activities in the past ten years are summarized. The 34 Technical papers cover almost all aspects of solar energy utilization. Among the speakers, Giovanni Francia and Giorgio

	Nebbia
14 April 1978	The Italian Section of ISES is legally instituted as a non-profit association. Its office continues to be in Naples. Vittorio Storelli is named President. In October 1978 Vittorio Storelli is elected President and Corrado Corvi Vice President.
Sept/Oct 1979	The first number of *Habitat Terrirorio Energia* (*HTE*), as the official magazine of the Section, replacing the *Rassegna Italiana di Eliotecnica*, is published. The magazine will be published for 18 years. The last number will appear in September/October 1996.
1980	Corrado Corvi is elected board member of ISES. The Section has 250 individual members and 50 collective members.

Acknowledgements

This paper was made possible by the decisive contribution of Vittorio Storelli. Without his writings and the documents in his personal archive, I could never have written it. Special thanks go to Giorgio Nebbia for his suggestions and comments, and for having allowed me to consult rare documents in his archive.

References

My major sources included the periodicals *Rassegna Italiana di Eliotecnica* (1964 – 76) and *Habitat Territorio Energia* (1978–80), the minutes of the board of the Italian Section of ISES from 1978 to 1980. Below are a few among the many other sources:

Bonetti E. (2000) Thesis, Lettura multimediale dell'opera lo specchio ustorio di B. Cavalieri, Università Cattolica del Sacro Cuore, Milano, 2000.

Butti, K., and Perlin, J., *A Golden Thread: 2500 Years of Solar Architecture and Technology.* Palo Alto, California: Cheshire Books, 1979.

Ciamician G. (1912) "La fotochimica dell'avvenire". *Scientia*, Vol. XII, Anno I, 1(346)-18(363), Zanichelli, Bologna. The lecture, given in English, was reprinted in journals and booklets in German, English, and Italian. The English transcript of the original lecture is available in Science, 36, 385 (1912).

Dornig M. (1956) "L'Energia solare e il Symposium dell'Arizona." Rivista di Ingegneria. 1956, Maggio vol. VI, n.5, 548-556; 1956 giugno, vol. VI, n. 6, 657–665.

Francia G. (1974) "Large scale central receiver solar test facilities." Proceedings of the National Science Foundation on International Seminar on Large Scale Solar Energy Test Facilities. Las Cruces, New Mexico, USA.

ENEL (1991) Progetto Eurelios – Utilizzazione dell'energia solare in impianti eliotermoelettrici, ENEL, Padova.

Polvani G., Fotoelettricità, "Un secolo di progresso scientifico italiano 1838- – 1938," in: Proceedings of the 28th SIPS Conference in Pisa, 11-15 October 1939, vol. I, 607-609. Rome: L. Silla, 1940.

Proceedings of the National Congress of the Italian Section of the International Solar Energy Society, Naples, 24-26 February 1977.

Righini G., and Nebbia G. (1966) L'energia solare e le sue applicazioni. Milano: Giangiacomo Feltrinelli Editore.

Silvi C. (2003) Can the History of Energy Technology and Use Educate Us for a Solar Energy Future—The Italian Case, ISREE-9 (International Symposium on Renewable Energy Education), June 14-15, 2003, Göteborg, Sweden.

Storelli V. (1964) Introduzione al primo numero della Rassegna Italiana di Eliotecnica della Sezione italiana della Solar Energy Society, Storelli V. (Ed), No. 1, 1.

United Nations (1962) Report on the United Nations Conference on New Sources of Energy—Solar Energy, Wind Power, Geothermal Energy, Rome, 21 to 31 August 1961. New Sources of Energy and Energy Development. E/3577/Rev.1 ST/ECA/72. New York: United Nations.

Walmsley H. (1964) "Message on the formation of the Italian Section of the Solar Energy Society." Rassegna Italiana di Eliotecnica, Storelli V. (Ed), No. 1, 1.

Chapter 11

Japanese Section of the International Solar Energy Society

by
Tetsuo Noguchi
Chief, Solar Research Laboratory *
Government Industrial Research Institute, Nagoya
Agency of Industrial Science and Technology
Ministry of International Trade and Industry
Hirate-machi, Kita-ku, Nagoya 462
JAPAN

Abstract

This is to briefly report the early activities of the Japanese Section of ISES and its background since 1955. After the announcement of the establishment of National Sections of the ISES in the respective countries by the board of directors meeting of ISES in 1970, the author started to organize the Japanese Section in 1970 and served up to 1984 as the international secretary, while section membership had been almost constantly at around 100–120. Major developments in solar energy technology from '50s to early '70s were: solar water heaters, photovoltaic power stations by PV cells, solar furnace studies, and solar heating and cooling systems studies (SHAC).

It is worthwhile to note that the Japanese Government (especially MITI) launched large- scale and long-range National Programs (Sunshine Projects) in which RD&D of Solar Heating, Cooling and Hot Water Supply Systems, Photovoltaic Conversion Systems, and Solar Thermal Power Systems were included as the Characteristic Three Topics since 1974. The further detailed developments of our Section beyond 1980 will be reported in the second volume of this history of ISES.

* Present Mailing Address: 63 Yoshinomaru Minami, Kuwana-City Mie 511-0032 JAPAN Telefax: +81-594-
   22-7748

11.1   Introduction

Since the first international Solar Energy Conference held in Phoenix, Arizona in 1955, some dozens of solar scientists in Japan have been dedicating their continued efforts to carry on research in the field of solar water heaters, solar cells, and high-temperature solar furnaces, working as a national part of the Association for Applied Solar Energy, which subsequently became the present International Solar Energy Society via the Solar Energy Society.

Encouraged by the AFASE World Congress in Arizona, USA, in 1955, early activity in the field of solar energy application was inaugurated in 1955 by the Solar Energy Application Committee under the Japan Society of Mechanical Engineers.

This was modified into the Japan Association for Applied Solar Energy (JAFASE) in 1961, with almost 100 individual members and 20 corporate members. Since then most of its efforts have been concentrated on the development of domestic solar water heaters, photovoltaic power generation by silicon cells, and high-temperature solar furnace research. Through the vicissitudes during the so called oil age in the '60s and the OPEC oil embargo in the '70s, solar energy established its firm position as one of the most promising energy sources for mankind. It ranks highest among other alternative and renewable sources of energy proposed since the first oil crisis in 1973.

After the establishment of the Japanese Section as a national Section of ISES, its membership increased rapidly: the growth of membership during 1973–1978 is shown below.

Table 1.   Membership Transition of the Japanese Section, ISES

	1973	1974	1975	1976	1977	1978
Individual Members	43	75	89	84	88	89
Sustaining Members	2	4	4	7	7	7

JAFASE was reorganized into the Japan Solar Energy Society (JSES) in 1971, and the office of the Japanese Section of the International Solar Energy Society was jointly operated by the JSES. (JSES Secretary: Noriyuki Takao)

11.2   Solar Water Heaters

The production of solar water heaters in Japan started around the '50s.

One might notice in the manufacturing data that the Integral Solar Collector and the Storage system comprised the majority of earlier DHW systems. The natural circulation type (thermo-siphon) gradually increased to a maximum production of approximately 690 thousand units per year in 1980.

Through 1977–78 the surface area of one unit of solar water heater was usually 1mx2m (2 m²). After 1980 one unit turned into two panels, i.e., 4 m² or more.

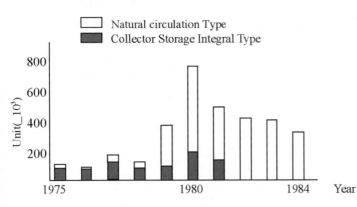

Fig. 1: Manufacturing Data of Solar Water Heaters in Japan

This development may have been caused by the Government's Incentive Measures to promote the development of active solar heating and cooling systems. Since then, the integral solar collector storage type was replaced by the natural circulation type (thermo-siphon type). (Based on the data from the Housing Equipment and Systems Association)

11.3   Development of Solar Heating, Cooling, and DHW System in the Early '70s

Fig. 2: Solar Research Laboratory Building, Government Industrial Research Institute, Nagoya. Agency of Industrial-Science and Technology, Ministry of International Trade and Industry

The Solar Research Laboratory Building was constructed in 1958, for solar heating (solar energy using air with unglazed A1 roll-bonded-sheet) and nocturnal radiation by unglazed collectors installed with a tilt angle of 30° for cooling. Two 20-ton water storage tanks were installed underground of the building. One was for hot water storage (45°C) and another for cold storage (5°C), to use with a heat pump (3HP). The floor area was 82 m² and the total area for three rooms was 300 m².

The storage tank of such a capacity was found to be enough for thermal storage of almost one week without solar radiation. Operation of the system stopped because the collectors failed in 1963.

On the first floor of the building, the paraboloidal mirror and heliostat-type solar furnace was installed with the optical axis horizontal and will be referred to later.

The Yazaki Research Co. Ltd. constructed the Yazaki Solar House in 1974 at Kosai City, Shizuoka. Design characteristics were

- Solar collections by 60 panels (120 m²) with stainless steel selective absorber surface
- Water storage tank of 6 tons
- LiBr-water absorption unit of 1.5 RT
- Auxiliary heat source by LPG
- Drain-down system for freeze protection
- Operated successfully until 1978, and stopped by the closing of the Yazaki factory.

Fig. 3: Solar Heating, Cooling and DHW System Courtesy Yazaki Corp.

11.4   High Temperature Solar Furnace Research

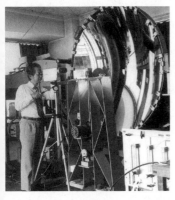

Fig. 4: Dr. Noguchi observing the surface of molten specimen at the focal point of the solar furnace that was coupled with the high-temperature X-ray diffractometer

High-temperature solar furnace research has been promoted at the Solar Research Laboratory GIRIN, AIST, MITI. Since 1955 solar furnaces of three different designs were constructed, the diameter of which were 2–3m, and with Heliostat plain mirrors of 3m x 3m.

The high-temperature emissivity and temperature measurements were studied in the temperature region above 2,000°C. Joining the International Cooperative Works on Secondary Temperature Standards, the melting points of alumina and yttria have been determined. Melting points of high-refractory materials as well as their binary phase diagrams have also been studied.

Heating curve analysis of high-melting refractory oxide were done, and vacuum fusion of refractories were studied with the second solar furnace facility. A high-temperature X-ray diffractometer coupled with the solar furnace was designed and the cubic zirconia phase above 2,450°C was verified. Digital pyrometry was another success at high-temperature measurements.

11.4   Photovoltaic Power System

In the early '70s, the cost of photovoltaic power of a single crystal silicone cell was more than JPY30,000/peak watt (approximately USD250), and the market of such an expensive PV power source was rather limited.

For terrestrial application, the Japan Coast Guard constructed more than 260 unattended navigational lighthouses along the Japanese coast. The PV power systems of 20-450 watts were mounted as the power sources for the lights. Other applications were power sources for wrist-watches.

Unattended snowfall depth measurement was another example of PV use.

Fig. 5: Unattended Navigation Light House
Courtesy Japan Coast Guard

It is also a well-known fact that most satellites have been equipped with PV power sources. Ga-As has been used rather than Si in outer space because of higher conversion efficiency. PV single crystal cells were manufactured in those days by NEC and the Sharp Co. in Japan.

11.6 Long Range National Program on the Development of Renewable Energy

In the early summer of 1973, the Japanese government announced the inauguration of "Project Sunshine," as a national project in which RD&D of renewable energy such as solar, geothermal, and wind energy were included, aiming at the security of energy balance on demand and supply in the year 2000. Since 1974 the solar heating and cooling program, solar thermal power, and photovoltaic conversion programs have been the three major energy programs in Japan. Hydrogen energy R&D was also organized.

11.7 Solar Heating and Cooling Program

System analyses, R&D on materials and components, construction of experimental buildings, and testing and monitoring on the following four systems were incorporated:

- Single-family residential house with evacuated tubular collectors coupled with LiBr -water absorption unit
- Retrofitting systems with high-performance, double-pane solar collectors with Rankine cycle unit

- Multifamily residential house with high-performance tubular collectors and Rankine cycle unit
- Large/commercial building with two-pane black absorber collectors and double-effect LiBr-water absorption unit

High Performance Solar Collectors R&D includes:

- Plastics, metallic and glass materials for selective absorber surface
- Convection suppression device such as honeycomb structure, etc.
- Selective transmittent materials

The above National Program was structured such that it could meet a considerable portion of energy demands by the year 2000. It was not reasonable to grasp by 1980 the total image of the program. In the following flow diagram, the Long Range National Program on Solar Thermal Technology is illustrated.

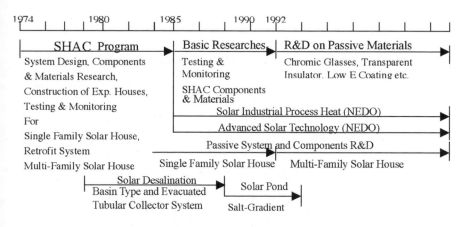

Fig. 6: Flow Diagram of Long Range National Program on SHAC Systems

11.8   Solar Thermal Conversion Program

Survey of irradiation intensity at the site, R&D on materials and system components, construction of pilot plants from 10 kWe to 100 kWe, and finally 1 MWe both of the central receiver type (CRT) and distributed type (DST) progress by the end of 1980. Followed with testing and monitoring for about three years at Nio-cho, Kagawa Prefecture, near the Seto Inland Sea.

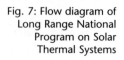

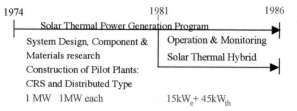

Fig. 7: Flow diagram of Long Range National Program on Solar Thermal Systems

11.9   Photovoltaic Conversion Program

System analysis, R&D of system components and materials. Temporary goal up to the year 1980 was the cost reduction of solar cells hopefully down to 1/100 of JPY30,000 per peak watt. R&D of technologies on silicon-ribbon crystals both by vertical and horizontal pulling methods; polycrystalline thin film both by ion-accelerating and non-ion-accelerating deposition procedures; concentrating irradiation technology for solar cells; and other semiconductor materials such as CdS, CdTe, and InP, as well as amorphous silicon, had progressed so far.

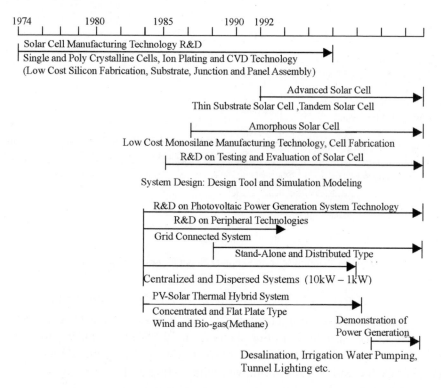

Fig. 8: Flow diagram of Long Range National Program on Photovoltaic Conversion System

In addition to these R&D efforts, feasibility studies on solar energy systems such as solar thermal, photovoltaic, solar heating and cooling, solar furnace as well as solar total system and heat storage subsystems were carried out within Project Sunshine. Technology assessment, meteorological survey, and other activities such as compilation of related patents, glossary, testing, and standardization were also included in the Project.

In the above feasibility studies, Japanese section members played the leading role in most of the workshops and in giving guidance in discussions.

11.10   Meetings and Other Activities

Every year dozens of symposia, seminars, and workshops on the above mentioned topics had been held by many organizations including governmental bodies, the Japanese Sections and JSES, and Private Sectors, etc.

The Japanese Section was honored to welcome visits by distinguished solar scientists from other Sections such as

Dr. Roger N. Morse	C.S.I.R.O. past president, ISES, Australia	July 1975
Prof. J. A. Duffie	Univ. of Wisconsin, USA	September 1976
Prof. S. Karaki	Colorado State Univ., USA	April 1977
Prof. J. I. Yellott	Arizona State Univ., USA	July 1977
Prof. G. O. G. Löf	Colorado State Univ., USA	September 1978
Dr. R. L. Datta	Past president, ISES, India	February 1979
Dr. W. Read	C.S.I.R.O. Australia	July 1979
Dr. J. Robbins	DSET, Arizona, USA	April 1980
Prof. A. H. Delyannis	Univ. of Athens, Greece	July 1980
Dr. J. D. Balcomb	Los Alamos Sci. Lab. USA	September 1980

It should be noted that the Japan Solar Energy Society (JSES) published Japanese journals semi-annually and has held an annual meeting since 1975. JSES membership remained between 500–650 members in those days. The Japanese Section membership of ISES overlapped with JSES members and remained constant between 100 and 120 during 1976–1984. Such a tendency might be ascribed mainly to language problems, while the journal *Solar Energy*, the *Sun at Work* and the Congress Proceedings gave up-to-date information to Japanese Section members.

In 1978, The Solar System Development Association was established as an affiliated association composed of 67 companies and manufacturers of solar heating, cooling and domestic hot water supply systems. This was very encouraging for the solar energy industry in Japan and for the promotion of market penetration.

On 30 May 1980 the "Development and Promotion on Introduction of Alternative Sources of Energy Act" was enacted. By an investment by the private sectors the New Energy Foundation (NEF) was established in September 1980 as a public service corporation. NEF has been proposing the application of renewable energy to the government; providing information dissemination; conducting surveys on renewable energy; and seeking subsidies for promotion of the introduction into the market etc,. Further, by the Act aforementioned, the Ministry of International Trade and Industry established the New Energy Development Organization in October 1980. NEDO has been very active in application of the achievements of the Sunshine Project, subsidizing local government sectors, and so forth in wide areas.

11.11 Some Achievements of Project Sunshine, 1980

One decade had already passed in the world community since the establishment of the national Section of ISES in 1970. Meanwhile, the first seven years had elapsed since the inauguration of the Sunshine Project as a national project on renewable energy RD&D as a response in Japan to the oil embargo of 1974. The Sunshine Project promotion headquarters (SPPH) of the Agency of Industrial Science and Technology (AIST), Ministry of International Trade and Industry (MITI), decided to cease funding of solar heating and cooling programs to eleven contractors because of increased market penetration by SHAC systems. However, basic research for materials and components as well as testing and evaluation of solar collectors and SHAC systems proceeded in the government research institution. Solar Industrial Process Heat (SIPH) had shown up as the new hot process and the New Energy Development Organization (NEDO) was subsidized by AIST. The Housing Industry Division (HID), MITI, also focused in 1981 on the new project of Passive Solar System RD&D as the "WISH 21 Project," including studies on materials, components, passive system configuration, and system simulations as well as monitoring.

Before describing new projects and topics, we will review the results of the active SHAC systems during the first seven years. Achievements of the active SHAC and DHW systems are briefly summarized as follows.

Table 2. Achievements in R&D on Active SHAC Systems

SUNSHINE PROJECT (1974 – 1980)				
Model	Solar Collector & Installed Area	Refrigerator & Capacity	Thermal Storage	System Performance
Single Family Residential Solar System	Evacuated Tubular Collectors, 40.6 m^2 μ=46%	LiBr- H$_2$O Absorption Unit, 1.8 RT	Water HT 1 m^3 85°C LT 8 m^3 10°/45°C	Solar Percent 95% SCOP: heating 8.6 cooling 6.75
Retrofitting Solar Systems	Double Pane Flat Selective Absorber Collector, 48 m^2 μ=35%	Rankine Cycle Unit, 1 RT	Latent Heat Storage Ammonium Alum 94°C LT 5.5 m^3 10°/60°C	Solar Percent 68% SCOP: heating 7.65 cooling 2.78
Multifamily Residential Solar House	Evac. Tub. Collector 366 m^2 μ=43% 100/130°C, Plus Flat Plate Collector for DHW120m^2	Rankine Cycle Unit, 20 US RT	Water HT 10 m^3 45°/95°C LT 80 m^3 60°C	Solar Percent 46% SCOP: heating 1.0 cooling 0.30
Large Scale (Commercial) Solar Bldg.	Double Pane Flat Selective Absorber Collector 508 m^2 μ=40%	Double Effect LiBr-H$_2$O Absorption Unit, 30 US RT	Water 45 m^3 x2 15°C /45°C	Solar Percent 72.1% SCOP: heating 2.77 cooling 1.85

In continuation of summarizing the SHAC system achievements, the appearance of new components and materials in solar heating and cooling technology are noted in the following table.

Table 3. Achievements of Components and Materials in Systems

SUNSHINE PROJECT (1974 – 1980)	
Components and Materials	Results
Solar Collectors	One Pane and Double Pane Flat Plate Selective Absorber Surface Collectors Heat Pipe Collector Evacuated Tubular Collectors Honeycomb Collector
Selective Absorber Surface Materials For Solar Collector	Black Metals Black Chrome Black Nickel (α= 0.90, ε=0.1) Black Copper Selective Paint Contain Mn (α= 0.8, ε=0.2)

Solar Collector Cover Materials	Selective Transmittant Glass (In$_2$O3 –SnO$_2$) (τ=0.84, $\rho_{8\mu m}$=0.80) Anti-reflecting Glass (ρ<2%) Glass Honeycomb Selective Transmittant Film (τ=0.76, $\rho_{8\mu m}$=0.77) Mirror Materials and Plastic Honeycomb
Heat Storage	Latent Heat Storage (Ammonium alum and Eutectic Salts) and Encapsulation Technique Latent Heat – Sensible Heat Hybrid System Seasonal Storage and Underground Heat Storage Chemical Reaction (ammoniated Salts, and Metal Hydrides)
Refrigerator	LiBr – Water Absorption Unit (Single and Double Effects) Rankine Cycle Units (3KW,and 20, 30kW)

Black Copper selective coating was found to deteriorate within a couple of years because of moisture in the air and the wet absorption surface of the collector, which dripped water from condensation on the back surface of the glass cover.

Other than the SHAC system program by SSPH, the Housing Industry Division, MITI, started subsidizing the housing industry on passive systems and components RD&D starting in 1980, firstly for single-family solar houses up to 1985, and then for multifamily solar houses. These programs will be described later.

Fig. 9: Solar Heating, Cooling and Domestic Hot Water System SANYO Hirakata Solar House

11.11.1   Sunshine Project

The Hirakata Solar House was developed as a single-family residential house by the Sunshine Project. Evacuated tubular collectors of 40.6 m^2 were installed on flat roof and of 10 m^2 on the vertical south wall for hot water supply. Operating temperatures: summer – 90°C; and winter, – 60°C. Tilt angle of rooftop collector fin was 15°.

11.12   Solar Desalination

The Small and Medium Enterprises Agency (SMEA), MITI, funded the Mechanical Social System Foundation on Solar Desalination Projects in 1977 – 1983. These projects were primarily to promote the production of drinking water from sea water for remote and/or isolated islands scattered in the Seto Inland Sea. In earlier days drinking water was distributed to these small communities of 20–400 people by fishing boats or ferry at a cost of more than 500 yens/ton.

Solar desalination plants of two types were constructed in 1978–1979. One of them was a basin type solar still installed on Byobushima Island, Kagawa. The plant capacity was 2 m^3 /day fresh water production with an effective still area of 620 m^2. This plant was operated for four years successively; however, some of the island people were frightened to find the ugly worm-like seaweed of about 1 meter in length in the hot sea water flowing path. This was the main reason why they rejected this desalination plant. While such phenomena could be suppressed by using some weed killer, nevertheless, the plant was abandoned for sanitary reasons.

Another system was constructed on Naoshima Island, Kagawa, which was a high-efficiency hybrid system of 10 m^3/day. The Vaporization process was composed of a multi-stage flush evaporator (90°C) with evacuated tubular solar collectors (336 m^2) coupled with an electrodialyser with flat-plate solar collectors (185 m^2) working at 55°C. After monitoring the operation of the system until 1985, the plant was accepted by the Naoshima Island people and was operated successfully, hitherto. A demonstration plant of a multi-stage flush evaporator-evacuated tubular collector type system of 120 m^3/day capacity was installed in Abu Dhabi, UAE, and survived the contamination of intake seawater from oil flow caused by the Gulf War.

11.13   Solar Pond

The history of the solar pond started when Kaleczinsky discovered the natural salt solar pond at Medve Lake in Hungary in 1902. Since then, many solar ponds have been constructed, e.g., in Israel, the USSR. Chile, India, and the USA, so far mostly as a relatively large heat source for low-temperature application.

The Small Scale Business Corporation (MITI) funded the Engineering Advancement Association of Japan for a Solar Pond Project, which was started in 1981 on mass and heat flow analysis of the salt gradient in a solar pond and for its conceptual design. The target was to supply hot water of 65°C to factories producing fishery products. As an auxiliary heat source, a heat pump using underground warm water was utilized.

The dimension of the solar pond constructed by NKK along the Notoro Harbor in Hokkaido was as follows:

Surface area of circular pond:	1,500 m^2
Depth:	3 m
Heat extracted from the pond:	418,000 MJ/m^2/Y
Hot water supply through heat pump:	501,600 MJ/h

To reach thermal equilibrium in a salt gradient solar pond usually requires more than a couple of years after its construction. Further, more than several years may be needed to achieve a stable condition.

Subsidies on the salt gradient solar pond project for testing and monitoring was terminated in 1987 and the local government failed to coordinate the fishery factories in the solar pond harbor area. Therefore, experimental works on solar ponds were transferred to the Kitami Institute of Technology.

11.14   Testing and Monitoring of SHAC System Components

In accordance with the outdoor collector performance test procedures developed at the Solar Research Laboratory, AIST, MITI, solar collectors of seven kinds, designed and built in the Sunshine Project, were tested and evaluated. The behaviors of the selective absorber surface materials were also studied and analyzed through visible and infrared inspection. Meanwhile the Solar Research Laboratory had participated in Task I in the IEA Solar Heating and Cooling International Program since 1977 (where the System Performance of Solar Houses and DHW were the task topics, Operating Agent (O/A): Mr. O. Jorgensen, Denmark); in Task II (in which coordination of national SHAC programs was discussed; O/A Dr. T. Noguchi, Japan); and Task III Solar Collector Testing—O/A Dr. H. Talarek, Germany.

Together with the achievements in Task III and in the Solar Research Laboratory's methods, the latter has worked to establish Japanese Industrial Standards for the Solar Collector Test Methods as well as for Solar Thermal

Storage Tank tests. Both standards were published as JIS A 1425 and JIS A 1426, respectively in 1985. Separately, Japanese Industrial Standards on solar collectors and solar storage tanks were revised and published in 1995. The drafts of these standards were prepared by the Solar System Development Association (SSDA).

11.15   Cost Reduction of the PV Cell

The PV conversion program started in 1974. The first six years were concentrated on cost reduction of silicon raw materials. At that time high-purity silicon raw material for PV cells production depended on Czochralski and Floating Zone methods or used wastes from the semiconductor industry.

The market for Si cells before 1974 was mainly limited to powering light sources for unattended navigation light houses. There were about 260 of those constructed by the Japanese Coast Guard, while the cost of PV power in those days was more than 30,000 yen/Wp, and space satellites were equipped with the Ga-As cell with higher conversion efficiency. The manufacturers of these Si single-crystal cells in Japan during these early days were the Sharp Co. and NEC.

The targets of cost reduction of PV cells in the Sunshine Project were 500 yen/Wp in 1990 and 100-200 yen/Wp in 2000, and the quality of silicon from SEG (semiconductor grade-ten to eleven niner) to SOG (solar grade-five niner). Yearly power consumption of the former silicon was 300 kWh/kg Si compared to the latter of 30 kWh/kg Si, i.e., a reduction to almost one-tenth.

In order to attain the first target during 1974 – 1980, both low-cost silicon fabrication technology and mass production procedures were pursued. In the development of the trichlorosilane production process, energy savings, the elimination of the reaction process and an increase of yields was sought. From 1981 to 1983, 200 tons of trichlorosilane were synthesized by an experimental set-up that succeeded during a 3,000 hr operation.

Chlorosilane reduction by hydrogen in the fluidized bed increased the reaction velocity and yields. SOG Si of 2.1 tons were derived in a 10 ton/year capacity experimental prototype plant during 1,170 hrs of operation.

Likewise, feasibility studies on cast substrate fabrications and ribbon crystal substrate fabrication technologies, p-n junction formation, module assembly, etc., were pursued, together with ion implantation and CVD technology in 1975 – 1980.

Interim targets for the cost of raw silicon were 6.8yens/gram in 1988. The results showed 10yens/gram (100 tons/year) and 4.6yens/gram (1,000 tons/year) and trial costs were accounted for in arriving at these values. On the other hand, to improve the conversion efficiency of the single-crystal silicon cell, casting of polycrystalline Si substrate was attempted with high speed and automatic production. Defects within the crystals were reduced in polycrystalline Si. Further, light input into the Si cell was increased by fine electrodes on a textured cell surface, by which reflection from the cell surface was minimized. In addition, back surface reflection (BSR) film was used, and passive technologies were developed with innovative technologies in the '70 and '80s.

In the early '80s, amorphous Si appeared and through a-SiC/a-Si hetero junction proposed by Prof. Y. Hamakawa at the Osaka University, the con version efficiency increased gradually. However, photo degradation of a-Si was observed; but some of this degradation was recovered after outdoor expo sure for several months. Therefore the conversion efficiency of an a-Si cell was calculated after the stabilized value was obtained. Such degradation was found to depend on the depth of layer in the p-i-n junction of a-Si. This should be controlled within 300 - 360 nm to suppress the so-called Staebler-Wronski effect. Also, tandem and triple junctions may be useful for enhanced per formance of the device. Recently an a-Si/a-SiGe stack-type solar cell module by Sanyo Co. showed a conversion efficiency of 9.5% after stabilization.

To improve the conversion efficiency and reduce the Staebler-Wronski effect, an optimum design is being developed.

II-VI compounds such as CdS and CdTe are fabricated by repeating coat ing-drying-sintering on a substrate layer. CuInSe2 is also a promising thin film solar cell material and showed a high-efficiency of 18.8% when tested recently by NREL, although Japan is rather behind on research of this cell material.

Including the thin-film polycrystalline silicon solar cell, amorphous and thin-film solar cells are contributing to material savings, and energy savings (lower temperature fabrication than silicon single crystal melting), so a lower cost is expected in future PV technology.

In addition to the above-mentioned solar cell groups, super high-efficien cy solar cells are being investigated including III-V compound semiconduc tor materials, such as those containing Ga, In, etc. GaAs cells are already showing 35% conversion efficiency. Their durability and reliability are very important future focuses for research, and the production of uniform large area solar cells is a key objective, together with the development of systems design and systems simulation.

This report will be continued in Vol. 2.

Chapter 12

Lebanese Section of the International Solar Energy Society

By
Eng. Mhamad Bakhour *
Assisted by
Dr. Fateh Sakkal**
Eng.Walid Baba***
LSES, Lebanese Solar Energy Society
Beirut-Lebanon
P.O. Box: 15-5044
Postal Code: 1101-2010
E-mail: mbkr69@hotmail.com

Abstract

In this part we report about our Lebanese Section of ISES that was formed in April 1980 on the initiative of highly educated engineers and was comprised of solar energy company owners; chairmen of university engineering departments; and chemical, along with mechanical, and electrical engineers, who became the heart of the Lebanese Solar Energy Society (LSES). In the following history of the Society, statistical data are given regarding its development; most important events including national events, conferences, local policy meetings; and national awards or recognitions. It is worth mentioning that war in Lebanon from 1975 to 1990, and its economic consequences, were a major hindrance to the development of solar energy in Lebanon, particularly limiting research funding and technological studies in manufacturing.

Eng. Mhamad Bakhour: B.E., mechanical engineering at American University of Beirut, 1991. Mechanical engineering consultant at Oger Liban.

*Dr. Fateh Sakkal: Ph.D, MI mech. Eng. Emeritus Professor American University of Beirut. Ex-chairman dept. of mechanical engineering AUB. Research Consultant energy division, Laurence Berkeley Lab, University of California Berkeley 1978 – 1988.

**Eng. Walid Baba: B.E. electro mechanical engineering, Ecole Superieure d'Ingenieurs de Beyrouth ESIB, 1974, Refrigeration Engineer.

12.1   Introduction: Solar History in Our Country and the Reasons for Tending to Renewable, Mainly Solar Energy, in Lebanon, and First Steps to Creating Our National Section

The idea of converting energy from the sun in Lebanon was developed for several reasons: First, Lebanon is blessed with 300 sunny days per year. Second, Lebanon, with approximately 200 km of shoreline on the Mediterranean Sea, has the potential to harness energy from the wind, where wind velocities exceed 40 km/hrs. Third, Lebanese geography is full of mountains with many valley areas where "wind corridors" make wind turbine installations possible. Fourth, the war crises in Lebanon made the government search for new sources of energy, to help lessen spending on fuel and lower the energy demands of the country. Last, but not least, since Lebanon is not a petroleum producing country, there is an urgent need to develop renewables such as solar, wind, and hydro plant energy.

12.1.1   The First Steps of Our National Section

On 22 April, 1980, the Lebanese Solar Energy Society was organized by a group consisting of:

Mr. Kamal Basilla, Solar energy company owner;
Dr. Fateh Sakkal, Ph.D, MI mech. eng. Emeritus Professor, University of California, Berkeley, Chairman of the Mechanical Engineering Department at American University of Beirut;
Dr. Raja Hajjar, Ph.D, physical chemistry, Ohio State University;
Eng. Burhan Kraitem, BA, chemical engineer, Aston University, UK;
Mr. Naser Mroueh;
Mr. Raja Fawwaz;
Mr. Fouad Shuwairy;
Mr. Rayan Badro.

The group also elected officers:

Mr. Basilla was elected President;
Mr. Mroueh, Vice President;
Dr. Sakkal, Secretary;

Mr. Kraitem, Membership head;

Dr. Hajjar, Treasurer;

Mr. Fawwaz and Mr. Shuwairy, Finance; and

Mr. Badro, Conferences, Exhibitions, and Research head.

12.1.1.1 The Growth of the Society

The first months of the Society were devoted mainly to stabilizing its basic foundations, and one of the most important tasks was distribution of committees and assigning each its responsibilities and activities. The initial four committees were the membership committee; the research-conferences-exhibitions committee; the general, public awareness committee; and the financial committee.

The Society, through its committees, progressed through several activities inside and outside the country:

a) Announcements through the Lebanese radio station: The president of the Society participated in a program on the local radio station describing the Society, its aims, and its future vision.

b) Announcements placed in local daily newspapers and in local weekly magazines: The news of the Society was published in these papers.

c) Announcements through correspondence: A briefing about the Society was sent through messages to more than 100 International scientific and relevant societies.

d) Direct coordination with the Lebanese government, along with public and private sectors: In this, the Society paid direct visits to the prime minister, minister of industry, the head of the Lebanese industrial and commercial sector, directors of industrial schools and factories, etc.

e) Advertisements through embassies: The Society contacted the foreign embassies and the commercial sections in them along with most of the Lebanese embassies in other countries.

The development of the Society continued moderately, although the war hindered and even stopped most of the technical and educational activities in the country.

In the late '80s and at the beginning of the '90s, Professor Dr. Fateh Sakkal, along with Dr. Nisreen Ghaddar, built a solar energy laboratory at the American University of Beirut. Moreover, Dr. Bassam Ouaida Chairman of the solar energy section in the National Council of Scientific research implemented between 1983 and 1988 a study of weather data together with compiling wind velocity data and an assessment of solar energy radiations monitoring in Lebanon.

At the beginning of 2000, the Society was reshaped through election of new board members and a restructuring of the committees. Through this reshaping, several activities were continued, including the society messages and aims that were put together in the early '80s (this reshaping will be discussed in a later section). Some of the outstanding activities were:

a) Seminars in collaboration with the Industrial Research Institute (IRI) to enhance the solar energy industry in Lebanon.
b) Seminars in collaboration with the Lebanese Syndicate of Engineers and Architects to clearly define the role of the Syndicate in the use of solar energy in Lebanon.
c) Press conferences in the presence of the president of the Lebanese Syndicate of Engineers stating the plan of the Society in the solar energy field.
d) Participating in "Project Lebanon" exhibitions for speeding solar energy development in Lebanon and participating in a workshop in the exhibition for this purpose.
e) Coordination with the National Center for Scientific Research (NCSR), IRI, and Energy Research Group (ERG) at the American University of Beirut, the Meteorological Station at Beirut Airport, and Kuwait Industrial Scientific Research (KISR), to enhance the use of Solar Energy.
f) Trying to develop a Solar and Wind Atlas for Lebanon.

12.2   Board of Directors and Society Activities

12.2.1   The Lebanese Solar Energy Society (LSES)

The Lebanese Solar Energy Society—LSES—was founded in Beirut on 22 April 1980 under registration of the Ministry of Interior N° 46/AD. Its elected board was composed of:

Mr. Kamel Basilla   President
Mr. Nasib Mroueh   Vice President
Dr. Fateh Sakkal   Secretary.

The activities of the LSES were stopped for some years due to the war in Lebanon and also due to the death of some of the founders, among them the president and the vice president.

The Lebanese Solar Energy Society resumed its activities officially in November 2001, with new members in key positions. A new administration board including eleven members was elected for two-year terms ending January 2004, comprised of:

Mr. Walid El Baba	President
Mr. Mustapha Ghaddar	Vice President
Mr. Moukhtar Beydoun	Secretary
Mr. Walid Zreik	Treasurer
Mr. Gaby Mourad	Accountant
Mr. Bourhan Kraitem	Relation with the government

and Messrs: Dr. Fateh Sakkal, Kamal Sioufi, Hussein Abdallah, Dr. Raja Hajjar, and Nouhad El Khoury as advisers.

The new board members elected in February 2004 for two years were:

Mr. Walid El Baba	President
Mr. Mustapha Ghaddar	Vice President
Mr. Muhamad Bakhour	Secretary
Mr. Youssif Ghantous	Treasurer
Mr. Jean Paul Sfeir	Accountant
Mr. Hussein Abdallah	Relation with the government

Dr. Fateh Sakkal, Mr. Kamal Sioufi, Mr. Moukhtar Beydoun, Mr. Rachid Bou Habib, and Mr. Selim El Khoury were also members of the board.

12.2.2   Objectives of the Association

1. To get together associations of professionals as well as individuals interested in the development of solar energy in all its various aspects in order to achieve the objectives of the LSES.
2. To develop education programs and training sessions regarding the various applications of renewable energies in general and more particularly solar energy.
3. To set up gradually a "Quality Label" with the view to guarantee the quality of services linked to the design, manufacturing, installation, and exploitation of solar energy in various fields.

4. To encourage development and protection of the manufacturing of solar systems in order to achieve a good quality of the equipment for the benefit of the users.
5. To inform and lead the public opinion on any matters regarding solar energy for the benefit of the national economy and environment in Lebanon.
6. To take part in scientific activities and to participate in exhibitions and seminars in accordance with the objectives of the association.
7. To back any initiatives in order to present to the public authorities (executive and legislative) as well as syndicates and financial institutions some proposals to elaborate laws and to improve the existing ones with the aim of enlarging the demand and developing the solar energy market as well as any other renewable energies.

12.2.3   Activities
The main target was to promote the use of solar energy with consideration for the protection of the environment, energy saving, and the quality of life.

12.2.3.1   Solar Radiation Map for Lebanon
Dissemination of information about solar energy in Lebanon, primarily solar radiation data, and in some places in Lebanon to do so on a regular basis.
In coordination with:
- A.U.B—the American University of Beirut—Faculty of Engineering and Architecture
- CNRS—National Center for Scientific Research

12.2.3.2   Market Study of Solar Water Heaters
Inventory of Lebanese manufacturers of solar water heater companies:
- Name and address
- Capacity of production
- Characteristics and quality of the products (solar collectors, water heaters, etc.)

In coordination with:
- Students at A.U.B./Mechanical Engineering faculty.

12.2.3.3   Quality Label in Solar Thermal System
Improvement of the Solar thermal market

- Quality of equipment
- Certified tools
- Calculation and design criteria
- Good installation procedure
- Good running procedure

In coordination with national and international associations and organizations.

12.2.3.4   Test Platform at IRI
Participating in a test platform for solar thermal collectors and solar photovoltaic in order to help in delivering the Quality Label based on standards and certification.
In coordination with:
- Industrial Research Institute (IRI)
- A.U.B.

12.2.3.5   Standardization / Normalization / Certification
Establishing Technical requirements concerning Solar material with respect to national certification for collectors and plumbing system
In coordination with:
- Syndicate of Engineers and Architects
- IRI
- LIBNOR
- and International norm institutions.

12.2.3.6   Training Programs Awareness Campaigns to Help in Good Solar Strategy
Training programs for plumbers, architects, and engineers; information and awareness campaigns for customers and professionals.
In coordination with national and international organizations.

12.3   Our Conferences
Our common efforts gave birth to the following events:

1st Solar Energy meeting on 18 March 2002
   Partner: Syndicate of Engineers and Architects, Beirut
   Subject: Role of the Syndicate of Engineers in developing and integrating the use of solar energy in buildings.

2nd Solar Energy meeting on 30 April 2002
  Partner: Industrial Research Institute, IRI Beirut
  Subject: Quality control and certification of Solar Energy Industry.

3rd Solar Energy meeting at BIEL Beirut Center on 16 May 2002 during the Project Lebanon 2002 Fair where LSES had a stand of 9 square meters to create awareness of the use of renewable energy sources (Lebanese Solar Energy Conference 2002).

Participation in the training session for solar water heaters held in Amman, Jordan, on August, 18–21, 2002, organized by the National Energy Research Center, Jordan.

Participation in Lebanese-Syrian Scientific Days in Beirut in March 2003.
  Subject: "Renewable Energy Sources and Application," organized by the National Council for Scientific Research (NCSR), Lebanon.
  Lebanese University
  Supreme Council of Sciences, Syria.

Participation in the exhibition of Project Lebanon 2003 at Biel Center Beirut in a stand of 9 square meters.

Signed an agreement for a convention for co-operation between the Industrial Research Institute (IRI) and the Lebanese Solar Energy Society (LSES) for a 3-year period starting 1 June 2003.

Published the "Solar and Renewable Energy Lebanon Guide 2003" in May 2003.

For the coming years our priorities will be to implement a rethinking of LSES priorities, including the development of new policies and advocating limited regulatory control, development of new and/or refinement of economic instruments, and increasing energy awareness in the civil society at all levels.

12.4   Financing of the Society

The main income for the society had been the yearly subscriptions of the members, where the society tried to coordinate with the public sector for this purpose, but the war crises and the economic situation of the country hindered this.

12.5   The Relation with ISES

Our LSES contacted ISES in the early '80s through its local center, which was in Australia at that time, for our society was a member of ISES at that time, but the war again stopped the continuation of cooperation and stopped our membership in ISES. Moreover, our society again contacted ISES a couple of months ago at its center in Germany and coordination between Engineer Muhamad Bakhour and the Deputy Director of ISES, Christine Hornstein, was pursued to continue the process of again having our LSES, Lebanese Solar Energy Society, as a member of ISES.

12.6   Our National Solar Energy Society

As per the latest coordination with ISES in Germany, 18 members of our Society were registered and they were:

Mr. Walid El Baba
Mr. Jean Paul Sfeir
Mr. Youssif Ghantous
Dr. Fateh Sakkal
Mr. Kamal Sioufi
Mr. Walid Zreik
Mr. Mustapha Ghaddar
Mr. Moukhtar Beydoun
Mr. Wassim El Baba
Mr. Ahmad Bitar
Dr. Saleh Chehade
Mr. Hussein Abdallah
Mr. Ramzi Abu Said
Dr. Kamel Abu Ghali (or Mr. Chafic Abu Said)
Mr. Selim El Khoury
Mr. Yafuz Alpan
Mr. Gaby Mourad
Mr. Rachid Bou Habib

These members simultaneously became members of ISES, taking into account that two of these members were already working members in ISES; they were Dr. Ahmad Houry and Engineer Muhamad Bakhour.

This made twenty members of LSES simultaneous members of ISES.

12.7   Value of ISES Publications to Our Section Members

It is always helpful to keep updated on solar energy news from ISES publications; they were the Refocus magazine, the cdmailer e-mails, the web site, and mail journals received from ISES by members; these will enhance the solar awareness of members and keep them updated with Solar Energy and the Renewable Energy World.

12.8   Most Important Research

Again, the war in Lebanon stopped all types of research programs in Lebanon, including solar energy research, not to mention the moderate experiments done by Professor Sakkal and Dr. Ghaddar in their laboratory at the American University of Beirut.

12.9   What Else Is Worthwhile to Mention about Our Society

It is always worth saying that, no matter what war might destroy, we will continue the effort to develop better solar energy alternatives and environmentally friendly energy in our country, originating from our faith that the sun is god-given to us, burning itself to give us heat and energy as a clean future source, that will generate a better future for all mankind in cooperation and peace, trying to make the world a better, safer, and cleaner place.

Fig. 1: Writer of this LSES chapter, LSES Secretary: Eng. Mhamad Bakhour

Fig. 2: Ffrom left to right: Eng. Yafous Alpan, Eng., Shafic Abi Saed,
LSES President Eng. Walid Baba, and Dr. Ahmad Houri

Chapter 13

The Mexican Section of the International Solar Energy Society

by
Eduardo A. Rincón Mejía
School of Engineering
Autonomous University of the State of Mexico
Cerro de Coatepec, C.U., 50130 Toluca, Mexico
MEXICO
e-mail: rinconsolar@hotmail.com

Abstract

In this chapter, the history of the twenty nine years of the Mexican Section of ISES, called Asociación Nacional de Energía Solar (ANES), is summarized. The initial association was formed on the initiative of a small group of enthusiastic colleagues led by Dr. José Luis Fernández Zayas, Manuel Martínez Fernández, Gustavo Best Brown, Enrique Caldera Muñoz, and Alfredo Sánchez Flores, among others academicians. This small nucleus was formed in 1976 and developed into a Section of ISES in the year 1981. Important events, including national conferences, local policy meetings, and international congresses, are listed here after a very brief history of ancient solar life in Mexico. A chronological listing of the presidents of the Section is also provided. Major solar developments in our country are presented. Finally, statistical data describing the Section are enumerated.

13.1   Introduction: Ancient Solar History in Mexico, First Studies on Solar and other Renewable Sources of Energy and First Steps to Creating the ANES

As a matter of fact, almost all archeological sites of ancient Mexican civilizations—Mayans, Aztecs, Teotihuacans, Olmecs, etc.—have great monuments dedicated to the Sun. An example of these is the pyramid of Tenayuca, which was built for solar worship. At summer and winter solstices its principal axis aims toward the sunset point, while the heads of two large serpents sculpted in stone, seems to look at that point. At the equinoxes, the shadows projected on the steps of El Castillo pyramid, located in Chichen Itzá, correspond to the pattern on the skin of a rattlesnake. These magnificent events are admired twice a year by thousands of tourists from all over the world, who gather around that great ancient construction. Calixtlahuaca pyramid, located about 100 km to the west of Mexico City, is dedicated to Ejecatl-Quetzalcoatl, the Mexican wind divinity, even more powerful than Aeolus, the corresponding Greek god of the winds. Nowadays, thousands of Mexicans have personal names like Tonatiuh (the Sun), Tlalok (the rain), Mistli (the moon), etc. Obviously, for ancient Mexico and for almost all millenarian civilizations, solar energy, and its manifestations as wind, rain, forests and thunder were powers to be worshipped, because life was always supported by these elements. Hence, it is not difficult to understand that the sun is now, as it has been for centuries, a matter not only of cult worship, but also and mainly of study.

Systematic research in Mexico about solar radiation began in 1911 with the actinometrical measures of Dr. Ladislao Gorcziñsky, which inspired a second period of research sponsored by the Mexican National Meteorological Service between 1923 and 1928. The data from these campaigns consisted of direct solar radiation measurements, carried out with an old pyrheliometer with electric-compensation.

Several years after, celebrating the International Geophysical Year, on June 1, 1957, almost three years after the birth of ISES, the Institute of Geophysics of the Autonomous National University of Mexico (UNAM) started uninterrupted observations of solar radiation in Mexico employing five solarimetric stations located at the Iztaksiuatl Volcano, near Mexico City; in San Cristobal de Las Casas, State of Chiapas; in the Atlantic port of Veracruz; and in the city of Chihuahua.

Renewed interest in solar energy in Mexico began in the early 1970s when, at the Institute of Engineering and the Institute of Materials, both of the UNAM, a small number of academicians under guidance of Dr. José Luis Fernández Zayas, Dr. Gustavo Best Brown, Dr. Manuel Martínez Fernández, M. Sc. Issac Pilatowsky Figueroa, and Professor Eric Mayer, along with graduate students Juan José Ambriz García, Rodolfo Martínez Strevel, Odón de Buen Rodríguez, and Hernando Guerrero Cazares, joined by other enthusiastic colleagues from other institutions like Eng. Alfredo Sánchez Flores, Eng. Enrique Caldera Muñoz, Dr. Jorge Huacuz Villamar, M. Sc. Ana María Martínez, and many other people, began to speak about sustainability and renewable sources of energy. Words like those stimulated commitment to study the technical and economic viability of converting solar energy into useful thermal and electric energy. The first studies were carried out on flat solar collectors. A growing interest in photovoltaic systems and other ways to convert solar energy led to the organization of some small symposia and forums about research and development of systems to measure solar input, taking the more recent technology into consideration for its application.

13.2   The First Steps to Creating the Mexican Section of ISES

The first national solar energy conference, called since then the Semana Nacional de Energía Solar, was held at the Autonomous Metropolitan University, campus Xochimilco, in June 1977. This meeting was attended by seventy people from universities, small industry, and government. The main conclusion of the meeting was interest in keeping in touch and sustaining a dialog among people interested on solar energy. Eight months later, in February 1978, a second national conference was held at Palmira, Morelos, organized by the Institute of Electric Research and the Center of Eco-Development.

This second national meeting was attended by more than 100 people, some from abroad, and at the end of the meeting the commitment was made to create a data base to support the public sector for the establishment of policies for the development of a national technology. It was concluded that renewable sources of energy would contribute to self sufficiency of energy in the country in the near future. It was decided to promote the demonstration of new technologies in pilot plants and to reinforce efforts toward a Mexican Chart on Solar Energy.

The third solar national conference was held at the Michoacán State

University of San Nicolás de Hidalgo, in Morelia, in February 1979. People from more than thirty five institutions discussed the state of the art of solar technologies and the possible beneficial social impact of these applications. At this meeting, the necessity to institute future conferences and to create the National Association of Solar Energy (ANES) was discussed, and three years later the discussion evolved into the Mexican Section of the ISES.

One year later, in October 1980, the constitution of the ANES became official, and Dr. José Luis Fernández Zayas was elected as its first president, for a two-year term. The fourth national solar energy conference was held in San Luis Potosi. In 1981 ANES became officially the Mexican Section of the International Solar Energy Society.

From 1977 to 2004 ANES has celebrated twenty-eight Semanas Nacionales de Energía Solar, and it has had thirteen boards of directors, also called Consejos Directivos. A brief compendium of the Mexican solar energy conferences is presented in Table 1, and Figures 1 and 2 show the photographs of the former presidents of the ANES, beginning with Prof. José Luis Fernández Zayas. The Presidents of ANES have been: Dr. José Luis Fernández Zayas (1980–1982); Manuel Martínez Fernández (1982–1984); Alfredo Sánchez Flores (1984–1986); Isaac Pilatowsky Figueroa (1986–1988); Jorge Huacuz Villamar (1988–1990); Hernando Guerrero Cazares (1990–1992); Juan José Ambriz García (1992–1994); Enrique Caldera Muñoz (1994–1996); Claudio Estrada Gasca (1996–1998); Gustavo Best Brown (1998–2000); Rubén Dorantes Rodríguez (2000–2002); Eduardo Rincón Mejía (2002–2004) and David Morillón (2004–2006).

Fig. 1: Former Presidents of ANES at its 25th Anniversary From left to right: Manuel Martínez Fernández, Gustavo Best Brown (Honorarium President), Enrique Caldera Muñoz, José Luis Fernández Zayas, and Roberto Best Brown.

Fig. 2:   Other Presidents of ANES, clockwise from top left: Alfredo Sánchez Flores, Jorge Huacuz Villamar, Juan José Ambriz García and Eduardo Rincón Mejía

13.2.1   The Growth of ANES

From the first meetings held in mid '70s, the number of people that regularly attend our national solar energy conferences has grown from a few tens to more than 500. For the first twenty three years of the ANES there was no budget to afford a professional office, hence the work was shared among the members of the board of directors. Six years ago (1999), ANES could afford hiring a part-time executive director to take over some of ANES' growing responsibilities. Mrs. Laura Hernandez worked in that position from 1999 to 2004 at our ANES office, located for four years in Cuernavaca, State of Morelos. Since ANES is a nonprofit organization, its operational expenses come from the conference and short courses fees, the sale of Proceedings, books and eventually some support from several institutions.

Mexico has more than 104 million inhabitants, and we have the conservative goal to get 1000 associates at the end of 2006, this way ANES would have only 10 members for each million of Mexicans. This is a rather low figure if we are trying to change the present fossil fuel-based national energy system with other sustainable based on renewable energy. But nowadays, ANES has members in each of the thirty two federative entities of Mexico, so it has the roots to begin to grow consistently year after year. Even though there are a lot of social, economic, political, health and poverty problems, and most of the systems intended to use renewable energies have purchase costs more expensive than the conventional ones, to bet for renewable energies is the best alternative in order to attain a sustainable future.

13.2.2   Our Principal Commitments

The main ANES commitments are the following:

1) The organization and carrying out of the annual national solar energy conference, publishing the corresponding Proceedings, and giving at least ten short courses on topics relating to renewable sources of energy;
2) To publish a quarterly magazine titled La Revista Solar, which contains papers of interest for our members and associates; and
3) To cooperate with other government and nongovernmental organizations to promote large-scale applications of renewable energy to further sustainable development.

ANES' work is guided by its internal by-laws that are legally registered according to Mexican laws.

13.3   Our Conferences

As it was mentioned, ANES annually holds a National Solar Energy Conference; besides this, a growing number of local and regional conferences about specific topics of renewable energies, such as biomass, wind machines, solar concentration, bio-climatic architecture, and many others, are more and more frequently presented due to the importance of renewable energy. Table 1 is a brief compilation of our first twenty eight National Solar Energy Conferences. Other interesting conferences are mentioned too.

Table 1
ANES Annual National Solar Energy Conferences

National Solar Energy Conference	Venues and Dates	Relevant Aspects
I	UAM – Xochimilco, D. F., 2-3 June 1977	1st annual meeting. About seventy participants from academia, industry and government.

II	IIE, Morelos, 2-3 February 1978	More than 100 participants noted the strategic importance of RE for sustainable development.
III	UMSNH, Michoacán, 1-2 February 1979	Creation of ANES is proposed. Twenty three papers on the state of the art in present solar technology were presented.
IV	UASLP, San Luis Potosí, 1-3 Oct. 1980	Dr. José Luis Fernández Zayas was elected president of the 1st ANES board of directors.
V	U. de Guadalajara, Jal., 7-9 October 1981	ANES became an ISES Section. More than 100 papers were presented.
VI	I. T. de La Paz, B.C.S., 6-8 October 1982	Dr. Manuel Martínez became president of the 2nd ANES board of directors. A short course on RE was given.
VII	I.T. de Saltillo, Coah. , 3-7 October 1983	ANES Regional Sections were created. Two courses on RE were given.
VIII	I.T. de Cd. Madero, Tam., 1-5 Oct. 1984	Ing. Alfredo Sánchez became president of the 3rd ANES board of directors. Papers on research, education and industry were presented.
IX	I.T. de Mérida, Yuc., 30 Sep -4 Oct 1985	Three short courses on bio-climatic Architecture, solar drying and electric generation with RE were given.
X	U. de Gto, Gto., 29 Sep -3 Oct 1986	Dr. Isaac Pilatowsky presided over the 4th ANES board of directors. Technical papers, round tables and short courses were given.
XI	UJAT, Tabasco, 28 Sep - 2 Oct 1987	More than seventy-five oral presentations. Strong participation of local government and an accompanying persons program were offered.
XII	BUAP, Puebla, 3 - 7 October 1988	Dr. Jorge Huacuz presided over the 5th ANES board of directors. Sixty- one technical papers were published in the Conference Proceedings.
XIII	UMSNH, Michocan, 2 - 6 October 1989	Morelia is the venue for a 2nd time. Four short courses on RE were given.
XIV	CIB & IT de La Paz, BCS, 1 - 5 Oct. 1990	Seventy-seven technical papers were published in the Conference Proceedings, and Dr. Hernando Guerrero presided over the 6th ANES board of directors.

XV	UAZ, Zacatecas, 30 Sep – 4 Oct. 1991	An agreement for trying to bring to Mexico an ISES WEC was accomplished in a plenary session.
XVI	CIIDIR-IPN, Oaxaca, 28 Sep - 2 Oct. 1992	Dr. Juan José Ambriz became the president of the 7th ANES board of directors.
XVII	U. de Colima, Colima, 4 - 8 October 1993	Electric cars contest was held.
XVIII	UNISON, Sonora, 3 - 7 October 1994	Eng. Enrique Caldera became the president of the 8th ANES board of directors. The State governor inaugurated the congress.
XIX	UABCS, BCS, 2 - 6 October 1995	Great international participation. Four plenary lectures and eighty-five technical papers were presented.
XX	U. V., Veracruz, 30 Sep - 4 Oct 1996	Dr. Claudio Estrada became president of the 9th ANES Board of Directors. Photographic exhibition on: "20 years of solar research in Mexico"
XXI	UACH, ITCh, Chih., 29 Sep - 3 Oct 1997	Industrial Exhibition, technical presentations & other events.
XXII	UABC, Baja California, 28 Sep - 2 Oct 1998	Dr. Roberto Best became president of the 10th ANES Board of Directors. ISES President and Vice-president attend the whole conference.
XXIII	UMSNH, Michoacan, 4 - 8 October 1999	Morelia is the venue for a 3rd time. Excellent social program.
XIV	Mexico City, 17-22 September 2000	ISES Millennium Solar Forum 2000 was celebrated.
XXV	UASLP, SLP, 1 - 5 October 2001	SLP is the venue for a 2nd time. A great celebration for the 25th anniversary of the ANES was carried out.
XXVI	UAQRoo, Q. Roo, 11-15 November 2002	Eduardo Rincón became president of the 12th ANES Board of Directors. Great international participation and massive student attendance.
XXVII	Chihuahua Gov., Chih., 6-10 Oct 2003	Chihuahua is the venue for 2nd time World-class industrial exhibition.
XXVIII	Oaxaca State Gov., 4 - 8 October 2004	Simultaneous celebration with the 12th International SolarPACES Symposium

Fig. 3: Official photograph of our colleagues at the venue of the XXVIII Mexican Solar Energy Conference held in Guanajuato, October 2004, jointly with IEA SolarPACES

Other relevant meetings on renewable sources of energy co-organized by ANES in the last months are listed below.

1. International Workshop on Clean Development Mechanism, Mexico City, 18–19 February 2004.
2. International Seminar on Solar Cooling of Buildings, Tuxtla Gutierrez, Chiapas, 3–5 September 2003.
3. International Seminar on Bioenergy & Sustainable Rural Development, Morelia, Michoacán, 26–28 June 2003.
4. International Seminar on Bio-climatic Architecture, Mexico City, 24–27 June 2003.

ANES is co-organizing many other international, regional and local solar forums in order to disseminate the benefits and realities about the use of renewable sources of energy among Mexican population. One particular conference was the ISES Millennium Solar Forum, held in Mexico City in September 2000 with almost 600 participants, with the largest industrial exhibition in the history of ANES. This Forum was inaugurated by Dr. Cesare Silvi, president of ISES; Dr. Roberto Best, president of ANES; and the Energy Minister of México, Dr. Luis Téllez. There were seven parallel workshops on: solar cities, world energy assessment and sustainable issues, bio-energy, ecological and economic perspectives by enhanced renewable policies: the German example, solar culture, renewable energy and gender, and history & art. Besides, six plenary conferences were dictated by universally recognized authorities. It was in this Forum where the ISES History Project, that culminates with the present book, became one of the main activities to be developed in order to summarize the experience and knowledge acquired during the 50 years of ISES, to see how it can best contribute to future developments and applications of solar energy, as Prof. Cesare Silvi has written about.

ANES also had the ISES support to organize the ISES Latin American Regional Conference, a great meeting intended to celebrate the 50th anniversary of ISES in the Latin American subcontinent. That feast was scheduled to be held on November 2004 in Guanajuato, Mexico. The president of Mexico, Vicente Fox and three of his Ministers were invited to speak about the commitment of the Mexican government on the promotion of the applications of renewable energies for the benefit of the people of Latin America and the whole world.

13.4   Our Relationship with Government

The governmental entity in charge of energy conservation and the promotion of renewable energy applications is the Comisión Nacional para el Ahorro de la Energía (CONAE). This is an agency that was created as an inter-secretarial commission in 1989, with a mandate that was specifically oriented toward energy efficiency and conservation, as M.S. Odón de Buen Rodríguez, former general director of CONAE, said. In 1995 due to the fact that there was no federal agency with a specific mandate on renewable energy, an agreement of its ruling body gave it a mandate to promote renewable energy. In 1996 CONAE, in alliance with ANES, organized a forum to analyze possible common strategies to boost the use of renewable energy, which concluded with the need to create an advisory council.

This council, known today as the Consejo Consultivo para el Fomento de las Energías Renovables (COFER) was created in 1997 and has been organizing open public meetings and press conferences, with support of private and public institutions, where general aspects and policies for renewable-energy promotion have been presented and analyzed.

However, ANES is a nongovernmental organization and with this character it often works against official decisions, when these are aiming at more fossil consumption instead of using renewable energy. Nowadays, about 75% of electricity, and more than 91% of total primary energy come from fossil fuels, despite that of Mexico is the land of the Sun, according to the ancient Anahuac inhabitants.

13.5   Our Most Important Research and Development Results

Being a small Section of ISES in a developing, oil-producer country, where support for research and development is very poor, one would not expect impressive research results. We have a much smaller number of researchers and research teams than other large countries, but we are proud to count with some interesting achievements. Figures 4 to 8 show some of most important results on research, development, and applications of renewable energy in Mexico. More than fourteen MW from small photovoltaic systems have been installed in rural areas in the countryside; the Tolokatsin solar ovens and solar hot plates are extremely efficient and effective. We also have produced important results in materials for solar energy applications, also in fundamentals of photovoltaic cells, and in solar dryers and distillers.

Fig. 4: Solar oven Tolokatsin been demonstrated to solar researchers by Dr. Claudio Estrada at his house in Cuernavaca

About 60 years ago the first commercial flat-plate solar collectors were manufactured in Guadalajara, the second largest Mexican city, by an engineer named Orozco. Some of these relics are still working. Nowadays, there are almost 50 small manufacturers of inexpensive solar flat collectors, but only 500,000 m² have been installed across the country. This is a ridiculous figure because according to ANES more than five million m² of these collectors should be today in operation in Mexico. In spite of this, more than 600,000 fossil-fueled water heaters were installed in 2002, even though there are many initiatives to install solar collectors in new buildings and dwellings. The combined application of solar heaters and solar ovens could help diminish the growing demand of natural and liquefied gas. Fig. 4 shows a photograph of a Tolokatsin solar oven, designed by Eduardo Rincón, been demonstrated to solar researchers by Dr. Claudio Estrada. Fig. 5 shows the Hot Plate Tolokatsin 2, intended for fried meals.

Fig. 5: The novel Hot Plate Tolokatsin 2, intended to fry meals

In 1966 the Centro de Investigación y Estudios Avanzados (CINVESTAV) of the National Polytechnic Institute, began research on semiconductor materials to manufacture solar cells. The first photovoltaic cells manufactured in CINVESTAV were employed in 1967 for meteorological balloons. Between 1979 and 1981 several dozen solar modules built in CINVESTAV were installed in more than 150 rural schools, and some pumping systems have operated successfully employing these arrays. Unfortunately, at the beginning of the neo-liberal federal governments in Mexico, the research on solar applications (and in many other fields of knowledge) was almost disappeared when all funds dedicated to investigation were cut.

A similar sad story is the 10 kW solar platform project of the Autonomous National University of Mexico (UNAM), which started in 1978 with the goal to develop an experimental facility to study electric generation by solar energy concentration, with a field of 550 m^2 of parabolic solar concentrators. Fig. 6 shows a picture of this plant in 1982, when it was ready to operate, and Fig. 7 shows the plant under construction in 1980. This project was one of the most important in the world at that time, and provided very useful experience and knowledge on big solar thermal plants. But the cutting of funds mentioned above impeded us to continue with this development, even though a few researchers still produce interesting new results, but far away from a large-scale industrial application.

Fig. 6: The concentrators of the 10 kW Solar Platform of the UNAM in 1982

Fig. 7: The 10 kW Solar Plant under construction in 1980

Many other interesting research and development results include solar distillers of great section, intended to provide large amounts of distilled marine water. Fig. 8 shows a photograph of a prototype of these distillers. Other interesting examples are the development of several photovoltaic-powered cars that have been designed and manufactured in Mexico. The first one corresponds to Tonatiuh, the "Son of the Sun" solar racing car, which participated in the USA Sunrayce'95, running 1850 km from Indianapolis to Golden, Colorado. In that contest, Tonatiuh won two awards: The Composite Award, given by DuPont, and the Max King Award, given by the race organizers. The second solar car was designed and built by very young students of the Chamizal High School, located in Ciudad Juarez, Chihuahua.

Fig. 8: Experimental solar water-desalination plant with great transversal section area in southern Baja California

Another important project on renewable energy application was carried out by FIRCO, an organism of the secretary of agriculture, with the support of GEF, which consists of the installation of several hundreds of photovoltaic pumping systems. More than 1200 of them were successfully installed in the thirty two federal entities of Mexico, and hundreds of technicians have been trained to operate, maintain and install these systems. The increase in land productivity due to these systems is impressive: they can transform arid or desert lands into very productive sown fields.

Mexico has a potential for electricity generation of more than 50.000 MW from wind with present technology. In the Tehuantepec Isthmus, the assessed potential is greater than 33,000 MW, but only a 1.6 MW small wind plant has been installed there. However, in the near future, at least three big wind farms with the following capacities will be installed: 100 MW for a project of the Federal Electricity Commission—the Mexican electric company—60 MW for the Cruz Azul cement plant enterprise, and a third of 120 MW to supply electricity for municipal lightning in central Mexico. A small part of the technology will be developed locally, and an important R&D Center on Wind Technology is planned to be installed near Juchitán, state of Oaxaca.

Finally, it is worth mentioning that relevant research on chemically-deposited films for solar applications, are conducted at the Center for Energy Research (CIE) of the UNAM and other Mexican institutions.

13.6   The Relationship of ANES with ISES

Formally ANES is the Mexican Section of ISES and as such our members are encouraged to also become full members of ISES. This has been a little bit difficult due to the extremely low incomes of most ANES members. Even though ANES has more than 300 formal members, only 38 are registered as ISES members according to data on Table 2. Thus, only one of each ten members of ANES is registered as a member of ISES. This is a concern, so a campaign to at least double the forgoing figures will be taken by the XIII Consejo Directivo of ANES this year, during the fiftieth anniversary of ISES. Fortunately, the relation between ANES and ISES is quite good; and the board of directors of ISES has authorized that in 2004 the ISES Latin America Regional Conference could be held in Guanajuato, Mexico, from November 8 to 12. Four years ago Mexico City hosted the Millennium Solar Forum, with broad participation of delegates from more than twenty countries. Improving even more that participation is a challenge that ANES has assumed.

Table 2
Membership statistics of the ISES Mexican Section

Membership	Number of Members
Regular Members	30
Senior Members	1
Student Members	1
Silver Members	5
Gold Members	1
Female	6
Male	32
Total Members	**38**

13.7   What Else Is It Worthwhile to Report Here about Our Society?

The Mexican Section of ISES is an active organization with a very low budget but with the willingness of its members to promote the application of solar and other renewable energies for the benefit of everybody, no matter the odds against. There are very high events in solar energy planned to be held in our country, many of those supported by ISES. Also we are tying to build bridges among academia, politicians, and people in general to convince everybody of the environmental, economic, and social benefits that a transition from the present fossil fuel-based world to a sustainable one, based on renewable energy, would bring. We are interested in communicating and sharing our modest experiences and to learn about successful results from all over the world.

Chapter 14

Norwegian Section of the International Solar Energy Society

by
Rolf Jarle Aaberg
Statkraft SF, PB 200 Lilleaker
NO - 0216 Oslo, Norway
Rolf.Jarle.Aaberg@statkraft.no

Abstract

The Norwegian Section of ISES was formally founded in 1981 under the name Solar Energy Association of Scandinavia—Norwegian Group, which later became the Norwegian Solar Energy Society, Norsk solenergiforening. Prior to the foundation of the independent section a few Norwegians were members of the Scandinavian Section founded in 1975. Over the years the membership figures have stabilized at around 100, about fifty being associated ISES members. Ever since its establishment, the Norwegian Section has been the only association for solar energy interests in Norway; thus it has served as the most important network and meeting place for academic and industry professionals in the solar energy field in the country. After more than thirty years of solar energy R&D in Norway, one now observes the growth of viable solar energy companies. Whether the Society as such has played a role in this successful development is hard to tell. Nevertheless, the Norwegian Section and its active members have provided an environment for public awareness and enthusiasm that has facilitated scientific interest and governmental funding in solar technology. In recent years the Norwegian Section has had a new boost in activity and visibility on the national energy policy scene. Being the home Section of Professor Anne Grete Hestnes, the Norwegian Section was proud to be the home Section of the first female president in ISES history when she took office in 2001.

14.1   Background and Foundation

Research and development in solar energy technology in Norway began in the early 1970s. In 1979 the Ministry of Petroleum and Energy formed a committee with the mandate to outline a national research programme in this field. Due to increasing scientific and technological interest in solar energy, many realized the need for a strong professional network, and the idea of an association developed.

The Scandinavian Section of ISES was founded in 1975, with members from Sweden and Denmark and a handful of Norwegians. The name of the Section was Solar Energy Association of Scandinavia, SEAS. The Secretariat was located in Stockholm. After some time, local Sections were set up in both Sweden and Denmark.

In November 1980 a Nordic seminar on "Hot air solar heating systems" was organized in Trondheim, Norway, gathering about 70 participants. A presentation of SEAS was given during the seminar that spurred significant enthusiasm for establishing a local section in Norway as well. Fritjof Salvesen, Harald Røsvik, and Ragnar Evensen were appointed to an interim committee to prepare the founding of a national ISES section.

The interim committee lead by Mr. Salvesen called for a founding meeting, and on the 23 of April 1981, twenty-eight people met in Oslo to accomplish the formal founding of the Solar Energy Association of Scandinavia – Norwegian Group, (SEAS Norge). The first board members in the section were Fritjof Salvesen (chairman); (Engineer, I/S Miljøplan, Sandvika); Øyvind Aschehoug (scientist, SINTEF, Trondheim), and Georg Parmann (journalist, Aftenposten, Oslo), Harald N. Røsvik (architect, own business, Stavanger). Architect Anne Grete Hestnes (SINTEF) was elected financial auditor. The objectives clause in the by-laws mandated that Norsk solenergiforening shall promote the rational use of solar energy in Norway by supporting research, and education, and by raising public awareness.

In November 1981 the Society had about 50 members, and a newsletter service was provided in the yellow pages of the Svensk VVS magazine. The Society had begun to find its profile. Two seminars were organized in the autumn of the founding year, titled "Solar energy in developing countries" and "Power from solar cells," respectively.

14.2   The First 18 years

As defined in the by-laws, SEAS Norge was primarily a network of professionals. The work of the society focused on scientific meetings and seminars. During the second year, five seminars on various issues were held around the country. The level of activity was high, reflecting the enthusiasm and interest related to solar energy in Norway and in the Society at the time. The Society soon became better known, and in 1983 the loudspeaker company SEAS complained about the Society operating under a similar name. To avoid conflict the board decided on a new name, "Norsk solenergiforening," The Norwegian Solar Energy Society.

14.2.1   Conferences and Seminars

The Norwegian Solar Energy Society was very active during its first years in existence. In the '80s and '90s, the Society organized several successful conferences, beginning in 1982 with Solar Energy Day ("Solenergidagen") held in Trondheim. In 1983 the next Solar Energy Days combined an exhibition and a conference in Oslo. About twenty exhibitors participated in the five day event. The exhibition had good visitor numbers and the evening seminar Praktiske råd for solbyggere ("Do-it-yourself solar collector construction") was attended by 100 persons. The following year a lecture series on building technology and solar energy was organized in cooperation with local architect and engineers associations in the cities Bodø, Narvik, Harstad, Tromsø, Alta, and Vadsø.

Over the last few years Solar Energy Day has become an annual tradition in the Norwegian solar community. Typically sixty to ninety persons attended the conferences. This is quite good for Norwegian conditions. The events have resulted in media attention as well as articles in professional periodicals. In addition to Solar Energy Day, the Society has organized several successful half-day seminars at the major universities in Norway. In this way we have reached students and scientists who are shaping the energy future of Norway. The objective is to establish an understanding of and interest in solar energy and the importance of solar energy technology in sustainable development.

Other seminars and conferences of significance were the Nordic Solar Energy Days, organized with Scandinavian SEAS co-operation, and the national conferences on renewable energy, Renewable Energy Forum in 1991, and the Havnaseminaret ("The harbour seminar") in 1996. These conferences gathered an audience from all fields of renewable technology, the Norwegian R&D community, industry, and authorities. In 1992 the international perspective was extended a bit further as the Norwegian Solar Energy Society hosted the North Sun Conference with northern European participants.

From 1994 to 2000 the Norwegian Solar Energy Society organized the national event of SunDay, a pan-European happening to promote public interest in solar and renewable energy. The event was organized as the finale in the educational program SOLIS (Solar energy in schools). An important part of the SOLIS program was to encourage pupils to build their own solar energy devices such as cookers and PV driven vehicles. Pupils from schools across the country met on SunDay to present their work. In 1997 the Solar Energy Society hosted SunDay in association with Oslo Energi ENØK (the information branch of the local utility) at the City Hall Square. The event was a huge success and attracted many visitors. The organizers received the award for the best SunDay event in Europe of 1997. The last SunDay to be held in Norway was in 2000. This SunDay had significant international participation as elementary schools, high schools and universities from Latvia, Finland, the Czech Republic, and Norway attended. After this the SOLIS program was closed. It was decided that the Solar Energy Society would be unable to organize similar events without the support of an external infrastructure, like that of an education program.

Fig. 1: Participants from Czech Republic at SunDay 2000 in Oslo

14.3   Membership

During the first ten years the membership numbers increased to about 100. The economy of the Society was based on membership fees. The income increased steadily and reached a level of about 40–60 000 NOK annually, equivalent to 5–7500 EUR. The Society received public funding related to particular conferences and dissemination projects. In the early '90s the membership numbers increased to 146 (1993). This coincided with a public subsidy and promotion program for solar heating technology, which raised public awareness and interest. However, after the closure of that subsidy program in 1993, the membership slowly dropped back to its previous level, around 100, from 1998 and onwards. About fifty to sixty of the members at any given time are regular members of ISES, while the rest are associated members, which is one of the highest per capita membership ratios of any ISES section. The annual budgets for the Society in this period were typically in the range from 50 to 100 000 NOK and a bit higher when conferences were organized.

14.4   A New Boost in 1999

In 1998 the Norwegian Water and Energy Directorate (NVE) granted financial support, enabling the Society to increase its activity significantly. A secretary general was employed in a part-time position. On 15 April 1999 Dr. Rolf Jarle Aaberg was appointed to the position, which he held until the end of September 2002, when he was succeeded by Dr. Stein Westad Ødegård. Partly due to the NVE grant, the average annual budgets increased substantially, and for the period 1999 to 2002 were on the order of 400,000 NOK, being significantly higher than previous years. This resulted in much more consistent and continuous work by the Society, in particular in the energy policy area.

14.5   Energy Policy

Since 1993 there has not been any national policy to support the introduction of solar energy on the Norwegian market. The reasons for this are many and complex. However, energy saving and renewable energy policy has gone through a major reorganization over the last three years. Because support now seems to be established it is time to start looking at the possibilities for new support mechanisms that can promote solar energy more actively.

Over the last few years, the Solar Energy Society has had several meetings with the Ministry of Petroleum and Energy, including personal meetings with the Minister. We also met with representatives from various members of Parliament to discuss policy measures to promote solar energy and sustainable energy solutions. The Society has also played an active role in several official reference groups, discussing important energy policy issues such as the introduction of green certificates in Norway. It has to be admitted the Society has not yet succeeded in establishing any specific national measures for solar energy. Based on the experience of recent political processes, it is obvious that the Norwegian Solar Energy Society can play a significant role in this area. Although no solar energy support programs are in place at the moment, we have been able to establish a network and a position in the public energy policy debate. Maintaining this position and actively promoting policies targeting the specific needs of solar technologies would hopefully result in the establishment of efficient support actions in the future.

Fig. 2: Since production started in 1997 the company ScanWafer AS in northern Norway has become the largest independent multi-crystalline wafer producer in the world.

14.5.1   Solar Energy Dissemination

A major contribution to the dissemination of solar energy information is of course the seminars and workshops. In addition to this the main channel toward the public is our web site at www.solenergi.no. When searching for the keyword "solenergi" at a Norwegian internet search engine, the home page of the Norwegian Solar Energy Society is likely to pop up on top of the result list. It is known that a great number of students and pupils contact us at the home page and use it for reference when preparing assignments on renewable and solar energy. We also receive a number of e-mails from organizations and individuals with specific questions or interests in solar energy.

Since appointing a secretary general, the Society has been able to distribute a bi-monthly newsletter named Solgløtt. Each issue contains two to five pages of relevant local and international information. The newsletter is distributed to every member in paper or electronic format, as well as to a number of authority and media representatives.

The work of the Norwegian Solar Energy Society has resulted in a number of attractive reports in newspapers and radio, where both the Society and its members have been able to present themselves and their activities.

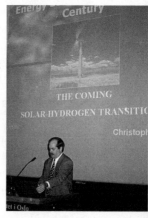

Fig. 3: Christopher Flavin of Worldwatch Institute speaking at the ISREE 7 symposium in Oslo, June 2000

14.6   The People

In any association there are always some people who are more active and enthusiastic than other members. It is of course the case in the Norwegian Solar Energy Society, too, but when asked to name those who really made a great difference it is difficult to define the criteria and find the people who played that special role. The author would nevertheless like to name three persons that have contributed to the life and success of the society in a special way. First of all there is Professor Anne Grete Hestnes, a founding member and member of the first board. Her enthusiasm and contributions through hard work has been a pillar in the life of the society from the beginning to the present day. She has been an active member of the board and chairwoman for many consecutive periods, and she has served as a significant link between the national section and the International Solar Energy Society, first as a member of the board of directors for several years and later as a member of the executive committee. In 2000 she was elected president of ISES and when she took office in 2001 she was the first female president in ISES history.

There are also a couple of other people who have been of particular importance due to their commitment and stamina. Another founding member who has followed the Norwegian Solar Energy Society since its birth, or even before that, is the first chairman Fritjof Salvesen. He served as chairman until 1986 in the very active first years of the Society, and in all the years after he has followed the Society both as a member of the board and later as internal auditor. Another prominent person in the life of the society would be Karl Torstein Hetland. He was a driving force in the SOLIS program and contributed to the introduction of solar energy education in Norwegian schools. The successful SOLIS initiative was a significant partnership for the Norwegian Section for many years in the '90s and an important channel to raise awareness among young people. Mr Hetland was chairman of the board during the "new boost" years, and his efforts have made a great contribution to the profile and visibility of the Society over the last years.

Fig. 4: Anne Grete Hestnes the first female president of ISES

14.7   Present Strategy and Future

The present strategy outlines three areas of importance for the Norwegian Solar Energy Society. These are energy policy, business policy, and education and information dissemination. Business policy is somewhat related to energy policy but also toward supporting research policies and various aid programs for developing countries. Currently, the activities in this field are limited.

Ever since the founding of the Society in 1981, there has been strong emphasis on supporting education and information dissemination. The plans at present are to continue developing the main tools in this work such as the seminars and workshops, the newsletter Solgløtt, the web page, and various targeted information projects.

At the time of writing (2003), the situation has been rather difficult due to very unstable financial circumstances, which occurred when some anticipated public funding was withdrawn. After negotiations, it seems as if the Society has obtained some funding after all and can continue its development as a network of competence in solar energy and sustainable development. Nevertheless, the challenges for solar energy development in Norway are significant, and the role at the Norwegian Solar Energy Society is as important as ever.

Fig. 5: The first active solar heated home in Norway, built in 1976 (still in operation) was based on technology developed at the University of Oslo. Since then this development has produced several viable companies involved in solar heating systems

Acknowledgement

The author is grateful for the contributions and documentation provided by Mr. Fritjof Salvesen.

Chapter 15

History of Solar Energy Development in Pakistan

by
Prof. D. Nasim A. Khan
Member Technical Secretary, Alternative Energy Development Board
344-B, Prime Minister's Secretariat, Islamabad
Director, Solar Systems Laboratory, Rawalpindi, Pakistan
Chairman ISES Pakistan Chapter
Tel: 92519223427 Fax: 92519223427,
e-mail: isesps_pk@yahoo.com

Abstract

Pakistan is amongst those countries that receive a very high intensity of solar radiation. Development of solar energy in Pakistan was initially based on the sporadic efforts of a few selected engineers and scientists at universities and research centres. This was followed by initiatives of some enthusiasts in selected government agencies that simultaneously resulted in new organizations in relevant ministries. Originally the Pakistan Atomic Energy Commission initiated projects in solar energy but this effort was soon transferred to other ministries. They include Solar Energy Research Centre under the Pakistan Council for Scientific and Industrial Research in the Ministry of Science and Technology; Appropriate Technology Development Organization (ATDO) in the Ministry of Science and Technology; a Directorate of Renewable Energy Resources (DGER) in the Ministry of Petroleum and Natural Resources; and a Directorate of Renewable Energy under the Water and Power Development Authority (WAPDA) in the Ministry of Water and Power. ATDO was later upgraded and renamed as the Pakistan Council for Appropriate Technology (PCAT). A new organization, the National Institute of Silicon Technology, was also created in the Ministry of Science and Technology to develop solar cell manufacturing. All organizations under the Ministry of Science and Technology were later merged into Pakistan Council for Renewable Energy Technology (PCRET), while DGER and the Renewable Energy Directorate under WAPDA were closed.

The initial efforts were led by scientists like Dr. Jamil Ahmad Khan, Dr. I. H. Usmani, Prof. Dr. M. Ikram Khan, Agha Hassan Abidi, Prof. Iqbal Hussain, Dr. Atiq Mufti, Dr. A. A. Junejo, Dr. Wajahat Hussain, Prof. S. H. Shah, Mr. Sohail Qureshi, M. H. Masud Butt. This was followed by a wave of comparatively younger scientists including Mr. Ajmal, Dr. Parvez Akhter, Mr. Tajjamul Hassan, Dr. A. Qayyum Qureshi, Dr. Z.I.Zaidi, Dr. I. Qazi, Mr. Shehyar Khan, Mr. Memon, Mr. Sarhandi, Mr. Asim Siddiqi, Mr. Rafiq Ghoto, Dr. Nazimuddin, Mr. Sarfraz Khan, Mr. T. Sheikh, and the author of this history, Dr. Nasim A. Khan.

15.1   Solar Energy Technology Development Organizations

The Directorate General of Renewable Energy Resources under the Ministry of Petroleum and Natural Resources took the initial step and planned to install village-level PV solar stations in 18 villages all over the country, as shown in Fig. 1. This was a big stride, and systems in all villages were successfully installed and started operation. The entire program was spear headed by Mr. Sohail Qureshi, but this effort was jolted by temporary closure of the department. Technical support to all the solar villages could not continue, which resulted in shutting down all the plants. These solar villages were located in remote areas of the country and in some places it was anticipated that grid connection would be reached in 10-15 years time in these areas. This also had the associated problem that in these areas the technicians were hesitant to stay or even visit. Lack of technical support, resistance from local residents, lack of maintenance by consumers, and closure by the department all led to failure of this very nicely executed project.

Fig. 1a, b, c, d, e: Several solar-lit villages in different parts of the country and a small wind turbine established by the Directorate of New and Renewable Energy Resources during the '80s

The Solar Energy Research Centre (SERC) of PCSIR under the Ministry of Science and Technology conducts research and development in solar thermal energy technology as shown in Fig. 2. SERC developed a solar desalination plant at Gawadar, Balochistan, with a capacity of 6,000 gallons per day output. It was a successful project that ended up in failure due to lack of support and further follow-up action. Dr. Wajahat was leading these research and development activities.

Fig. 2a, b: Solar Energy Research Centre of Pakistan Council for Scientific and Industrial Research at Hyderabad, Pakistan, and 6,000 gallons/day seawater solar desalination plant built by them at Gawadar, Balochistan

The Appropriate Technology Development Organization (ATDO) that was later changed to Pakistan Council for Appropriate Technology (PCAT) assumed charge in low-tech solar appliances like solar cookers, biogas digesters and micro hydro power plants, as shown in Fig. 3. Dr. A. A. Junejo, Mr. Shah, Mr. Majeed, and Mr. Shehryar made a decent contribution in these fields. It had an initial success in all fields, especially biogas digesters, with the help of Chinese technology, but the effort starved due to lack of continued government support and failure of some initial projects.

Fig. 3a, b: Biogas plants and micro hydro power plants built under the supervision of the Pakistan Council for Appropriate Technology

The National Institute of Silicon Technology (NIST) that was later renamed as the Pakistan Council for Renewable Energy Technology (PCRET), as shown in Fig. 4, assumed responsibility for solar energy promotion in Pakistan in a big way and became Solar Energy Technology Centre for SAARC and the Islamic World, and the only body in Pakistan to have international linkages in this technology. The main role of NIST was to promote solar cells manufacture in Pakistan and transfer of technology to manufacturers to reduce the cost of solar cells. It was unable to do both missions; however, it initiated good international seminars and R&D activities mainly concentrated on PV technology. This effort was spearheaded by Dr. Atiq Mufti. Several years of inaction shattered the confidence of decision makers in the country, who developed the misconception that solar energy is very costly and cannot be developed indigenously. Other lobbies were also very strong that ensured lack of investment in solar technology. The problem was aggravated due to the absence of a central body in solar/renewable energy technologies. Most of the technologists and researchers also got discouraged and changed their profession due to lack of government support. The merger of PCAT and NIST into PCRET has resulted in reduced effort in the manufacture of solar cells, despite the fact that all the equipment held in the organization is for fabrication of solar cells and modules. However, biogas digesters are being installed on a larger scale as compared to the previous state.

Fig. 4a, b: National Institute of Silicon technology, now Pakistan Council for Appropriate Technology, Islamabad, along with solar modules installed in a restaurant in Islamabad

No international society related to ISES was formed in solar energy to develop collaboration amongst scientists and engineers working in renewable energy. Individuals became members of international societies but could not continue due to unaffordable membership costs and lack of government initiatives. The Pakistan Chapter of the International Solar Energy Society was created in 1997 and since then a lot of effort has been put into developing consensus in decision makers to enact favorable policies, promote use of solar energy in villages and towns, develop low-cost products, disseminate information on solar energy, develop human resources, publish solar technology books, extract from international activities/experiences, and develop manufacturers, financiers, and market acceptance among the masses.

During the period before formation of the ISES Chapter a lot of technology demonstration initiatives, with the help of national and international and UN bodies, resulted in good progress, but the momentum died down due to lack of continued government support and incoherent policies. During this time, solar radiation data were collected and compiled as shown in Fig. 5.

Fig. 5: Solar radiation data compiled for all parts of the country.
Source: Khan, N. A. Solar Energy Guide and Data Book for Pakistan, EME College, Pakistan

Countries like Pakistan have a majority of their population that cannot afford to experiment on new technologies because of the costs involved. They are completely dependant on the government to provide them with energy solutions. The existing infrastructure of energy provision in Pakistan is city-biased, and most of the power generated is consumed in major city centers. The energy source used in households is based on natural gas that will remain available for the next decade at quite low rates.

15.2   Solar Culture Development (ISES-Pakistan Chapter History)

Solar energy development in Pakistan lacked the missionary zeal and requisite organization to produce positive results. The establishment of the Pakistan Chapter of the International Solar Energy Society was followed by planning a few sets of activities during a series of meetings, as shown in Fig. 6, to ensure long-lasting development of a solar culture.

Fig 6: Meeting of members and supporters of
solar energy at the College of EME,
Peshawar Road, Rawalpindi

15.2.1   Awareness in Decision-Making Circles

Awareness had to be awakened in the intelligentsia, bureaucracy, decision-makers, and the masses, and was conducted with the help of demonstrations, visiting lectures, seminars, workshops, and confidence-building measures. These were conducted all over Pakistan on personal invitations and official levels. Thousands of people have been shown the utility of solar and wind-energy-operated products in collaboration with private NGOs, semi-government, and government and international organizations that include the National University of Sciences and Technology, the Commission for Science and Technology (COMSATS), the OIC Commission for Science and Technology, COMSTECH, Pakistan Science Foundation, NICELINK Education Trust, SZABIST University, the Sustainable Development Policy Institute, the Ministry of Culture, the Ministry of Defense, the Ministry of Petroleum and Natural Resources, Forest Departments of various provinces, Provincial Governments, and Ministry of Science and Technology. Based on these efforts the year 1997 was declared as the year of Solar Energy in the Pakistan Army and the year 2002 was declared as The Year of Solar Energy by the Ministry of Science and Technology. The Prime Minister of Pakistan has declared the year 2003/4 as the year for Alternative/Renewable Energy.

The project was initiated at the grassroots level with the general population and students. This was later shifted to bureaucracy and decision makers, and subsequently the project is being implemented at the national level of policy making. Thousands of consumers have been motivated to shift to renewable energy resources. To meet their demands, around 50 investors were mobilized to convert products into mass manufacturing with adequate government support.

Heads of State like President Farooq Ahmed Khan Leghari (Fig. 7), Prime Minister Muhammad Khan Junejo, President General Pervez Musharraf (Fig. 8), the governor of Balochistan (Fig. 9), Prof. Dr. Atta-Ur-Rahman, the Minister of Science and Technology (Fig. 10), and Prime

Minister Mir Zaffarullah Khan Jamali (Fig. 11), have all been persuaded to support and adopt renewable energy friendly policies. Ministers and Secretaries responsible for introduction of renewable energy technologies in Pakistan include Syeda Abida Hussain, Lt. Gen. (Ret.) Qazi Javed Ashraf, and the chairman of the Planning Commission, have also been educated to become advocates of renewable energy technologies.

Fig. 7: President being shown the operation of a solar steam generator

Fig. 8: President along with other army general staff being briefed on solar products

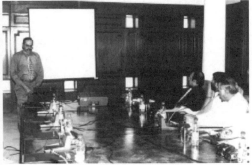

Fig. 9: The goverernor of Balochistan being briefed on solar energy

Fig. 10: Minister for S&T being shown the operation of a wind generator

Fig. 11: Prime Minister Jamali being given a demonstration of solar energy products

15.2.2   Technology Development and Demonstration with ISES Assistance

Solar Products Development. To ensure providing renewable energy products at affordable prices the use of indigenous material is an essential ingredient. Local vendors, students and manufacturers have developed the following products indigenously based on the low-cost designs provided to them and shown in Figs. 12 to 16.

- Solar Cooker Box Type
- Solar Cooker Concentrating Type
- Solar still/Desalination Plant
- Solar Cell Manufacturing Machine
- Solar Tent
- Field Solar Shower
- Solar Heat Resisting Roof Tiles
- Solar Stirling Engine
- Passive Solar Heated House
- Passive Solar Heated Hospital
- Solar Shower

- Solar Room Air Heater
- Solar Steam Generation System
- Dish Parabolic Mirror Fabrication System
- Components of PV Lighting System including charge controllers, inverters, AC/DC lights, repair of solar cells etc.
- Design and Development of Evacuated Heat Pipe for water heating and steam generation

- Solar Water Pumping
- Solar Geyser of a variety of materials
- Solar De-hydrators

- Wind Turbine Blades (small size)
- Wind Turbine Generation System (small)

Fig. 12a, b: Solar passive house with Trombe wall at Solar System Lab, College of EME, Peshawar Road, Rawalpindi, which acts as ISES' Pakistan Section

Fig. 13a, b, c: Solar geyser manufacture and installation in Pakistan

Fig. 14a, b, c: Experimental solar thermal power plant at the Solar Systems Lab, College of EME, Peshawar Road, Rawalpindi, Pakistan

Fig. 15a, b, c: Stirling engine, solar cells, and solar heat resisting roof tiles designed and manufactured by members of ISES Pakistan

Fig. 16a, b, c: Solar box cooker, solar concentrating cookers, and solar tent designed and manufactured by members of ISES Pakistan

Product Display/Demonstration/Installation. Most of the products developed by selected members of ISES-Pakistan have been installed at different sites around the country. There was lack of confidence in solar energy systems, so it was decided to develop confidence-building measures, and installation of a series of solar-lit parks was initiated. At this time solar-lit parks (Fig. 17) have been installed at Rawalpindi/Islamabad, Peshawar, Bahawalpur, Karachi, and Manser, The installations in these parks have resulted in building the confidence of consumers and technologists. Student members were encouraged to develop solar electric cars as shown in Fig. 18 and a water pump for irrigating fields during sunny hours only was also installed as shown in Fig. 18. A solution to provide clean drinking water at places where only brackish water is available was also proposed in the form of vertical solar desalinator as shown in Fig. 19. Wind turbine development in the world has also been closely studied by our students and a set of wind turbines was developed and installed at the Karachi coast as shown in Fig. 19.

Fig. 17a, b, c: First solar lit park in Rawalpindi, Gilgit, and its light during the night

Fig.18a, b, c: Solar lighting system at a public park, solar car, and solar water pumping station

Fig. 19a, b, c: Solar vertical desalination system and micro wind turbines

Water heating at remote locations was also demonstrated with indigenous designs installed in remote locations of Pakistan as shown in Fig. 20 that are performing satisfactorily. A hospital is also being heated with solar heated air and energy stored in a Trombe wall in a solar wall facing south, as shown in Fig. 21.

Fig. 20a, b, c: Solar water geysers installed at different localities in Pakistan

Fig. 21a, b, c: Solar hospital heating system in northern areas of Pakistan

15.2.3   Human Resource Development/Products Dissemination

To ensure development of adequately qualified manpower, a curriculum was developed for undergraduate engineering, and a book, *Energy Resources and Utilization*, was written and introduced by the author. This book has been followed to train 400 engineers under direct supervision of the author. Books for introduction of fresh minds at school grades six and seven on solar and wind energy have also been written and are in the stage of introduction in various schools. The book on solar energy has already won first prize from the National Book Foundation of Pakistan in the year 2002. More than forty-five projects have been developed by undergraduate students, including a solar car.

A series of presentations and demonstrations were made in the cities, towns, hill stations, and villages listed below during the extensive Solar Culture development initiative. Most of the activities were initiated without any government support, and a large number of personal contacts were used to even make presentations at hotels and government departments.

1.	Karachi	16.	Gilgit
2.	Lahore	17.	Khaplu
3.	Hyderabad	18.	Dansum
4.	Islamabad	19.	Manser
5.	Rawalpindi	20.	Vinjore
6.	Bahawalpur	21.	Paiju
7.	Multan	22.	Muree
8.	Gilgit	23.	Gultari
9.	Quetta	24.	Kel
10.	Awaran	25.	Plundri
11.	Taftan	26.	Jambar
12.	Chor	27.	Ziarat
13.	Ranak dhar	28.	Gharo
14.	Goma	29.	Pind Dadan Khan
15.	Skardu	30.	Uran Kel

Chapter 16

SPES—
Sociedade Portuguesa de Energia Solar—
Portuguese Section of the
International Solar Energy Society

by
J. Farinha Mendes and M. João Carvalho
INETI - Department of Renewable Energies
Estrada do Paço do Lumiar, 1649-038 Lisboa, Portugal
farinha.mendes@ineti.pt

Abstract

This is an overview of the most relevant activities of SPES—Sociedade Portuguesa de Energia Solar, the Portuguese Section of ISES, during the last two decades from the day it was born in December 1980. It has featured a very intensive solar energy promotional activity, which up to now used almost all available tools, including organization and participation in Congresses, conferences, seminars, and workshops; publication of a periodic magazine, newsletters, press releases, books, brochures, posters, and other dissemination papers; participation in national and international projects for dissemination of solar energy applications; creation and maintenance of a web site; the annual celebration of SunDay and so on. Unfortunately, these activities had no direct correspondence with the Portuguese market for solar collectors, which did not grow accordingly. Reasons for this discrepancy, proposed measures to overcome it, and perspectives for our section are also discussed in this review.

16.1   Introduction: A Brief Historical Overview of Solar Energy in Our Country and the First Steps Leading to the Creation of the Solar Energy Society

Almost one century before the oil crisis of 1973, the Portuguese scientist, Father Manoel Antonio Gomes, knicknamed Father Himalaya because of his tall stature, devoted a part of his life to the research and developement of solar energy devices, inventing a number of highly innovative solar concentrators and ending up getting the Grand Prix at the 1904 Universal Exposition in St. Louis, USA, with his Pyrheliophoro (Fig. 1). This was a solar furnace, with which he claimed to have reached, on three very bright days, 3,800° C. For it, he planned a number of applications, like the production of drinkable water in desert places, the production of steam, steam for industrial machines, melting refractory materials, and the production of nitrate fertilizers, through the oxidation of nitrogen existing in the air at the very high temperatures produced in the furnace! [1].

Fig. 1a, b: Father Himalaya (above) and the Pyrheliophoro (below) that won the St. Louis Grand Prix (1904)

Father Himalaya was a visionary who, in many ways, was 100 years ahead of his time. His inventions and writings were abandoned for almost one century, but the importance of his work has a planetary magnitude, as can also be seen in [2]. For us he is like the grand-father of solar energy studies and applications in Portugal.

In more recent times there was a noticeable increase in research for solar thermal apllications, in particular during the '60s, carried out at a state laboratory in Lisbon, LNEC [3], through projects on solar drying, solar dessalination, solar cooling, and solar cooking, which led to the construction of prototypes in those areas (see Fig. 2) and studies of bioclimatic architecture. This work was connected initially to the Ph.D. thesis of our member Salgado Prata, integrated in the dams team, but no research policy in this field, governmental or otherwise, was implemented at the time, and so the work continued for some time, but stopped in 1966.

Also in the '60s, in sync with Israel's policy for the widespread use of solar energy thermal applications, the first Portuguese company commercializing solar thermal collectors [4] imported from that country began its operation and installed the first solar system in Lisbon. It was possible to document that some of those first systems were still in operation in the '80s and this company is still in operation today.

The '70s in Portugal, as in many other countries of the world, saw more serious attention being paid to solar energy. Our country has always been one of the most energy-dependent countries in the OCDE, and 1973's oil crisis had a real impact in all economic sectors in Portugal. The adhesion of Portugal to IEA was immediate, and a new beginning of solar research took place in another state laboratory, through the effort and personal interest of scientists and engineers working in the Mechanical Test Laboratory (LEM) of the General Directorate of Combustibles [5].

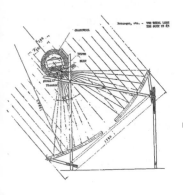

Fig. 2a, b: Parabolic solar cooker (on the left) and solar dryer prototypes (on the right), Salgado Prata, LNEC (1963)

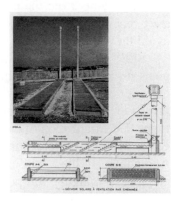

In 1974, a very important change in the political situation occurred, with the ouster of the dictatorial regime by the April Revolution and the implementation of a democratic regime (1976), after a transition period (1974-1975) overseen by the Army. The impact in all activities was enormous, mainly because democracy opened new doors to the public discussion of political, social, economic, cultural, and scientific issues. Energy dependence was among those discussions, in parallel with a more technical/scientific planning for energy policies. The debate around the nuclear energy solution was a central debate at the end of the' 70s as well as discussions related to environmental issues.

The scientists and engineers initiating solar energy work at LEM, university researchers, and other technicians participating actively in energy planning, and colleagues who got their high-level education abroad (in particular in the U.S.A), had the opportunity to participate in those public discussions about the energy future of Portugal, in seminars, workshops, congresses and press articles – where the important solar resource we have (Fig. 3) at the European level, was always stressed in opposition to the lack of fossil fuel energy. By this process a kind of mutual knowledge started to be gathered and it was, in fact, a contribution to the origin of our Society (SPES), created in December 1980.

During the twenty-four years of its existence, SPES has lived through the different phases of exaggerated claims and enthusiasm followed by disbelief and even discredit in solar energy and other renewable energy in Portugal. The origin of these cycles were economic, financial, and political reasons as well as technical ones, which are well-known and common to similar instances in other countries. A good systematic analysis of those cycles was presented in the Forum das Energias Renováveis 2001 [6], which gathered all relevant partners in the renewable energy area and identified the more important constraints from the past. The point is that the renewed effort to jump-start renewable energy, and in particular solar energy in Portugal, should avoid the same pitfalls.

SPES had a prominent role in that Forum, as it was fully in line with its goals for the use of renewable energy in Portugal. From SPES' point of view there is no question about the benefits: i) to the environment, ii) to the reduction of external energy dependency, iii) to the increase of energy security, iv) to the decentralization of energy production and v) to the development of the economy, with the creation of thousands of new jobs, export capacity, etc. And above all, there will not be sustainable development without renewable energy assuming the full potential of its contribution.

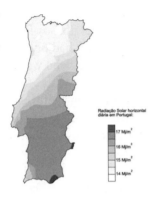 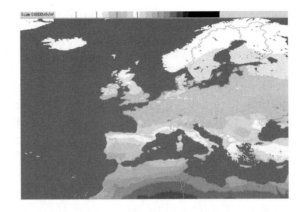

Fig. 3a, b: Solar radiation map of Portugal (on the left) and Europe (on the right)

16.2   Founding, By-Laws and First Members of SPES

The Portuguese Solar Energy Society (SPES) was formed in the beginning of the '80s by a group of people interested in the development of solar energy and other renewable energy sources. These people represented different sectors of activity, including researchers, investors and other people interested in renewable energy—technicians, economists and others.

The legal creation of SPES as a non-profit organization and adoption of its by-laws was done in 1980, on December18, in the eighth Notarial Office of Lisbon. The legal paper was signed by the 1st, 2nd, and 5th members representing the first ten members of SPES:

1. Manuel Collares Pereira
2. Jorge Cruz Costa
3. Humberto Duarte da Fonseca
4. Eurico da Fonseca
5. António de Melo Queiróz
6. Sidónio Paes
7. Armando Viana da Rocha
8. Antonio Xavier
9. António Adragão
10. Antonio Forjó

The first two persons on this list had the leading role bringing together the rest of the group: Prof. Manuel Collares-Pereira (Fig. 5), had just arrived from the University of Chicago, where he had participated in the first phase of CPC type optics development and its application to solar energy, and had obtained his Ph.D. under Prof. Roland Winston and Dr. Jorge Cruz Costa, who was the leader of the team that initiated the first experiments in Portugal within LEM, the public research institute where the first solar collectors testing-facility was built. Prof. Collares-Pereira, was a member of the American Section of ISES and introduced it to the rest of the group, orienting them to the idea that the new society should, from the start, be a member of ISES.

On 20 November 1996, in the official journal, *Diario da República (II Série) nº269*, SPES was officially recognized as a non-profit organization with the Public Utility, which gave it an important statute, simplifying its administration and providing tax exemptions, which were important for its development.

The by-laws of SPES establish as a major objective for the Society:

"to join, to inform, to promote and to develop the efforts of those that, interested in the future, are worried about the energy problem and specially, interested in solar energy, which is the origin of all other energy sources. The evolution of Mankind is deeply dependent on several sources of energy discovered and used up in succession. The energy problem, which constitutes a principal problem for Mankind, brings to the foreground an urgent necessity to adopt renewable energy sources, more immediately dependent on the Sun."

One of the first paragraphs also establishes the connection between SPES and ISES, recognizing the important role of ISES at the global scale and the contribution of SPES at our national scale:

"On the global scale there are institutions devoted to the promotion and valorization of these (renewable) sources of energy, that do not damage quality of life and contribute to the reduction of air pollution. It is the case of ISES—the International Solar Energy Society Incorporated, which has National Sections in several countries in the World. Through the creation of SPES it is expected that Portugal—a country with almost no conventional energy sources and with a great potential for renewable energy sources (sun, biomass, wind and ocean)—will benefit as soon as possible from the use of these energy resources, associating all those that are interested in them, increasing their number and their enthusiasm by the promotion of activities, information, dissemination, exchange of knowledge and affiliation in the international entities with the same task."

Fig. 4: Logo of SPES adopted from the logo of the 2nd Solar Energy Iberian Congress

During the first years of SPES there was strong support for its activities from the Gulbenkian Foundation, as well as from the Directorate General for Energy, whose director at the time, Eng.° Sidóneo Paes, was one of the founders of SPES. At that time, two oil companies (Petrogal and Shell) had already created their own solar collector companies/departments to look into the possibilities behind the solar business, and thus also got interested in SPES. From them came two of our founders, the seventh affiliate, Eng° Viana da Rocha (Shell), and the ninth affiliate of SPES, Eng° Antonio Adragão (Petrogal), who gave strong support to SPES activity for the first fifteen years.

Another name deserving specific mention, given his enthusiasm and dedication to the objectives of the Society is that of Eurico da Fonseca, unfortunately he is no longer with us.

It is also important to mention Prof. Eduardo Oliveira Fernandes (Fig. 5) as an important member of SPES, not only because of his work for SPES but also for ISES, where he occupied the vice-presidency in '92–'93 and the presidency in '96–'97. In Portugal we have to stress his work as Secretary of State of Environment, in 1977, and Deputy Minister of Economy, in 2001–2002, where he was the driving force behind the creation, for the first time in Portugal, of a general policy on energy, the so called E4 Program—Energy Efficiency and Endogenous Energy—in which a central role was given to the rational use of energy and to renewable energy, a basis for the present energy policy in this area.

Fig. 5: Prof. Oliveira Fernandes, President Jorge Sampaio, and Prof. Collares Pereira (from left to the right in first line) visiting the Technological Fair of Solar Equipment in Vilamoura during the Iberian and Iberoamerican Solar Energy Congress (CIES2002)

SPES now has more than 1,000 regular members, but also created the category of Honorary Member. At present, two members have that distinction: Prof. Franklin Guerra, who was also one of the founders and unfortunately, is no longer with us, was instrumental in founding the first regional section of SPES in the north of Portugal, SPES Norte, located in Porto, and Dr. Jorge Sampaio, the president of the Republic of Portugal for the period 1996-2006 and member number 1,000 of SPES. Dr. Sampaio's Honorary Member Diploma was given to him in September 2003 during an audience conceded to the board of directors of SPES in his presidential palace in Belem, Lisbon (Fig. 6).

In fact, in 2002, the board of directors of SPES invited the Portuguese President, Dr. Jorge Sampaio, to become its 1,000th member. He accepted, and this membership was publicly announced in his presence during the opening session of CIES2002, the XI Iberian Solar Energy Congress, September 2002 (Fig. 8), giving great visibility to renewable energy through the media present at the Congress. Since then, and already on several public occasions when he has the opportunity, Dr. Sampaio continues to talk about the necessity to enhance the role of renewable energy, which truly helps provide impact to the message of SPES.

To summarize, it is fair to say that among the members of SPES since the time of its founding, are the most relevant people in the field of solar energy and renewable energy in Portugal, including businessmen, researchers, professors, engineers, architects, and politicians—and, following the market growth, a number of companies and individuals.

Fig. 6: Honorary Member Diploma given to Dr. Jorge Sampaio in September 2003 by members of the Board of Directors of SPES. From left to the right – Eng. João Saraiva, member of SPES; Dr. Pedro Sassetti Paes, vice president of the board of directors; Dr. Nuno Ribeiro da Silva, vice president of the General Assembly; Eng. João Farinha Mendes, president of the board of directors; Dr. Jorge Sampaio, President of the Portuguese Republic; Dr. Adelino de Souza, president of the fiscal council; Dr. Hélder Gonçalves, former president of the board of directors.

16.3 General Operation, Board of Directors, and Regional Sections

SPES is an association, that every two years elects a board of directors with seven members, including a president, a vice president, a secretary, and a treasurer. The election takes place during the General Assembly, which is led by a president, a vice president and a secretary. The third body of SPES is the Fiscal Council also composed of three members.

During the last (almost) 24 years, corresponding to the lifetime of SPES, there were ten elections, and the number of persons who served in at least one of those bodies is now up to 130. The list of Board of Director's Presidents of SPES, follows:

Manuel Collares Pereira	April '81 – March '83
Manuel Collares Pereira	March '83 – March '85

Jorge Cruz Costa	March '85 – June '88
Manuel Collares Pereira	June '88 – July '90
Jorge Cruz Costa	July '90 – April '94
Manuel Gonçalves Santos	April '94 – May '96
Helder Perdigão Gonçalves	May '96 – October '98
Helder Perdigão Gonçalves	October '98 – January '01
João Farinha Mendes	January '01 – January '03
João Farinha Mendes	January '03 – January '05

Since April 1981, when the General Assembly took place for the first time, there have been thirty-two General Assemblies. The last one took place in March 2004.

It must be stressed that participation in the social bodies of this society, has always been a voluntary one, and its most important activities have been possible with the dedication, not only of those directly involved in social bodies of SPES, but also with that of a great number of interested members, providing work and expertise in a voluntary manner when requested by the Society.

SPES was constituted in Lisbon, but during its first Assembly there was a proposal for the constitution of a Regional Section in Porto, where there was also a strong interest in solar energy, from researchers of the faculty of engineering, architects, and local companies.

Members of SPES pay a small annual fee, presently 25.00 Euros for individuals and 125.00 Euros for companies and institutions, receiving the two annual issues of our journal, without any other payment.

16.4   SPES: Activities Between 1980 - 2004

16.4.1   SPES Journal

Since the first years of the Portuguese Society, one of the objectives was to have a journal that would be distributed to the members but should also be a form of dissemination of RE among other people, namely schools and at selected events (Fig. 7).

This journal had its first issue in March 1983 and the title was "Journal of Solar Energy and Biogas" (*Revista de Energia Solar e Biogas*), being published four times per year during the first years. The periodicity changed over time because it was not possible to keep it due to financial reasons. The contents were a mixture of technical, scientific, and press news related to RE.

In 1994 the name of the journal changed, after the 34th issue, to: "Solar Energy. Renewable Energy and Environment Journal" (*Energia Solar. Revista de Energias Renováveis & Ambiente*) and in the second half of the '90s, its was published two times per year. There was also a shift in contents associated with the participation of SPES in several national and international promotion and dissemination projects, sponsoring the publication of the journal and demanding the publication of dedicated issues to topics under contract, which nevertheless, never ceased to be within the framework of SPES as defined in its by-laws.

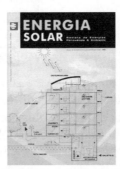

Fig. 7: The front cover of some of the fifty-two issues already published. Although it has been a difficult task to maintain its publication with regular periodicity, fifty-two issues have nevertheless been published. An archive of all of them is available in SPES installations, which can be consulted by anyone interested in it. Some of those issues are also available for purchase.

Information about the journal can also be obtained on the web page of SPES—www.spes.pt—where the front cover of the different issues, the index of each one, the list of authors indicating the name of the article and number of the corresponding issue, and also a list of subject matter are available. Subjects are listed in the following way:

- Biomass
- Biogas
- Wind
- PV

- Solar Thermal
- Geothermal
- Ocean
- Mini-hydro

- Renewable Energy
- Energy Prices
- SPES
- Others

16.4.2   Iberian and Iberoamerican Solar Energy Congress

Since the beginning it was perceived as very important to provide a forum for researchers in the Iberian Peninsula to meet, exchange ideas and publish their results. Thus was born the idea of organizing Iberian Congresses. It is perhaps fair to say that, without them, not so many and such good groups would have developed and matured in both Portugal and Spain.

Fig. 8: Opening ceremony of CIES2002 during the speech of the President of the Portuguese Republic, Dr. Jorge Sampaio (on the right)

Thus, Iberian congresses were some of the first events organized by the Portuguese and Spanish sections of ISES. The first one took place in Madrid in 1982 and the proceedings of this congress had an impressive 119 communications in different fields of renewable energy.

The Iberian congress takes place every two years (even years alternating with the World ISES congresses), being organized, alternatively, by the Portuguese and Spanish sections.

After the third Iberian Congress it was agreed with most similar Latin American societies to extend it to their participation. This third congress was then the 1st IberoAmerican Congress on Solar Energy. The relationship continued and some of the following congresses were also Iberoamerican ones. The last one was organized in Vilamoura in the south of Portugal and was the eleventh Iberian and sixth Iberoamerican Congress (CIES2002). Its theme was: "Sun, Energy and Life" ("Sol, Energia e Vida").

Fig. 9: Front cover of some Proceedings of the Iberian and Iberoamerican Solar Energy Congresses

It was an important moment for promotion of solar energy and other renewable energy sources in Portugal, because the President of the Republic decided to accept the invitation to come for the opening ceremony (Fig. 7). In his speech he presented his view for our future, which must be envisaged in the framework of "Sustainable Development," stressing the role of solar and all renewable energy. He also visited the exhibition of solar equipment that was simultaneously organized by SPES (Fig. 5). The event was widely announced in the different media and coincided with the launching of the solar thermal part of the E4 Program already referred to above, called "*Solar Hot Water Program for Portugal.*"

It is fair to say that since then more media attention is being dedicated each day to the topic of renewable energies.

In Fig. 9, the front cover of some Proceedings of the Iberian and Iberoamerican Solar Energy Congresses are shown, and in Table 1, locations, dates, and other relevant data related to the organization of the Congresses, is presented. As can be seen by the number of communications, those congresses had large participation, especially if we take into account the regional level and the financial difficulties for the participation of people coming from Latin American countries.

Related to the Congresses the important role of the CYTED Program,— *Programa de Ciência Y Tecnologia para El Desarrollo, V Centenario*— should be stressed as it is a program to commemorate 500 years since the discovery of America, sponsored mainly by Spain, with a large number of participant institutions - research institutes, universities, and companies—from Portugal, Spain, and all Latin American countries. The rationale of this program, covering broad areas of research in both humanistic and science fields is that it consists in joining teams from both sides of the Atlantic Ocean and working on research projects mutually agreed upon. CYTED provides the funds for travel, allowing for meetings taking place once or twice per year to discuss results and to prepare new projects, funded by national money. CYTED was launched in the late '80s and is still ongoing. In the area of solar energy, projects have been carried out in the fields of desalination, drying, water purification, solar cookers, solar cooling, and PV. Other projects include wind energy, renewable resources assessment, and so on. Since the beginning, project meetings were organized to coincide with the Iberoamerican Congresses, as a way to finance the participation of a large number of colleagues from the other side of the ocean.

Table 1—List and main data of Iberian and IberoAmerican Solar Energy Congresses.

Date	Title	Proceedings Edition	Location	# vol & # papers
27–30 Sept 1982	I Congresso Ibérico de Energia Solar	M. Collares Pereira A. Luque	Madrid, Spain	3 volumes 142 papers
7–13 Oct 1984	2º Congresso Ibérico de Energia Solar	J. Doria M. Collares Pereira B.R. Arguelles R. Urculo	Lisbon, Portugal	1 volume 104 papers
22–24 April 1987	III Congresso Ibérico e I Ibero-americano de Energia Solar	J. Doria M.C. de Andres C. Armenta	Madrid, Spain	2 volumes+ 1 Annex 103 papers
July 1988	4º Congresso Ibérico e 2º Ibero-Americano de Energia Solar "Renewable Energies for a Sustainable Development"	E. de Oliveira Fernandes Eduardo Maldonado José Manuel Mendonça	Porto, Portugal	1 volume + 1 vol. supl. 96 papers
15–18 Oct 1990	V Congresso Ibérico e IV Ibero Americano de Energia Solar	J. Doria M.C. Andres C. Armenta	Madrid, Spain	1 volume 50 papers
5–7 April 1993	VI Congresso Ibérico de Energia Solar	SPES	Lisbon, Portugal	1 volume 50 papers
20 May – 1 June 1994	VII Congresso Ibérico de Energia Solar "Clean Energy in Progress"	Manuel Vázquez Jorge Morán	Vigo, Spain	1 volume 117 papers
May 1997	VIII Congresso Ibérico de Energia Solar "Solar Energy and Quality of Life"	E. de Oliveira Fernandes E. Maldonado M. Guedes de Almeida	Porto, Portugal	1 volume 121 papers
27-29 March 2000	IX Congresso Ibérico de Energía Solar "Renewable Energies and Sustainable Development"	A. López E. López R. López F. Casares	Cordoba, Spain	1 CD-ROM 145 papers
August 2000	X Congresso Ibérico de Energias Solar "Renewable Energies for the New Millennium"	Marcelo Roméro Hélder Gonçalves	Sao Paulo, Brasil	1 CD-ROM 158 papers
30 Sept – 2 Oct. 2002	XI Congresso Ibérico e VI Congresso Iberoamericano de Energia Solar "Sun, Energy and life"	J.Farinha Mendes M.Joao Carvalho Pedro Horta	Vilamoura, Portugal	1 CD-ROM 204 papers

The Solar Energy Iberoamerican Congress covers all renewable energy areas, although tradition continues to refer to them as "solar." They deal with the realities of the different countries that are represented, in resources, available technologies, and renewable energy development, leading to the exchange of experiences and to the gathering of scientific and business communities from both sides of the Atlantic Ocean. In all Congresses the leitmotif has been to join efforts and to find commitments between all those who are involved in the energy area: consumers, research laboratories, factories and service companies, promotion agents, and finally the politicians able to approve the laws that will constitute the base of a general solar energy policy, in agreement with SPES ideas about sustainable development.

16.4.3   National and International Projects

With the small annual fee paid by the members of SPES, it has been very difficult to keep up our effort in solar energy promotion, but with time, there was a clear need to increase such work because of decline of the solar market that occurred in the second half of the '80s, despite the contradiction with energy-related environmental problems that became more and more important after Chernobyl.

In the middle of the '90s, with Portugal as a member of the EU and because no increase in the fees was adopted, an alternative to find funds able to help us in our promotional work, was to participate in national and European projects, mainly through the ALTENER Program, just with national partners, or with other European partners: institutions, companies and other nongovernmental organizations (NGOs).

This was a very good decision, since in that way our Section could considerably increase its activity, joining European work and spreading in Portugal some of the latest news in the solar energy area and developing important work on information, education, and dissemination. This placed our Society in the first line of support for the energy policies in Portugal, at the beginning of the new century.

As an example we can refer to the case of the QUALISOL project, whose working program included developing the criteria for a certification program for installers. In the course of the work there was a request from a national program in the same direction, i.e., asking for the terms of a certification program for Portugal. The results of QUALISOL, as well as of a previous project on information and education, were quickly extrapolated to the Portuguese situation and in cooperation with other Portuguese institutions.

Some of those projects were only 50% financed by the European Commission, and in those cases we had to find financing for the other 50% in Portugal. That came through national programs like Programa Energia, and in this regard we have to acknowledge the support given by the Directorate General for Energy (Direcção Geral de Energia).

The list of projects, with the most relevant data related to them is outlined in the following text.

Fig. 10: Dissemination Actions of Solar Thermal Energy in Portugal

ALTENER Program (1996–1999), Contract No. XVII/4.1030/Z/96-104. Coordinated by SPES with two national partners: CCE (Energy Agency) and INETI.

The main objective of the project was to promote Solar Thermal Energy in Portugal through a series of technical courses and workshops on solar systems. Six training courses were completed with the participation of eighty installers and designers. This was an important training activity with the future certification of installers in mind.

A large promotion program called "Para melhor aproveitar o sol" ("For a better use of the Sun"), was also developed. This promotion was carried out at fairs, exhibitions, seminars, and through advertisements in newspapers, magazines and on the radio. A series of three posters were created as well as T-shirts and caps that were offered to members of SPES and distributed at those promotional actions and in schools and factories.

Fig. 11: The Use of Solar Thermal Energy in Social Equipment in Alentejo and Andaluzia

ALTENER Program (1999-2000), Contract No. 4.1030/Z/98-329, national support of the ENERGIA program.

The project was again coordinated by SPES and involved two national energy agencies, CCE and ARECBA, and another energy agency from Spain, SODEAN.

Solar energy is already being used in Europe in a series of installations, such as for swimming pools and gymnasiums, or for water heating and air conditioning of those spaces. As owners of those structures, municipalities and associations have an important role in showing the technical and economic viability of these solutions through the reduction of operational costs.

The objective of this project was to study the potential of the use of solar energy systems, in those structures just mentioned, as well as in private residences, in firehouse installations, campgrounds, hospitals, prisons, etc. Two regions close to each other, on the border of Portugal (Alentejo) and Spain (Andaluzia) were analyzed. The population of these regions is approximately 9 million and the available solar resource makes them the best place in Europe to implement large-scale solar energy utilization.

Fig. 12: Solar Thermal Process Heating in Industrial Applications. A Stimulation Plan

ALTENER Program (1999–2000), Contract No. XVII/4.1030/Z/98-205.

This was a project coordinated by a research center in Greece, the Center for Renewable Energy Sources—CRES, having SPES as partner, as well as the Greek Solar Industry Association-EBHE, SODEAN (Spain) and DFS (Germany).

The main objective of this project was the implementation of a strategic plan for participating countries, to promote and develop the national market for solar thermal energy, focusing on process heat applications of industry.

Fig. 13: The Potential of Solar Heat in Industrial Processes

Fifth Framework Program (Key action No. 5—Cleaner Energy Systems), Contract No. NNES5-1999-0308 (2000–2001).

The project was coordinated by AIGUASOL (Spain), and the other partners of SPES were INETI (Portugal), IDAE and ICAEN (Spain), ZAE and DLR (Germany).

The project sought evaluation of the potential of solar thermal systems in industrial applications. The results of the project were presented and discussed in several meetings and workshops and were published by SPES in its journal Energia Solar (No. 48). One of the workshops was integrated in the program of commemoration of the SunDay 2001, which was held in Palmela, 40 km from Lisbon, the location for what could be the biggest solar system in

Portugal, with 4,000 m², studied and proposed, in the framework of this project, for one malt factory.

It was possible to show, as a result of the project, that the economic justification for solar thermal in industry was now easier because of the international oil price increase and because industry has a tax incentive while calculating its annual corporate tax, since the investment in solar equipment can be amortized in a period of just four years. SPES is hoping that this provision in combination with the quality changes that are taking place in a number of companies—e. g., certification by the ISO 14000 series—will help the introduction of solar thermal into industry.

Fig. 14

QualiSOL - an Update of Installer Qualification for Solar Heating Systems

ALTENER Program (2001-2002), Contract No. AL/2000/Cluster No. 4.

The project was coordinated by Ambiente Italia srl; the other partners of SPES were: INETI (Portugal), Associazione Nazionale Impiantisti Manutentori—ANIM (Italia); Target GmbH (Germany;) and Sol*id CV (Netherlands).

The main objective of the project was to promote and disseminate information about the quality of solar thermal energy systems, through the creation of a certification program in the countries participating in the project - Germany, the Netherlands, Italy, and Portugal.

SPES and INETI shared their participation, working in the work program foreseen for Portugal. The opportunity for and interest in this work was proposed in time for the Portuguese Government AQSpP Program (Solar Hot Water for Portugal), which was presented in November 2001 and which requires, among other things, qualified solar thermal system installers. The input from QualiSOL was obvious, and it included the certification program.

Fig. 15: Forum: "Renewable Energy in Portugal"

Forum

Energias Renováveis
em Portugal

Organized by INETI, ADENE and DGE and sponsored by the Economy Minister, the forum "Renewable Energies in Portugal," took place in 2001, to study the potential and feasibility of development of renewable energies in Portugal up to the year 2010.

Several working groups were created, involving competent entities and persons concerned with the several areas of RE, as in the case of SPES. In fact SPES was involved in all the working groups both as an association and through the participation of many of its members. Results of this study contributed to the definition of the so-called E4 Program, the energy policy for Portugal that had been defined when one of our members, Prof. Oliveira Fernandes, was deputy minister of economy.

Fig. 16: IP AQSpP—A Public Initiative to Promote the Program "Solar Hot Water for Portugal"

This was a project coordinated by DGE (General Direction of Energy) and involving ADENE (Energy Agency), INETI (state laboratory), SPES, and APISOLAR (Portuguese Solar Industry Association), to promote the program "Solar Hot Water for Portugal" (a sub-program of the E4 Program), whose main objective was to attain 1 million square meters of solar thermal collectors in Portugal, installed and in proper operation, by the year 2010. This objective was connected to the development of quality in the solar market through establishment of collectors and installer certification programs. The project also developed a series of informative materials (technical, economic/financial, educational) to be used in a series of dissemination actions during the project's duration (2002–2004).

Fig. 17: Solar Challenger Father Himalaya

In 2004, SPES is organizing, with the collaboration of INETI and sponsorship by Ciência Viva, which is a national program for science education, the Solar Challenger Father Himalaya, at the same time celebrating the 100th Anniversary of the St. Louis Grand Prize attributed to him as previously mentioned

The focus of the Solar Challenger is to promote and develop interest and expertise in using solar and other renewable energy technologies by Portuguese school students. The construction of solar models of different technologies used in solar energy conversion will accomplish simple and inexpensive experiences where students and teachers are invited to use principles of physics, chemistry, biology, mathematics, geography, and art education.

The teams are challenged to design and construct solar models. They are also led to develop skills in leadership, school teamwork, time management, competition, and problem solving ideas, by exploring science and technology in the field of solar energy.

The Solar Challenger presents four different levels of participation according to Portuguese degrees of primary and secondary school. For each of the three levels in primary schools the challenge consists of the production of a model powered by the sun: sun clock, solar oven, and a miniature PV car. For the secondary degree, the challenge consists of building a solar model of a thermal collector, showing that hot water can be produced without pollution.

The winning team will be taken to the "Plataforma Solar" in Almería, Spain, which is really a European Centre for Solar Energy Applications and high temperature applications like those of Father Himalaya. State and private schools were invited to enter teams of students and teachers. Regulations and details were posted on the Internet site. http://www.cienciaviva.pt/rede/himalaya.

The competition itself will be included in the event organized to commemorate SunDay 2004 at Pavilhão do Conhecimento—Ciência Viva (Pavilion of Knowledge in the Nation's Park), Lisbon, Portugal, on June 26, 2004.

16.4.4   Publications

Table 1 reports all relevant data related to Solar Energy Iberian Congresses, and for the ones that took place in Portugal, the corresponding Proceedings were published by SPES, as is the case of the following ones:

> 2nd Solar Energy Iberian Congress (Lisbon)
> 4th Solar Energy Iberian Congress (Porto)
> 6th Solar Energy Iberian Congress (Lisbon)
> 8th Solar Energy Iberian Congress (Porto)
> 11th Solar Energy Iberian Congress (Vilamoura)

In the framework of our first ALTENER project—*"Dissemination Actions of Solar Thermal Energy in Portugal—a Handbook"* was published with materials used in the courses for installers realized at that time: Thermal Conversion of Solar Energy: a Handbook for Installers (Fig. 18a) (*Conversão Térmica da Energia Solar. Manual Sintese para Instaladores*). This handbook is available (free download) at the SPES site (www.spes.pt), and is being widely used by students and interested people who visit our site.

Fig. 18a, b: The two books published by SPES

In 1998, SPES also published a book *Renewable Energy, the Option that Can No Longer be Postponed* (Fig. 18b) (*Energias Renováveis. A Opção Inadiável*). This publication had sponsorship from other institutions in Portugal. The book was written by our member number one, Prof. Manuel Collares-Pereira, to contribute to the statement of national policy in the renewable energy area. This book starts with an analysis of the energy question in connection with the environment and concepts of development. It then compiles the available technical and statistical information about energy and about all renewable resources in Portugal, also presenting a review of renewable energy technologies. It makes specific proposals for an energy policy for renewable energy in Portugal, listing main actions, laws, and incentives necessary to implement it. In a very conservative scenario, the author estimates that the final energy consumption in 2010 that could be covered by renewable resources in Portugal is close to 30% (from the 12%—final energy—1996 that was produced by large-scale hydro and the traditional use of wood and industrial residues). This book made a strong contribution to the governmental E4 Program, which was published three years later, when our member Prof. Oliveira Fernandes was Deputy Minister of Economy

16.4.5   Other National Actions

16.4.5.1   SunDay Celebration

SPES has participated in the SunDay celebration since 1997, promoting actions in accordance with its objectives. Some relevant events related with SunDay were realized in the following years:

Fig. 19: SunDay 1997—This celebration day was included in the promotion actions carried out for the Altener project "Dissemination Actions of Solar Thermal Energy in Portugal," and involved a radio campaign and a postcard production. The radio spot of 20 seconds was broadcast on two main radio stations, in a total of 72 airings, with the following message: "The sun is an enormous energy source…Don't be indifferent! Take advantage of it!!"

SunDay 1999—There was an exhibition of solar thermal collectors, PV, and wind applications in the Municipal Garden of Oeiras (near Lisbon), in collaboration with a scout team from the area, which also involved distribution of promotional and technical information. An advertising campaign was also held, with a series of advertisements in newspapers and magazines. The message was: "This Sunday is a SUN-DAY! Sun is an energy source. Using it you are contributing to the sustainable development of our society and protecting our environment!"

SunDay 2001—Organized by SPES and by the Palmela Rotary Club, with close contribution by the Palmela Municipal Council. It took place on 22 June in the "Largo D. João I" in Palmela. Games occupied the whole morning. A large number of students, about 150 belonging to some basic and secondary schools from Palmela, took part in pedagogic activities related to the subject of SunDay. In the afternoon, a Technology Exhibition took place, and during the late afternoon a workshop on the results of the POSHIP Project was held in the auditorium of the "Caixa de Crédito Agrícola." The assembly, which drew a large and interested attendance provided a lively discussion and was supervised by the town councilor for the environment, as a representative of the mayor of Palmela.

SunDay 2003—SPES got the cooperation of QUERCUS, which is the main Portuguese NGO for nature protection, to celebrate this day, which occurred in one of the main squares in the Lisbon historic zone, where a solar collector exhibition also took place, together with solar cookers. This place always attracts lots of people, who then had the opportunity to taste food cooked in the solar cooker and to see solar collectors in real operation. The event got great coverage by the media—press, radio, and TV—announcing it through the day and commenting on it on following days, giving details and promotion materials about the on-going program "Solar Hot Water for Portugal". This celebration used the theme "The way for peace is also the way for sustainable development."

Another action also took place and was held in cooperation with INETI, involving a large number of students from the basic schools in the region of Lisbon. They visited the Renewable Energy Department of INETI, the science museum Ciência Viva—INETI, and prepared their lunch using solar cookers developed by themselves.

16.4.6   Site of SPES and SPESNews

SPES News—This was a pamphlet, published and distributed by members of SPES between 1999–2001. Since 2001 it has only been available on the SPES web site, because of the necessity of reducing costs and the difficulty of publishing it monthly. The digital solution made it possible to renew it and to keep it up to date all the time.

Fig. 20: Home page of SPES site (www.spes.pt)

SPES site (www.spes.pt)—The site was created in 1999 and was renewed in 2001 (Fig. 20). Since then permanent assistance was contracted to keep the web page and the SPES News edition up to date. This strategy has been successful enough as the number of visitors to the site has increased very much and compliments on it are received regularly. This also gave us more responsibility and a permanent mission to include on the site new and actual-ized materials in order to be useful to our visitors.

SPES press releases—During the last two years, on an irregular sched-ule, SPES produced and distributed several press releases in order to capture the attention of the media to relevant events or to main difficulties standing in the way of regular development of the solar collector market. Special mention should be made of the highlights of our history—the Iberian Congress in 2002 and the involvement of the President of the Republic of Portugal, and more recently of solar energy dissemination in buildings and the Father Himalaya Challenger activities.

16.4.7   General Matters

Relations with Other Associations and Groups—Contacts and cooper-ation were made with numerous groups such as: AEDES (Spanish Section of ISES); with INETI (Innovation, Technology and Engineering National Institute); with DGE (General Directorate for Energy); with FCT (Science and Technology Foundation); with FEUP (Engineering Faculty of Porto University); with EST/UA (University of Algarve); with ADENE (the main energy agency in Portugal); and with APREN (Renewable Energy Association of Portugal). Closer cooperation was recently established with QUERCUS (Environment Protection Association), given its strong interest in energy matters.

SPES staff—We have to mention the important contributions of Mr. Onésimo Barata and Mr. Fernando Carvalho (1900-2001). They both gave more then ten years of their lives to the regular secretariat of SPES in such a way that for a long time they were in fact the face of SPES for the public and even for most of the members of SPES. To the work of the secretariat, a strong contribution has been made by Dr. Maria da Graça Amado, since 1995, Eng° Eduardo Peres between 1997 and 2000, Arq° Pedro Nunes between 1999 and 2002, and in last three years by Dr. Ana Solano. SPES is deeply indebted to their dedication and kindness and wishes to specifically acknowledge their contribution in this document.

SPES Office Locations—For a long time SPES used office space offered by other institutions: 1) Sociedade de Ciências Agrárias de Portugal (1981–1983); 2) Portuguese Industrial Association (1983–1995); 3) General Directorate for Energy (1994–1999); 4) INETI (1999–2002). SPES wishes to acknowledge to all of them this very important contribution they made dur-ing these years. After 2002 SPES rented from INETI, on an annual base, a dedicated space inside the INETI campus—three rooms in Building M1, where INETI has lodged several other associations with activities that have relevance to INETI itself.

16.5   Perspectives

In Portugal, SPES has tried to play a role, alongside research and other institutions and companies, determined to promote and follow the development of solar thermal applications, participating actively in international projects, and developing independently its own projects of research and promotion of solar and renewable energy in general. The Portuguese solar collector industry also did its share of this work, producing solar collectors with standard and improved technology, sometimes highly innovative on a world level.

The market, however, has been very resistant to real growth due to low economic capacity and low environmental concerns in Portugal, together with energy policies which by and large ignore renewable energies most of the time. Unfortunately there was an initial phase of exaggerated claims, poor collectors, and poor engineering and installations.

To change this situation, the ongoing governmental program AQSpP—providing financial and fiscal incentives, by imposing quality requirements on installers and equipment, and making guarantees for installed equipment; producing a series of technical and economic information and publicizing the technology—is going in the right direction to increase the credibility of the technology and to promote good products in the market, towards a goal of 1 million square meters of solar collectors, installed by the year 2010 in Portugal.

Now SPES is conscious that more than ever, an additional effort, by all agents involved in the sector including politicians, industry, technicians, researchers, and media, should be mounted, because the market is showing difficulties to increase at the desired rate. But important Portuguese solar energy resources, in conjunction with available technology, are excellent, creating favorable conditions to implement solar thermal energy use on a large scale in Portugal. Demonstration projects, dissemination of information and promotion—where SPES intends to continue playing a role—and more favorable policies are also a necessity that will give confidence to the public and will help to achieve such objective.

We hope that Portugal will soon be singled out as an example to others, actively in the first row of users of solar energy, not waiting to be pushed, but pushing others to act in the same way as Father Himalaya did, in the beginning of last century!

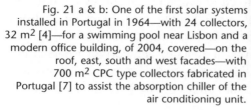

Fig. 21 a & b: One of the first solar systems installed in Portugal in 1964—with 24 collectors, 32 m² [4]—for a swimming pool near Lisbon and a modern office building, of 2004, covered—on the roof, east, south and west facades—with 700 m² CPC type collectors fabricated in Portugal [7] to assist the absorption chiller of the air conditioning unit.

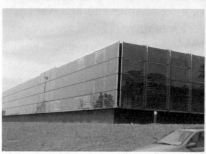

Acknowledgement

The authors wish to thank the contributions from Dr. Collares Pereira and Engº Salgado Prata, and a revision of the paper by Dr. Cruz Costa, Dr. Helder Gonçalves, Engº Lopes Prates, Engº David Loureiro, and Prof. Oliveira Fernandes.

References

[1] Jacinto Rodrigues, *A Conspiração Solar do Padre Himalaia*. Edited by Cooperativa de Actividades Artisticas, Porto (Portugal), 1999.

[2] Manuel Collares-Pereira, "A highly innovative, high temperature, high concentration, solar optical system at the turn of the nineteenth century. The Pyrheliophero" EuroSun 2004, Freiburg (Germany), June 2004.

[3] A. Salgado Prata. "Actividade sobre utilização de energia solar desenvolvida no LNEC"—SPES, 2003.

[4] Falconer (Import-Export) Ltd., Av. Duque de Loule, 47-3ºDto, 1050-086 Lisboa, Portugal.

[5] J. Costa, L. Valle, N. Silva, S. Prata, A. Martins, C. Costa. "Relatório Final da 1ª Fase dos estudos do GTAES"—LEM (DGC), 1976.

[6] Forum Energias Renováveis em Portugal Edited by H. Gonçalves, A. Joyce and L. Silva, ADENE/INETI, 2002.

[7] Ao Sol, Energias Renováveis Ltd, Apartado 173, 2135-402 Samora Correia, Portugal.

Chapter 17

Russian Section of the International Solar Energy Society

by
D. S. Strebkov and I. I. Tyukhov
All-Russian Research Institute for Electrification of Agriculture
2, 1-st Veshnyakovsky proezd
Moscow 109456, Russia
viesh@dol.ru

Abstract

We discuss here the activities of the Russian scientists, scholars, and researchers in solar energy, whose activities show interest in the practical usage of solar energy, in theoretical and practical research, and in envisioning strong connections between Sun and Earth in developing new clean energy technology. The Russian Section of ISES was formed because solar energy enthusiasts understood the necessity of international exchange and co-operation. Economic difficulties during the political transition period at the end of the '80s and having almost no financial support forced us to find new forms of work. Some research and educational activities of the Russian members of ISES are described.

17.1   Introduction

The history of solar energy in Russia is quite involved, especially in regards to our relationship with ISES. Although all of our researchers formally belong to the Russian Section of ISES, we consider all solar energy enthusiasts to be members of our community.

Interest in the use of solar energy has been sustained among scientists, engineers, common people, and businessmen at all times during the rule of different political systems and despite all political changes and economic difficulties.

We consider our task is to write about the development of solar energy in Russia a bit more widely than just to tell about our relatively small national Section and our formal affiliation with ISES.

We would like to write first about our enthusiasts, working in solar energy, who belong to the worldwide community of "solar people" making contributions to solar energy use.

The main task of our Russian Section of ISES is to support the activity of all such enthusiasts.

17.1.1   Solar History in Our Country

17.1.1.2   Research of Our Predecessors (Early Investigations)

Many ancient people, including Russian, revered the Sun as their supreme god. This simple belief was rational in that the Sun is the ultimate source of almost all of the energy used by man; it is the source of life. Solar energy is the first to have been used by man. Understanding this fact intuitively, Slavonic people worshiped the pagan God of the Sun—Yarilo. Some folk celebrations, connecting the Sun and agricultural works, are preserved into the twentieth century.

In writing about Russian solar energy history, we have to tell about some outstanding personalities who made significant contributions to many aspects of solar energy: to the understanding of physics, developing meteorology, investigating solar-terrestrial connections, etc.

Let us mention first Mikhail Vasilevich Lomonosov (1711–1765), the first Russian scholar to create encyclopedic knowledge at the world level and who made outstanding contributions to Russian science. He was a founder of the Russian sciences (Fig. 1). Most important were his achievements in optics. Even the word optics was entered into the Russian language by M. V. Lomonosov. Many outstanding results of his work in the field of optics and optical engineering are well-known: the technology of glass melting—the material basis for any optical device, creation of the first ever "night-vision" telescope, the invention of a one-mirror, extra-axial astronomic telescope (twenty-seven years before the English astronomer William Hershel did so); manufacturing high-quality metal mirrors; discovery of the atmosphere on Venus; and many other achievements.

It is interesting to look at Fig.1 and Figs. 2a and 2b, where probably the first Russian concentrator systems are depicted. Lomonosov discussed the technological and economic difficulties of the production of "burning glasses" with a diameter of 75 cm and a focal length of about 2 m (F. Willet, French mechanic and optician) and suggested use of an ingenious system with 8 smaller lenses and 7 mirrors (Fig. 2), understanding that solar rays conserve their "heat power" after reflection from polished metallic mirrors [1].

Unfortunately many of his scientific views were ahead of his time by one or two centuries (the period of reaction in Russia) and were not understandable to his contemporaries (and were practically unknown to foreign scientists).

It is necessary to note here that Russian scientists during long periods of time had difficulties in communicating with foreign scientists (M. V. Lomonosov lived in a time of deep reaction and extreme conservatism; Russian scientists in Soviet times were behind the iron curtain and unable to communicate with Western colleagues in spite of substantial financial support from the government). Even now our freedom is restricted, this time by lack of financial opportunities for research and traveling.

Fig. 1: M. V. Lomonosov. Portrait by an unknown artist

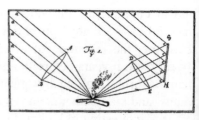

Fig. 2a: Drawing from original M. V.Lomonosov paper [1]

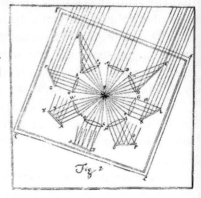

Fig. 2b: Drawing from original M. V. Lomonosov paper [1]

Moscow State University, named by M. V. Lomonosov, is one of the world-class universities; it has an excellent tradition of teaching fundamental courses in combination with applied sciences. For example, Prof. Brashman (teacher of the famous mathematician P. L. Chebyshev) in a course on mechanics, introduced the theory of water wheels, spill-ways, water-engines, etc., and offered to post-graduate students such themes for dissertations as "Water as engine," "Theory of water wheels," and so on (1840s).

Prof. V. A. Tsesarskii obtained extraordinary results in 1890 in focusing sunlight. He managed to obtain temperatures up to 3,500°C using concentrated sunlight, and he melted many metals and nonmetals by using his solar system.

The outstanding Russian chemist Dmitry Ivanovich Mendeleev (1834–1907) is famous, not only for his Periodical Table of Elements (Fig. 3), but also for his contribution to improving vodka production (this fact is probably not known to foreign readers). In 1865, the final definition of vodka as a national alcoholic beverage was possible only due to the works of Mendeleev. There was a lot of hearsay about him: it was said that he discovered the secrets of making Russian vodka, or that he produced false French wines. All these rumors appeared because of his thesis, "About the combina-

tion of spirit with water."
We would like to emphasize other aspects of Mendeleev's work. Rapid development of industry in the XIX century generated the problem of pollution of water and air and accumulation of waste products as a result of manufacturing. But these difficulties were considered to be technical, and the correction of them to be a matter of time. Also, he took an "ecological" view of wildlife management. Mendeleev's interests were rather extensive, and besides physics and chemistry included an industrial economy and agriculture, statistics, and demography. All his various activities were directed to one purpose—to promote an economic boom of Russia. His ecological plans (to again use the modern form) and his unshakable optimism were based on belief in the omnipotence of knowledge, sciences, i.e., of scientism. He supposed, that "dross, wastes or the by-products of manufacture," demanded complex processing, repeated inclusion in a production cycle; i.e., he was sure it was possible to manufacture without wastes. Actually, he did not have an ecological program (and, perhaps, could not have yet), but some of his ideas about wildlife management and industrial pollution remain useful today. His dictum is widely known: "to burn petroleum is all the same as to burn bank notes."

Fig. 3. Cartoon of D. I. Mendeleev (from the Internet)

In the book *Chemistry and Modern Life* he clearly describes the looming problem of exhaustion of natural resources and the necessity of their rational use; he also discusses the problem of what energy sources should replace petroleum and coal. In a separate chapter he discusses chemistry and problems of food. From the following words his position on some global ecological questions is clear:

"The use of raw materials throws a dark shadow on the destiny of mankind. The future will discover that the aspiration to continue to consume raw materials has become the cause of an enormous misfortune that has overtaken mankind, or, more truly, so-called civilized peoples. Clearly, sooner or later one should come to the conclusion that it is self-destructive to leave decisions on use of raw materials to national egotism or self-interest, to greedy industrialists. Mankind will come to the truth that, as far as it is possible, we should protect fossil fuels for the future and replace them with alternative sources of energy, which, apparently, the Sun sends to us in inexhaustible amounts, directly as in the tropical countries, or as energy indirectly dependent on the sun and consisting of rough, stormy streams and turning vegetation green."

Mendeleev also formulated a concept of manufacturing that looks like a contemporary idea: "The main purpose of modern technology is to search for ways of producing useful things from waste."

Solar energy meteorology is most important for the design of practical solar conversion systems. Recently we celebrated 125 years of practical measurements by V. A. Mikhelson at the Meteorological Observatory (Moscow). Vladimir Aleksandrovich Mikhelson (1860–1927), Russian physicist and geophysicist, was one of the founders of domestic actinometry, and a professor at the Moscow Agricultural Institute (now K. A. Timiryazev Agricultural Academy) Department of Physics and Meteorology. He organized the first systematic measurements of incoming solar radiation near Moscow (Fig. 5). He designed, tested, and improved a number of actinometers and pirheliometers (Fig. 4). See, for example, his papers: "About application of an ice calorimeter in actinometry" (Saint Petersburg, 1894) and "New actinometer" (1908). The results of probably the first systematic solar radiation measurements are represented therein [2].

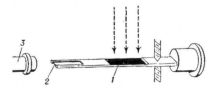

Fig. 4a & b: Prof. V. A. Mikhelson (above) carrying out actinometric measurements with his actinometer of bimetallic type (below) (1 - blackened bimetallic receiver, 2- quartz fiber, 3 – microscope)

Fig. 5: The 125-year old Mikhelson Meteorological Observatory building with meteorological equipment on the roof, in 2004

17.2 Russian Solar Energy Researchers and Systematic Work Before the Second World War

One of the greatest Russian solar schools was started in Saint Petersburg and is connected with the name Abram Fedorovich Ioffe (1880–1960). At the beginning of the 1930s A. F. Ioffe concentrated on semiconductor physics, formulated many important practical tasks of direct conversions of solar energy, and as a result created a world-class school of semiconductor physics. Many interesting historical facts connecting solar energy research to the Ioffe Institute are described in the books listed at the end of this review [3, 4]. This research helped us establish systematic works in the semiconductor industry.

Fig. 6: The old Ioffe Institute building and the bust of A. F. Ioffe in the fall of 2003

Chizhevskiy Alexandr Leonidovich (1897–1964) worked in space biology and space medicine. From a young age on, he devoted his life to observations of the sun and investigations of the influence of solar radiation on the Earth. He started to work with P. P. Lasarev in his Institute of Biophysics. He was a founder of heliobiology (now seen as astrobiology), and he was a pioneer in this field. He established connections between solar cycles and many processes in the biosphere. Some of his papers are available on the Internet in Russian (see, for example, the URL below). He investigated the influence of ionized air on people's health and developed many devices for generating negative ions in the air, which are now very popular in Russia.

Чижевский А._Физические факторы исторического процесса_ - Калуга, 1924.htm

Kondratyuk Jury Vasil'evich (1897–1942) was one of the pioneers of Soviet rocket engineering and for the first time stated the idea of the enormous value of space flights for the national economy. Before Obert and Noordung, he offered to concentrate sunlight with the help of parabolic mirrors from space.

The systematic work on the direct use of solar radiation started in 1926 with applications mainly in the southern regions of the USSR. Later the leading role in the complex use of solar energy was taken up at the Krzhizhanovsky Power Engineering Institute (ENIN) as the head scientific institute. This field developed in promising directions for the development of solar-power engineering.

The scientific institute was founded in 1930 and for more than a quarter of a century it was headed by the academician G. M. Krzhizhanovsky. He was an outstanding scientific and public figure, under the direction of whom the first state plan for electrification of Russia (plan GOELRO) was developed. The scientific nucleus of the institute was made up of leading scientists who were participating in the further development of this plan.

According to the ideas of the GOELRO plan, ENIN, as the Institute was called, was established to solve major complex problems facing Soviet power engineering. Under a guidance of G. M. Krzhizhanovsky the scientific principles for creation of an Integrated Power Grid (EES) of the USSR, nowadays "EES of Russia," were developed.

The Institute proposed planning and development of power systems, using analysis of optimization of a fuel and energy balance throughout the country and its separate areas. On the basis of these ideas basic rules were established for the forecast of development of power in the near and distant future. Thus the influence on the environment of power stations of different types was considered and the necessity of accounting for ecology influenced the choice of sites for their location.

ENIN proposed a number of fundamental ideas that were subsequently further developed. The expediency of creation of large power stations with powerful units and systems of centralized heat supply for large and medium-size cities was economically justified; technological charts of burning and use of low-grade solid fuel in the power stations were developed; technical decisions to use solar and geothermal energy were offered.

Wind energy had been used in Russia for hundreds of years for milling grain, pumping water, and other mechanical power applications. At the end of the seventeenth century tower mills (where only the cap and rotor were rotated in response to changes in wind direction) became wide-spread. The last windmill in the Perm region (first part of the nineteenth century) is shown in Fig. 7. At the end of the nineteenth century tower mills with a wheel diameter of 24 meters provided high-quality milling of grain by using two millstones and achieving high productivity. Engineer Vasili Petrovich Davydov designed the first Russian multi-bladed wind engine, which was demonstrated at Nizhnii Novgorod in 1896. Davydov's design boosted industrial production of multi-bladed wind engines in Russia.

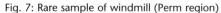

Fig. 7: Rare sample of windmill (Perm region)

The theoretical basis of the use of wind energy was developed in the second half of the nineteenth century by the great Russian scientist Nikolai Egorovich Zhukovskiy (1847–1921); he was the founder of modern aerodynamics and the "father" of Russian aviation.

Prof. N. E. Zhukovskii had organized a wind engine department at the Central Aero-hydrodynamic Institute (TsAGI). Between 1920 – 1925 he created the theory of wind engines, which was expanded by his followers to include practical applications. In the USSR, from 1925 on, new designs of wind engines for energy-plant production were developed. These wind engines were produced with a production rate of 7,000 per year at the plant named after Petriovski in Kherson and were used for water supply on collective farms, in railway stations, and on steppe pastures. Up to 1940 more than

45,000 windmills were in use mainly in southern regions of the country. The first big windmill in the USSR was built at Karanskie hills (Balaklavskaya in Russia the wind mills industry station), and produced a current in 1931 (now this territory belongs to the Ukraine). In 1930 TsAGI designed a Balaklavskaya 100 kW capacity wind station, which was at that time the most powerful station in Europe. A special cabin with the generator and blades 30m in diameter was installed on a metal support structure of the height of about an eight-story building. The system had a weight of about 9 tons. This unique windmill was destroyed during the Second World War.

Biomass for energy in Russia historically started, as elsewhere, from using firewood. In most areas of Russia, in cold climatic zones, firewood was the only energy source that helped many generations of peoples to survive the long snowy winters.

In Table 1 we show the technology, which was popular for transport needs (producer-gas from wood) before the Second World War and which helped during the war in times of fuel shortages with a technology that does not demand a special fuel except for wood.

Table 1:   Producer-gas from wood technology in Russia.

October 27, 1905	At the meeting of the 8th Department of the Russian Imperial Technical Society, Colonel A. Oditsov suggested the use of both diesel and producer-gas engines for rail transport. A schematic layout of the locomotive engine fueled with producer-gas was designed by engineer N. Ruznetsov and A. Oditsov.
1900–1907	The regional newspaper "Uralsky Kray" reported on a project by Russian merchant Alexander Borchaninov to construct a new flour-mill plant equipped with the steam producer-gas engine (capacity: 500 horsepower) "…driven by gases produced from peat burnt in an airless environment…."
1931	The all-Union contest for development of producer-gas engines for tractors was launched. The winner was engineer Dekalenkov with his engine that was installed in tractors "Kommunar-50."

1931 – 1939 	These "Mug2" locomotives had GAZ-42 producer-gas engines (29 h. f.) and were produced at the machine shop in Kaluga.
1932–1936 	A number of projects of producer-gas- engine locomotives were designed in Leningrad (at the Institute of Railway Transport Engineers), including an 1860 h. p. locomotive type "2-6-1."
1935	According to Instruction #228 of "Stroykrasmash" dated September 21, the production of producer-gas engines for motor ships was designed for gold-mining enterprises.
Summer 1938 	Twelve cars and trucks with producer-gas engines took part in the 11,000 km rally. By that time, 10% of cars, trucks, and tractors were running on solid fuel in the USSR.

17.3   Russian Solar Energy Researchers and Systematic Works after the Second World War

After the Second World War (we say Great Patriotic War) practically half of the country was destroyed. Scientific activity started to shift from the war (although rocket and nuclear researches were among the main priorities) to developing technologies oriented to people.

The publication in 1947 of a book devoted to energy problems reflects a growth of interest in the new energy technologies [4]. In this book, of Prof. P. P. Lasarev (1879–1942) surveyed all energy technologies known to that time.

In the second half of 1940s a group of wind-energy specialists under the leadership of academician A. V. Vinter started scientific and development projects for the creation of autonomous wind- water supply systems generating energy for uninterrupted supply to consumers. Many research institutes and universities were involved in this complex problem; including the Krzhizhanovsky Power Engineering Institute of the USSR Academy (ENIN), the Bauman Technical University, the Moscow Aviation Institute, and others. From 1956 till 1958 TcAGI wind laboratory developed and built multi-unit wind stations of 400 kW capacity (VES-400), comprising twelve wind engines with a capacity of 42 kW each with a 12-meter wind wheel diameter. This energy plant had reserve diesel generators. VES-400s regularly supplied energy to three big collective farms and produced 11.7 billion kWh of electric energy during seven years. One should emphasize that the multi-unit VES-400s were built for the first time in the world; practice and seven years of exploitation proved the concept of energy supply in regions with wind speed in excess of 5 m/sec and higher to be economical.

Important research results were obtained in our former Soviet Republics, particularly in the Middle Asia and Caucasus regions. Many interesting and useful research projects on the complex use of solar energy were developed in the 1950s and 1960s and were coordinated by ENIN. The scientists from ENIN and branches from a number of central institutes and local laboratories in Tashkent, Ashkhabad, and Tbilisy made important contributions to the development of solar thermal collectors and to various solar systems such as dryers, greenhouses, water heaters, high- temperature solar furnaces, desalters, boilers, steam boilers, cookers, refrigerators, thermal concentrators, etc. Great contributions to solar energy, were made by the world-famous scientists V. A. Baum, V. B. Veinberg, P. P. Aparisy, V. B. Petukhov, G. I. Markov., D. I. Teplyakov,. and many others.

In 1961 V. A. Baum wrote words that sound like modern thoughts to us:

Just imagine for a moment that mankind had based his power on solar radiation, not fuel, and then the proposal to use different kinds of fuel was put forward. Probably there would have been very many objections. One could imagine that one of the most important arguments in defense of solar energy would be formulated as follows:

Solar radiation is a "noble" form of energy, and it was under its influence that life originated and continues to develop on Earth; therefore, its use, no matter on what scale, could represent no danger or inconvenience for either the flora or fauna of the world. The use of any other kind of fuel would inevitably be connected with the poisoning of the atmosphere, water, and land. Fuel should be used only where there are no other possibilities of obtaining energy, and in the many sunny regions of the world the energy of the sun should be used.

Now former Soviet republics are independent states and our contacts with them depend on the political situation. Many former branches of leading Moscow and Saint Petersburg Institutes and enterprises (ENIN, KVANT, VEI) are working now as independent research centers in the Middle Asia and Caucasus regions.

The Ioffe Institute became a great research center on semiconductors for solar energy applications. See, for instance, the semiconductor thermoelectric generator TG-1, that was developed by the Ioffe Institute for partisan radio stations just after the beginning of the Second World War and in the shortest possible time (Fig. 8).

Fig. 8: Thermoelectric generator TG-1

Prof. V. D. Rumyantsev from the same Ioffe Institute has developed a modern version of a converter from combustion heat of organic fuel into electricity, based on GaSb cells, resulting in a thermophotovoltaic generator for autonomous applications (Fig. 9).

Let us mention here that the first thermoelectric freezer in the world was created by L. S Stilbans under the supervision of A. F. Ioffe and Yu. P. Maslakovets in 1951.

D. I. Nasledov (1903–75) developed technology for growing monocrystals of GaAs, InAs, p-n-junctions, and solar cells. We refer here to the Zh. I. Alferov's book [4] for detailed information.

Many applied research subjects were carried out in the Crimea (now Ukraine). One of the first geothermal heat supply systems was created there in the beginning of the 1980s.

An active group led by Prof. Povarov (Moscow Power Engineering institute) developed big geothermal projects in the Far East.

The first solar power station in the USSR (SES-5) was built in 1986 in the

Crimea near the village of Lenin, with a capacity of 5 MW. The height of the central tower together with a steam and gas generator was 89 m. Mirror concentrators (heliostats), rotating around the vertical and horizontal axes, sent solar energy onto the boiler that was placed on the central tower at a height of 78 m. The total area of mirrors equaled 40,000 m². The steam with a temperature +225° C and pressure 2.6 MPa was generated by heating water in the boiler. Steam then powered turbines and consequently the rotor of an electric generator. From 1986 to 1996 the SES-5 system generated approximately 2 million kWh of electric power (much less than estimated, but this was caused by the political transition period with ensuing complicating economic problems).

Many systematic investigations were carried out at research centers in the big cities, such as Moscow and, Leningrad (now Saint Petersburg), at NPO "Kvant," ENIN, VEI (the All-Russian Research Institute for Electrical Engineering), Ioffe Institute, and FIAN ((Physics Institute of the Academy of Sciences). All of them were involved in solar technology. At the same time new branches and centers for field tests were created in the southern Soviet Republics for developing terrestrial applications of solar energy.

Fig. 9: Modern TPV technology in action (radio receiver is working from the spirit lamp with TPV generator)

17.4   Official Steps to Creating our National Section of ISES

17.4.1   The Official Steps

The German ISES section gave generous support from 1990 on during several extremely hard years for Russian scientists. After visiting the All-Russian Institute for Electrification of Agriculture (VIESH) and some other institutes in Moscow, St. Petersburg, and Tashkent, Prof. Adolf Goetzberger (director of the Fraunhofer Institute for Solar Energy Systems (FhG-ISE) and chair of ISES) and Prof. Dmitry Strebkov (director of VIESH) signed a joint plan of action to stimulate the exchange of research results and to establish cooperation between the two institutes in the fields of photoelectricity, thermal conversion of solar energy and other research areas. The German section of ISES and FhG-ISE paid the membership fee for twenty leading Russian scientists, who were also members Russian Council on Renewable Energy (Andreev V. M., Evdokimov V. M., Strebkov D. S., Tarnizhevsky and others). After many political and legislative changes the Russian Association of Solar Energy Investigators was officially registered.

17.4.2   What About the Next Steps?

The next steps could be made only during the building of a civil society in our country. The average salary of Russian scientists is much lower than the salary of foreign scientists (including usually a part-time job in a university), especially in such areas as solar energy. While Russia is a key producer and exporter of energy resources and is actually one of the richest countries in terms of fuel and mineral resources, the situation in sciences and education is rather bad, with an undeveloped infrastructure. We hope that the building of a civil society can decrease such a big disparity.

Especially difficult is the situation with young scientists in the solar energy field. Russia is now home of an excess number of economists, accountants, lawyers etc. To be an engineer is not a very popular career in Russia, many pragmatic young people choose more successful professions in order to earn an attractive salary.

Grassroots organizations (particularly environmental) could help solar activity. But without state or external assistance and the systematic efforts of many groups of people, it is unrealistic to expect significant results in the near future. We have to emphasize, though, that our activists, even in dire economic need, do not sit passively, but try to find new forms of ideas.

17.5   Our Conferences and Exhibitions

There are different types of conferences devoted to solar energy, renewable energy, and energy efficiency in our country, all related to promoting solar energy.
Let us mention only some of them to show our efforts (Table 2).

Table 2:   List of some Russian renewable energy conferences and events with the active participation of Russian Section ISES members.

1.	Moscow Solar Summit—International Conference in the framework of World Solar Summit–UNESCO initiative, Moscow, 1996
2.	SunDay-97: event was devoted to the active use of solar energy, Moscow Power Engineering Institute; leaflets, special issue of a newspaper, and excursions to research institutions, June 1997
3.	IV International exhibition "Power Engineering and Electrical Engineering-97," Seminar: "Problems of development and using small and renewable power engineering," Saint Petersburg, 11 – 15 November 1997
4.	Small and nontraditional power engineering: Current state and future trends, The All-Russian Exhibition Center, Scientific Seminar and Exhibition, 15 – 19 June 1998
5.	Scientific and practical conference "Ecology and agricultural machinery," Saint-Petersburg, 1998
6.	International Congress and Exhibition, "Business and Investment for Renewable Energy in Russia," carried out in Moscow, 31 May – 6 June 1999
7.	University Conference, "Modern energy-saving technologies and installations," Goryachkin Moscow State Agro-engineering University, 2 – 4 February 1999
8.	Second International Conference at VIESH, "Energy saving in agriculture" (with a special section on renewable energy), Moscow, 2000
9.	Many Russian scientists took part in a Ukrainian conference "Nontraditional power engineering in the twenty-first century," Crimea, Yalta, 17 – 22 September 2001.
10.	Third International Conference at VIESH "Energy saving in agriculture" (with a special section on renewable energy), Moscow, 2002
11.	International Conference and Exhibition, "Renewable energy 2003. Modern situation, problems, trends," November 4 – 6, 2003, St.-Petersburg
12.	International School—seminar UNESCO: "Education and training on renewable energy. Problems and trends in the twenty-first century," Makhachkala, Dagestan Republic, Russia, 15 – 19 September 2003.
13.	Fourth International Conference at VIESH, "Energy saving in agriculture" (with a special section on renewable energy), Moscow, 2004

Within the framework of cooperation between Russia's Energy Ministry and the U.S. Department of Energy, joint research on wind power engineering and photovoltaics was initiated. Russia was represented in the project by the Renewable Energy Sources Company, VIESH, and the Intersolarcenter Company; and the United States was represented by the National Renewable Energy Laboratory (NREL). A new environment-friendly, chloride-free process of obtaining silicon for solar cells was developed. Russian scientists and specialists recently had a meeting at NREL (March 2004). Quite regular Russian-American seminars on renewable energy problems are held.

17.5.1   The Relation of Our Section to ISES

Formally we are now a Section of ISES and as such our members are encouraged also to become a full member of ISES. We collect the dues and transmit its part to ISES (it is not simple because our banking system is far from being perfect, especially for people with small incomes, there are many restrictions on transferring money abroad).

Our key members of ISES are supporting personal contacts. We have good contacts with ASES, ISES of Italy, ISES of Germany, and ISES of Europe. It helps us to visit international events and to participate in conferences of world level (as ISES Congresses, EuroSun Conferences, and ASES Conferences).

The main task for us is to involve young people in this activity. They have now much more opportunities for studying foreign languages for communication and have a chance to study abroad in foreign universities. Our old generation with technical background usually had opportunities (in Soviet times) to study foreign languages only for reading technical literature – not for communication. It would be very useful to organize joint international schools for our students, postgraduate students and young specialists. At the same time young specialists with good command of foreign language(s) are looking for positions in the prestige foreign (or in joint Russian-foreign companies) with high salary and very often leave our scientific area for better financial positions.

17.5.2   Our Most Important Research Results

Being a smaller Section of ISES, one would not expect large scale research results from us. At the same time we are proud that many members of our Section were involved in great projects, which are now famous in the world. As an example, we list some important key events in Russian photovoltaics (space industry, terrestrial application, and researches) in Table 3.

The following Russian scientists made a large contribution to the development of the photovoltaic industry: N. S. Lidorenko, Zh. I. Alferov, V. S. Vavilov, A. P. Landsman, A. M. Vasilev, V. M. Evdokimov, V. M. Andreev, M. V. Kagan, D. S. Strebkov, M. M. Koltun, D. N. Nasledov, C. M. Ryvkin, and others.

Table 3:   Development of Photovoltaics in Russia

Year	Key events
1958	First satellite, "Sputnik-3," with solar arrays was launched
1964	A 0.25 kW solar PV concentrator plant for water pumping was tested in the Kara-Kum desert near Ashkhabad (Turkmenistan).
1967	New class of silicon multijunction (with vertical p-n-junctions) and high voltage cell technology was developed
1970	Ion implantation technology was applied to a solar cell manufacturing line.
1970	Bifacial silicon solar cell technology was developed and applied to space solar cell production.
1975	Testing of 32 kV, 1 m² solar arrays for ion plasma space engine
1975	Development of GaAlAs-GaAs solar cell technologies. In 1981 this technology was applied in the lunar space program.
1980	Multijunction solar cell technology using GaAlAs-GaAs was developed.
1981	New types of compound, holographic, and prism concentrators were developed.
1983	A 1 kW PV plant with glass parabolic mirrors and heat tube cooling system was installed in Tashkent (Uzbekistan)
1984	A 10 kW PV plant with plastic parabolic trough for linear concentration was installed in Ashkhabad (Turkmenistan).
1985	Efficiencies up to 36% with electric power density of 3,6 kW/cm² was demonstrated for laser PV energy conversion.
1987	The technology for purification of metallurgical-grade silicon for solar cell applications was developed.
1989	A 500-W solar power plant with glass compound concentrator was developed and 40-kW solar PV village in Krasnodar region was installed.
1989	Special technology in production of solar cells for terrestrial applications was initiated.
1993	A 30% efficiency of cascade GaAlAs-GaGeAs heterojunction with concentrated solar radiation was demonstrated.
1996	The technology of 100-square shape bifacial solar cells was developed.
1997	A 1 kW, 10 kW single-wire electric power system for renewable-based electric grid was developed.
1998	Chlorine-free solar grade poly silicon technology was developed.
2000	Stationary concentrator PV module with ratio concentration of 5-30 was developed.

17.6   What Else is Worthwhile to Report Here About Our Society?

There are many events we could list here in solar energy in our country; many of those are credited to ISES members (some of them we mentioned earlier).

In our fast-changing society (during the transition period we jumped quickly from a centralized socialism to wild capitalism) it takes time to build a well-balanced civil society. In these conditions we are looking for and trying different strategies and means of joining with all people who are interested in solar energy.

The main problem in more actively developing the Russian ISES Section is the great disparity between the salaries of ours scientists and engineers, and the financial support of their research, and the real cost of life, contrasted with the incomes of our new extremely rich businessmen, especially those who work in the oil and gas industry. Searching for new forms of activity is a very important issue for us.

There are many barriers and obstacles in the way of solar energy: economical, financial, technical, legislative, educational, psychological, and cultural, worsened by the lack of information. All these barriers are traditional for any country. But we also have a language barrier.

That is why we (active members of the Russian Section of ISES) organized several new institutions such as Intersolarcenter and the UNESCO Chair, "Renewable energy and electrification of agriculture," at VIESH.

In 1998 the "Intersolarcenter" started to publish the *Renewable Energy Bulletin* for Russia and CIS countries. The bulletin contains:

1. Information about international and regional projects and programs, which are accomplished by the European Community, UNESCO, UNDP, and other international organizations.
2. Review papers and opinions of political and public authorities and scientists concerning energy strategy and renewables in particular.
3. The thematic selection of 2–3 analytical scientific articles on renewable energy application.
4. Abstracts of publications in domestic and foreign information sources.
5. News of economical efficiency and practical results of renewable energy application.
6. News of Russian and CIS regional projects and programs, information on renewable energy potential and priorities, consumers, renewable energy equipment manufacturers.

7. Advertising of Russian and foreign energy equipment and renewable energy technologies.

The Bulletin is distributed in Russian regions and CIS countries through Energy Commissions, Regional Administrations, and Renewable Energy Centers. Some papers were in English.

In 2000 Intersolarcenter became Associated Member of the OPET network. Within the framework of this project, Intersolarcenter publishes the new Renewable Energy Bulletin. All materials now are in Russian.

The UNESCO Chair "Renewable Energy and Electrification of Agriculture" took part in the preparation of international projects within the frame-work of the World Solar Summit (1996–2005). Diploma projects, practical works for students at different universities, the teaching of postgraduate students, and educational seminars are our main activities. From 2003 on, the regular teaching of courses on renewable energy and energy-saving technology has been offered for students of the Moscow State Agricultural Engineering University.

We have mentioned the most important issue: how to attract young people to our field. The Moscow State University jointly with VIESH (UNESCO Chair) organized regular "All-Russian Schools for Youth on Renewable Energy" (first: 4–9 October 1999; second: 20–24 November 2000; third: 4–7 December 2001; fourth: 2-4 December 2003). Many leading scientists, specialists, and experts lectured at these schools (two volumes of lectures have been published), many young specialists, students, and postgraduate students made presentations (three volumes of papers have been published). The next problem: how to involve our young scientists in international activities?

During many years the teaching and training of specialists (experts on renewable energy) at different levels—engineers, bachelors, technicians was conducted at the Moscow Power Engineering Institute (Technical University), the Bauman Technical University, the Lomonosov Moscow State University, the Moscow State University of Environmental Engineering, the Saint Petersburg State Technical University, the Dagestan State Technical University, the Institutions of Ekaterinburg, Novosibirsk, and Khabarovsk, etc. Academic councils on the awarding of candidate and doctor's degrees on renewable energy run continuously. However, there is a lack of technicians and workers for practical service and maintenance of renewable energy installations.

A stock company, Vetroen, is another form of organization for our active ISES members. They recently published the *Renewable Energy Equipment Catalog* and a book on renewable energy resources [6].

17.7   Photo-report

Here we have collected some photos that should illustrate our activities and show our active members of the Russian section of ISES. We hope it will bring our members closer to the international ISES community. Readers are welcome to visit Russia and to co-operate with Russian solar energy activists in any possible way.

Fig. 10: Prof. Strebkov, director VIESH, chairman of the Russian ISES section and chairholder of the UNESCO Chair

Fig. 11: Prof. Vissarionov (Moscow Power Engineering Institute) lecturing at the All-Russian Youth Renewable Energy School (winter 2003)

Fig. 12: Prof. Rumyantsev and Prof. Andreev at the lab in the Ioffe Institute, (St. Petersburg, October 2003)

Fig. 13: Dr. M. Y. Lyamin describes how artificially cultivated microalgae are producing in an artificial environment (Laboratory for renewable energy sources, Department of Geography, M. V. Lomonosov Moscow State University, winter 2003)

Fig. 14: Dr. Sokolskii, head
of wind and hydro energy
laboratory (VIESH)

Fig. 15: Prof. Frank Vignola (r) (a member of ASES) and
Sidney Clouston(l) with Russian bifacial solar cells at the
University of Oregon

Fig. 16: Dr. Chirkov at UNESCO, chair of VIESH (PV films and biomass specialist)

Fig. 17: Prof. Evdokimov, deputy director of VIEN (VIEN), PV chief specialist

Fig. 18: Engineer Pinova (Intersolarcenter)

Fig. 19: Dr. Starshiov, chief technologist and chemist (solar cells workshop of VIESH)

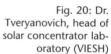

Fig. 20: Dr. Tveryanovich, head of solar concentrator laboratory (VIESH)

Fig. 21: Dr. Kargiev (Intersolarcenter)

Fig. 22: Dr. Zadde, head
of PV laboratory (VIESH)

Fig. 23: Prof. Generalov (Rector of Moscow State University of Engineering Ecology) and Prof. Shpilrain (Institute of High Temperature) at the test field in Makhachkala (Dagestan)

Fig. 24: Dr. Nikitin, PV systems specialist (VIESH)

Fig. 25: UNESCO seminar on renewable energy education at Makhachkala (Dagestan, September 2003)

Fig. 26: Dr. Arbuzov, director of VIEN, photovoltaics specialist

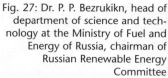

Fig. 27: Dr. P. P. Bezrukikn, head of department of science and technology at the Ministry of Fuel and Energy of Russia, chairman of Russian Renewable Energy Committee

Fig. 28: Dr. Tyukhov, deputy chairholder of UNESCO Chair (PV and concentrators specialist)

Conclusion

Let us finish this review paper with the words of V. A. Baum (1960), who actually formulated the program for all of us living in the twenty-first century:

The problem of utilizing solar radiation could be formulated as studying the interaction of the radiation energy of the sun with live and dead matter and determining possible ways for the practical use of this interaction. However, when the problem is formulated in such a general way, the volume of research becomes too large and ill defined. It is expedient to conduct the research first in those directions that can be expected to produce the most important practical results in the shortest time. From this point of view, we believe the primary directions of research should be the following: (1) Studies of the Earth's climate and the extent to which it should be controlled. These studies would include both the elaboration of methods for controlling climate conditions in large territories and also the changing of microclimates. (2) Studying photochemical processes, particularly photosynthesis, both for the purpose of increasing crop harvest and for determining the possibilities of creating artificial chemical systems for obtaining food products and energy. (3) Studying photoelectric and thermal-electric processes in order to create economically acceptable devices for transforming the energy of solar radiation into electricity. (4) Studying the processes of heat and mass transfer in different solar installations. (5) Investigations connected with designing and manufacturing special materials and their products with definite properties (materials for photo- and thermal-elements, transparent and metal films, selective coverings, and so on). (6) The search for new methods of transforming and utilizing solar energy. (7) At the same time, engineering work should be continued on designing prospective solar installations and calculating their technological and economic characteristics.

The authors thank the organizing committee for the invitation to write this review, and they would be glad to support any international cooperation in solar energy.

The authors also thank Dr. Tveryanovich and Dr. Chirkov for some ideas we used in this review.

All photos (except Fig. 27 and Fig. 28) were done by Dr. Tyukhov.

We understand that "Russia goes on her own way" but would like to cooperate significantly more than our current economic situation allows. We strongly believe that international cooperation with Russia in the transition period for developing solar energy can and should be more active. It will help us to build a much better infrastructure for consumer-oriented technologies.

We hope that the Russian ISES history is just starting and after a transition period and with our strong roots we will be able to work jointly with the world solar energy community, as it should be with the help of our educational activity and our solar (read here, inexhaustible) enthusiasm.

Our motto is "High Solar Technologies, for Humans and Society!"

Literature

1. Lomonosov, M. V., Investigation of catoptrico-dioptric burning-glass device described in August 1741, *Complete Collection of Proceedings*, v. 1, Academy of the USSR, 1950.

2. Mihelson, V. A. "Results of solar radiation measurements in Petrovsko-Razumoskoe from 1910 till 1924." Proceedings of the Agricultural Academy, 168 p.

3. Ioffe, A. F. "On Physics and Physicists, Papers, lectures, letters," Leningrad, "Nauka," 1985, 544 p. (in Russian).

4. Alferov, Zh. I. *Physics and Life*. Moscow-Saint Petersburg, "Nauka," 2001, 288 p. (in Russian).

5. Lasarev, V. P. "Energy, her sources in the Earth and her origin," *Gosenergoizdat*, Moscow, Leningrad, 1947.

6. Baum, V. A. "Research on the use of solar energy made in the Soviet Union." Proceedings of the National Academy of Sciences of the USA, 1961 August; 47 (8): 1262–70.

7. Bezrukikh, P. P., Arbuzov, J. D., Borisov, G. A., Vissarionov, V. I., Evdokimov, V. M., Malinin, N. K., Ogorodov, N. V., Puzakov, V. N., Sidorenko, G. I., and Shpak, A. A., *Resources and efficiency of the use of renewable sources of energy in Russia*, Saint-Petersburg: Nauka, 2002.

Chapter 18

Solar Energy Utilization in Singapore

by
M. N. A. Hawlader* and K. A. Jahangeer
Department of Mechanical Engineering,
National University of Singapore
9 Engineering Drive 1
Singapore 117576
*e-mail:mpehawla@nus.edu.sg

Abstract

This paper describes the applications of solar energy in Singapore for the past four decades. It includes meteorological conditions; solar thermal applications, such as, water-heating, air-conditioning, and drying; solar energy storage; photovoltaics. Solar air-conditioning comprises both space heating and cooling. Considerable research efforts have been devoted to meteorological data collection and analyses, which is an essential element for solar applications. Solar collectors, both flat and tubular, showing good performance, were used for various solar thermal applications. The largest solar application in Singapore is the solar water heating system at Changi International Airport, which provides 60% of the total hot water required for the flight kitchen of the airport. Solar domestic water heaters are also in use in different parts of Singapore. Thermo economic analyses of solar systems required the development of simulation programs. These enabled performance evaluation and optimization of the systems. Solar energy applications for water heating and drying show favorable economics. The future directions of solar energy applications in Singapore have also been identified.

18.1   Introduction

The modern world economy is dependent upon energy derived from fossil fuel, and any disruption in its supply affects the whole world economy. The growing demand for oil, since 1973, leads to a significant difficulty in the world market. For the past two decades, the world has become aware of the fact that the supply of energy is of utmost concern to mankind. It is important that measures are undertaken immediately to conserve the dwindling supply of costly fuel and, at the same time, to develop alternative sources of energy. Experience shows that reliance on fossil fuel alone is not wise due to the various socio-political and geographical factors underlying its availability and usage. Even if fossil fuel is readily available in some parts of the world, as proven by various researchers over the years, its usage should be controlled because of global warming that it causes. The discomfort and unhealthy living of the human race caused by global warming is a by-product of the quest for our basic need; energy. This, along with the depletion of the fossil energy resources on the globe, compelled researchers to look for alternate energy sources. Solar energy has been in the front line among all the renewable energy resources, e.g., wind, wave, and biogas energy.

Singapore being a tropical country located near the equator (1° 21'N latitude and 103° 55'E longitude), the availability of solar energy is more than adequate even to replace other expensive sources of energy currently available to support its population of less than 5 million. This may be cited as one of the reasons behind the research that has been done on solar energy in Singapore for the last four decades. Of these, the ongoing research on an integrated solar system for air-conditioning, water-heating, and drying deserves a special mention. Both the local universities, the National University of Singapore and Nanyang Technological University, are staunch supporters for solar energy-related research and have been the epicenter for all the solar energy-related developments in Singapore. The following sections describe the research and development that have taken place in Singapore in the different fields like solar water heating, solar air-conditioning, and solar energy storage. Brief discussions about the future direction of the research and development of the solar energy in Singapore is included near the end of this review.

18.2   Meteorological Data of Singapore

In Singapore, global solar radiation on a horizontal surface has been measured by the meteorological department at the airport since 1961. In 1962,

Tan Beng Cheok, under the supervision of Dr. Rajaratnam, investigated solar radiation in Singapore [1]. This investigation included the measurement of total and diffuse radiation falling on a horizontal surface. Hawlader [2] developed a model, in which global radiation was separated into diffuse and direct components. In addition, equations were developed for frequently used meteorological variables, based on the hourly meteorological data of Singapore for a period of six years, 1975-1980, by Hawlader et al. [3]. These variables include global radiation, dry bulb temperature, relative humidity, and wind speed. Monthly averaged hourly values of these variables can be calculated using these equations. Fig. 1 and 2 show the monthly mean hourly values of global radiation, dry bulb temperature, relative humidity, and wind speed, respectively, for a typical day in Singapore.

The annual mean daily global radiation in Singapore contributes about 45% of the extraterrestrial radiation on a horizontal surface. Whereas, on clear days it will be about 67%, the annual mean daily value of 16.06 MJ/m2 accounts for 66.5% of the days. Sunshine data have been measured for more than 40 years. The average daily sunshine hours amount to 5.61 hours, that is 46.4% of the maximum possible sunshine.

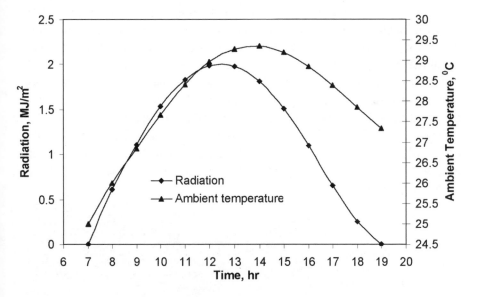

Fig. 1: Variation of solar irradiation and ambient temperature for a typical day in Singapore [3,4]

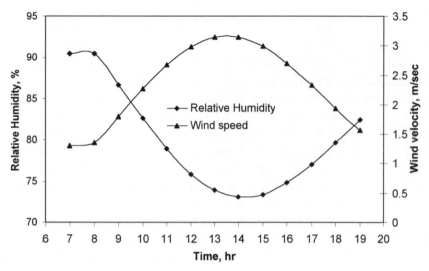

Fig. 2: Variation of relative humidity and wind speed for a typical day in Singapore [3,4]

18.3   Solar Water Heating

The introduction of solar hot water installations in Singapore in 1978 was only the beginning of the advancement of solar water heating application in the years to come. The main components of the solar water heating system, as shown in Fig. 3, are the solar collector and storage tank; it supplies hot water to the airport, sports/social clubs, hotels, restaurants, hospitals, commercial/institutional buildings and industry. Considering the rising fuel and electricity costs, the solar water heating installations are currently considered to be economically viable. It is generally found that such installations operate efficiently and effectively. The demand has grown steadily for such systems, and, with the active encouragement of the Government, the future for such systems appears to be promising.

Fig. 3: Installation of a domestic solar water heater in Singapore

In April 1978, two solar hot water systems were first installed in Singapore at the Changi Golf Club and the Tanglin Club. The total solar collector areas installed were relatively small, 16 and 40 m², respectively. Since the setting up of these installations, the demand for such systems has grown steadily and a large solar plant was set up at the passenger terminal building of Changi International Airport in Singapore [5]. The collector area used in the installation at the Changi International Airport is 630 m² with a storage tank volume of 40 m³. The existing solar installation can provide about 60% of the total energy required by the catering facility for water heating. A computer program is also available, developed by Hawlader et al. [6–8], for the performance evaluation of the system. Table 1 shows some solar water heating installations in Singapore with the total collector area used.

Table 1
Some of the water heating installations in Singapore

Location	Solar Collector Area, m²
Changi Golf Club	16
Shangri-La Hotel	32
Tanglin Club	40
Singapore Island Country Club	64
Orchid Inn Hotel	96
Singapore International Airlines	120
Tanglin Club Phase-II	144
Changi International Airport Passenger Terminal	630

18.4   Solar Air-conditioning

In the tropical climate of Singapore, the average daily temperatures can exceed the comfort level for long periods, resulting in the requirement for air-conditioning for space cooling. Installations of conventional air-conditioning using high-cost electrical energy is considered expensive. This encourages the use of an alternate source of energy for running air-conditioners in a cheaper and more affordable way. If solar energy could reduce the overall cost of air conditioning, it would be beneficial for a large section of the population of Singapore living in multistory buildings.

As in mechanical air-conditioning, the system shall be working either on a vapor compression cycle or on a vapor absorption system. The major difference between the two is the presence of a compressor in the vapor compression system, which is replaced with an absorber and generator in the absorption system. In Singapore, most of the research on solar air-condition-ing consisted of vapor absorption systems driven with the help of the solar energy collected from flat-plate collectors or from a solar pond.

In 1978, Tan and Tan [9] reported a solar powered air-conditioner for Singapore that worked in conjunction with an absorption refrigeration cycle. The refrigerant used in the air-conditioner was LiBr-Water, and a YAZAKI WFC 600S-model chiller was used in the system. Flat-plate solar collectors were used, which could operate at a temperature sufficient to drive the absorption system.

A solar fridge/cooler working on an intermittent vapor absorption sys-tem was reported by Teng and Chng [10]. The refrigerant used was NH_3-water and a flat-plate solar collector was used. Research by Hawlader [11] on the use of solar ponds for space cooling was reported in 1981. In the work, a description of the solar pond, its method of operation, and the likely problems to be encountered during the operation of the pond were included. A computer program was developed and run with the daily aver-age insolation data recorded at a location near the Singapore airport. It was reported that the solar pond attains fairly high temperature suitable for space cooling in conjunction with an absorption refrigeration cycle. In 1982, in another work of Hawlader [12] on solar ponds, a mathematical model was developed to predict the performance characteristics of the pond under different operating conditions. Hawlader had reported that the temperature of the pond strongly depends on the extinction coefficient, the depth of the surface mixed layer, and the ground loss. In his work on the performance characteristics of solar ponds operating at different lati-tudes, Hawlader [13] compared the performance of a solar pond operat-ing at two different latitudes. For the comparison, the hourly meteorolog-ical data of Kew (UK) and Singapore were used. He had found that the pond operating at higher latitudes, i.e., Kew, where seasonal variations are significant, must be deeper than a pond near the equator. It was also proven that a pond operating at a location in Singapore attains a fairly high temperature, but the temperature requirements are also high for the desired applications such as space cooling in conjunction with a refriger-ation cycle. In comparison, a pond in Kew attains a lower temperature and it can supply a considerable amount of thermal energy to support a space-heating load.

A double exponential model for transmittance in solar ponds was devel-oped by Hawlader et al. [14] in 1989. An analysis of the measured and esti-mated data has shown that a single profile of transmittance is unlikely to be applicable for different quality and clarity of salt solution in solar ponds. An empirical equation was proposed to include the effect of different values of transmittance in the simulation and design of a solar pond. The equation takes into account the variations of the quality and clarity of the salt-water, dependence of absorptance on wave length of solar radiation, and the effect of zenith angle.

Kho et al. [15], in 1990, designed a solar pond for delivering 54 m3 per day of hot water at 600 C for a catering facility in Singapore. An experimental pond with an area of 14 m^2 and a depth of 1.5 m was built and tested over a period of time under the meteorological conditions of Singapore. The design of the pond was carried out in two steps. First, the depths of the different layers of the pond were determined by considering the maximum temperature of the storage zone and the useful energy gain. Table 2 shows the different layers and their depth for the given load and for the Singapore meteorological conditions.

Kho et al. had used the minimum payback period as the economic figure of merit to determine the optimum area of the pond. The optimum area of the pond was found to be 6,000 m^2. It was found that the payback period depends on the transparency of the pond and, for the particular pond, varied between 3 and 4.5 years.

Table 2
Depths of different layers of the solar pond

Layer/zone details	Depth in m
Surface mixed layer	0.32
Insulation zone	1.00
Storage zone	1.00
Total pond depth	2.32

In his work on solar assisted open-cycle absorption cooling in 1994, Hawlader [16] highlighted the advantages and disadvantages of an open-cycle absorption refrigeration system for Singapore meteorological conditions.

18.5   Solar Photovoltaic

Photovoltaic solar electricity is the conversion of sunlight into electricity by efficient photovoltaic solar cells. High conversion-efficiency silicon solar cells became commercially available on the world market in the late 1950s mainly for space applications. A photovoltaic system typically consists of a solar cell array, energy storage system, and control devices. A solar cell array is made up of several photovoltaic modules, each of which encapsulates an assembly of solar cells which convert sunlight into electricity. Modern solar cells with reasonable efficiency were invented in the early 1950s and have been in use to power satellites since 1959. They began to be used for Earth-based applications in a big way in the 1970s mostly for remote telecommunication and navigational aids. They have been in use to provide power for urban applications, such as road side emergency telephones and traffic sign boards, since the mid 1980s. With the price dropping steadily due to more advances in technology and mass production, they are now becoming affordable for urban homes and businesses.

In 1980, Chew and Tay [17] studied the performance of a silicon solar cell system under the local meteorological conditions. They had used 128 silicon solar cells in an experimental power generation system. In 1986, Chandratilleke and Ho [18] had tested a water pumping system comprising a 1.14 kW photovoltaic array and an 860 W centrifugal pump for its performance. A system simulation procedure was also developed and used for comparative study.

Currently, in Singapore, the following commercial solar photovoltaic products are available in the market for wide variety of uses:

1) Solar power system for homes and schools
2) Solar educational products
3) Solar light products
4) Solar power system products
5) Energy saving bulbs

In Singapore the application of the solar photovoltaic can be seen in garden lights, street lights, electric lamps, advertisement boards etc. There are public bus stops with a photovoltaic system running the lights and fans. The solar power of the commercially available lights in the market ranges from 0.33 to 30 W and these are mainly used for street and park lighting applications. Table 3 shows the details of the commercially available solar panels in Singapore.

Table 3
Commercially available solar panels in Singapore.

Model	Peak Power (W)	Working Voltage (V)	Current (A)	Dimension (LxWxH) mm	Weight (kg)
TDB60-20-P	4~4.5	>=8.5	0.47~0.53	390x161x28	0.93
TDB60-38-P	8~10	>=16.5	0.48~0.60	550x207x28	1.46
TDB60-20-P	5~6	>=8.5	0.58~0.70	459x191x28	1.23
TDB60/2-38-P	5~6	>=16.5	0.30~0.36	340x240x28	1.10
TDB60-38-P	10~12	>=16.5	0.60~0.72	639x240x28	1.95
TDB75-20-P	8~10	>=8.5	0.94~1.17	558x227x28	1.75
TDB75-38-P	17~20	>=16.5	1.03~1.21	789x294x28	2.90
TDB100/3-36-P	10~12	>=16.8	0.60~0.71	500x300x28	1.80
TDB100-38-P	36~42	>=17.3	2.08~2.42	1356x296x32	5.70
TDB103x103/4-36-P	10~12	>=16.8	0.60~0.71	360x340x28	1.58

18.6   Solar Energy Storage

Because solar energy is a time-dependent energy source, the storage of energy or other products of solar processes are necessary if solar energy is to meet a substantial portion of the required energy. The optimum capacity of an energy storage system depends on the expected time dependence of solar radiation availability, the nature of load dependent on the process, the degree of reliability needed, the manner in which auxiliary energy is supplied, and an economic analysis that determines how much of the annual load should be carried by solar energy [19].

The performance of solar applications in Singapore is also strongly dependent on the energy storage associated with the system. To address the issue of energy storage in the solar system, studies have been carried out on the problem. In the water-heating system of the Changi International Airport Services (CIAS), four storage tanks of 10 m^3 each are used for energy storage. In 1988, Hawlader et al. [20] investigated theoretically and experimentally the thermal stratification and fluid motion in the storage tanks like the one used at Changi International Airport. An electric water heater was used to simulate a solar collector and the experiments were conducted under several different conditions in which a solar system is likely to operate. From the experiment, it was found that the location of the inlet/outlet ports has considerable effect on the mixing of the fluid. Equations were developed to predict temperature distribution in the storage tank.

A recent trend in energy storage research is to seek novel solar storage materials like micro- encapsulated phase-change materials. Preparation and evaluation of a novel storage material, namely microencapsulated paraffin, was conducted by Hawlader et al. [21] in 2000. The preparation of the micro-encapsulated paraffin was done by the complex coacervation technique. The performance evaluation was carried out by considering encapsulation ratio, hydrophilicity, energy storage capacity, and size distribution. The experiments were designed, based on a surface response method, to optimize the processing conditions. The microencapsulated paraffin had shown large energy storage and release capacity during its phase-change, depending on different ratios of paraffin wax to coating. Another work on the microencapsulated phase-change material was performed by Uddin et al. [22] in 2002. He investigated the effect of cyclic operation on the performance of the micro-encapsulated phase change material. The result had shown that the microencapsulated phase-change material has large energy storage and release capacity during its phase change and maintains its energy storage and release capacity, chemical characteristics, and structural profile even after 1,000 thermal recycles.

18.7   Performance of Solar Collectors

In general, collectors used in solar installations in Singapore are mainly of the flat-plate type. These flat-plate collectors are manufactured based on the type of applications they are intended to be used for. Other types of collectors used in Singapore are evacuated tubular collectors, particularly for higher-temperature applications. Flat-plate collectors installed in Singapore are equipped with either selective or nonselective black coatings. Local firms are manufacturing these solar collectors. Studies have been conducted to evaluate efficient solar collectors for various applications. In 1988, Wijeysundera and Hawlader [23] applied the single-blow technique to obtain the performance parameters of solar collectors [23]. Both simulation and experiments were performed on two flat-plate collectors of different designs. The predicted fluid outlet temperature agreed well with the experimental results over a wide range of flow rates and fluid temperatures. Wijeysundera et al. [24] also developed a test procedure for the evaluation of solar collector characteristics from the measured variation of the storage tank temperature. Two flat-plate collectors were tested over a period of eleven days each to study the feasibility of the test procedure. From the test, it was found that the standard deviation for the daily mean values of the collector characteristics were about 2.8 to 4 percent. In 1999, experimental studies of three types of solar air collectors were performed by Karim and Hawlader [25]. These collectors included a flat-plate, finned and v-corrugated collector suitable for solar-drying applications. These collectors were tested using ASHRAE standards for solar collector testing. The v-corrugated collector was found to be the most efficient one. In 2002, Minn et al. [26] formulated a distributed model for a tedlar-foil flat-plate solar collector and performed experiments for the validation of the model. For a given meteorological condition and collector design parameters, the model describes a 2-D absorber plate, where its temperature distributions along with the coolant channels can be predicted.

The solar water heater at Changi International Airport consists of 630 m2 of flat-plate collectors. and Fig. 4 shows part of the solar collector arrays in use. Fig. 5 shows evacuated tubular collectors used for domestic water heating applications.

Fig. 4: Part of flat plate solar collector used in Changi International Airport

Fig. 5: Evacuated tubular collectors

18.8   Future Directions

As far as future prospects are concerned, there are no economic and technical constraints that would inhibit the demand for solar energy installations in Singapore. Increasing petroleum fuel prices on one hand and a high year-round availability of solar radiation in Singapore on the other hand are positive factors for increasing demand for solar energy installations, purely out of economic considerations. In the future, on a national scale, solar energy installations will assist, not only in energy conservation and pollution abatement, but also in the conservation of foreign exchange. Rapid advancement in fabrication technology, even on the micro and nano scale, along with the well-advanced solar technology attained over the years by Singapore-based researchers, is motivating and promising a bright future for solar energy applications in Singapore.

Currently, most of the solar energy installations in Singapore are confined to applications in hospitals, schools, canteens, clubs, and commercial and institutional buildings. There is still room to adapt solar energy installations in industrial applications. It may be noted that extensive studies in countries with established solar technology have shown that the prospects of solar thermal technology in industry are promising. The general trend from these studies is optimistic and shows that at least 50% of process heat can be derived from solar sources. This shows that the prospects of applying central solar heating systems in food, drink, and the tobacco industries in Singapore are promising.

In Singapore, there are also bright prospects for domestic applications of solar energy for air-conditioning, drying, and water heating. The Singapore housing system is under the strict regulation of the housing and development board (HDB), which is under the direct control of the government. With full support and encouragement from the government in the national interest to minimize environmental pollution and increase conservation of conventional energy sources like oil, the three domestic applications can be met with the major share from solar energy. For example, a proven integrated solar energy system comprising air-conditioning, water heating, and drying can be added in any future building design by the housing board [27,28]. Existing buildings can be retrofitted with the integrated system. This is a scenario that would reap direct and indirect benefits for the population of Singapore. On a national scale, it will help to address the increasing oil price, while on the domestic scale, tenants can save appreciable amounts of utility payments.

Closure

Solar energy activities and application in Singapore for the past decades have been reviewed by highlighting the salient features of the research. Being a tropical country and ideal for solar energy applications, future prospects for the development of the solar industry in Singapore are promising. With the help of interest by and encouragement from the government and the exploitation of the untapped market in the industrial sector, the prospects seem to be much enhanced and realistic.

References

1. Tan Beng Cheok, "An investigation of the solar radiation in Singapore," "Master of Science Thesis, National University of Singapore, 1962.

2. M. N. A. Hawlader, "Diffuse, global and extra-terrestrial solar radiation for Singapore," *International Journal of Ambient Energy*, vol. 5, no.1, pp. 31–8, 1984.

3. M. N. A. Hawlader, T. Y. Bong, and Wan Mahmood, "A method of estimating monthly global radiation for Singapore," *International Journal of Solar Energy*, vol.5, pp. 279–88, 1988.

4. M. N. A. Hawlader, T. Y. Bong, and Wan Mahmood, "Some frequently used meteorological data for Singapore", *International Journal of Solar Energy*, vol.8, pp. 1–11, 1990.

5. M. N. A. Hawlader, K. C. Ng, T. T. Chandratilleke, Kelvin Koay H. L, "A solar installation for industrial hot water," *Renewable Energy Review Journal*, vol. 6, no.1, pp. 40–7, June 1984.

6. M. N. A. Hawlader, K. C. Ng, T. T. Chandratilleke, and Kelvin Koay H. L., "Performance prediction of CIAS solar water heater," *International Journal of Ambient Energy*, vol. 9, no.1, pp. 23–9, January 1988.

7. M. N. A. Hawlader, M. S. Uddin, and Low Eng Siang, "A PC based simulation and optimization program for domestic solar water heaters," *Asian Journal on Science Technology for Development*, vol. 7, no. 1, pp. 43–61, 1987.

8. M. N. A. Hawlader, K. C. Ng, T.T. Chandratilleke, D. Sharma, and Kelvin Koay H.L., "Economic evaluation of a solar water heating system," *Energy Conversion Management*, vol. 27, no. 2, pp. 197–204, 1987.

9. Tan Chuan Jin, Tan Seng Chee, "Solar Powered Air-conditioner," Bachelor of Engineering Thesis, National University of Singapore, 1979.

10. Teng Chong Heng, Chng Teck Lam, "Design and Construction of a Solar Fridge/Cooler," Bachelor of Engineering Thesis, National University of Singapore, 1978.

11. M. N. A. Hawlader, "Solar ponds for space cooling," Proceedings of the third convention of engineering institution of the south east Asian nations, pp. 311–33, 1981.

12. M. N. A. Hawlader, "The use of solar ponds for air conditioning" Proceedings of the I. I. F.-I. I. R.-Commissions E1, E2-Jerusalem, pp. 61–73, 1982.

13. M. N. A. Hawlader, "Performance characteristics of solar ponds operating at different latitudes," *Applied Energy*, vol. 17, pp. 97–115, 1984.

14. M. N. A. Hawlader, J. C. Ho, N. E. Wijeysundera, and T. H. Kho, "A double exponential model for transmittance in solar ponds," *International Journal of Solar Energy*, vol. 7, pp. 227–35, 1989.

15. T. H. Kho, M. N. A. Hawlader, J. C. Ho, and N. E. Wijeysundera, "Design and performance evaluation of a solar pond for industrial process heating," *International Journal of Solar Energy*, vol. 10, pp. 83-101, 1991.

16. M. N. A. Hawlader, "Solar assisted open cycle absorption cooling," *RERIC International Energy Journal*, vol. 16, no. 1, pp. 27–41, 1994.

17. Chew Hock Kee, Tay Siang Lee, "An Experimental Study on the performance of a solar cell system under local conditions," Bachelor of Engineering Thesis, National University of Singapore, 1980.

18. T. T. Chandratilleke and J. C. Ho, "A study of a photovoltaic array for water pumping" *Solar and Wind Technology*, vol. 3, pp. 59–71, 1986.

19. John A. Duffie and William A. Beckman, *Solar Engineering of Thermal Processes*, second edition, 1991.

20. M. N. A. Hawlader, T. Y. Bong and T. S. Lee, "A Thermally stratified solar water storage tank," *International Journal of Solar Energy*, vol.6, pp. 119–138, June 1988.

21. M. N. A. Hawlader, M. S. Uddin, and H. J. Zhu, "Preparation and evaluation of a novel solar storage material" *International Journal of Solar Energy*, vol. 20, pp. 227–38, 2000.

22. M. S. Uddin, H. J. Zhu, and M. N. A. Hawlader, "Effect of cyclic operation on the characteristics of a microencapsulated PCM storage material," *International Journal of Solar Energy*, vol. 22, pp. 105–14, 2002.

23. N. E. Wijeysundera and M. N. A. Hawlader, "An application of the single-blow technique to obtain the performance parameters of solar collectors," *International Journal of Solar Energy*, vol. 7, pp. 63–72, 1989.

24. N. E. Wijeysundera, M. N. A. Hawlader, and K. Y. Foong, "Estimation of collector performance parameters from daily system tests," *Transaction of the ASME*, vol. 118, pp. 30–6, 1996.

25. M. A. Karim and M. N. A. Hawlader, "Development of solar air collectors for drying applications," *Energy Conversion and Management*, vol. 45, pp. 329–44, 2004.

26. M. A. Minn, K. C. Ng, W. H. Khong and T. Melvin, "A distributed model for a tedlar-foil flat-plate solar collector," *Renewable Energy*, vol. 27, pp. 507–23, 2002.

27. M. N. A. Hawlader and S. K. Chou, "The performance of a solar assisted heat pump water heating system," *Applied Thermal Engineering*, vol. 21, pp. 1049–065, 2001.

28. M. N. A. Hawlader, S.K. Chou, K. A. Jahangeer and S. M. A. Rahman, "Solar assisted heat-pump dryer and water heater," *Applied Energy*, vol. 74, pp. 185–93, 2003.

Chapter 19

Solar Energy Society of Southern Africa

by
Brian Schaller
with contributions by Dieter Holm
and Charles Eduard Barnard
Private Bag X010
Howick, 3290, KwaZulu-Natal,
South Africa
e-mail: brian7@netfocus.co.za
Cell 083-448-3390

Abstract

This report covers some of the early history of the Southern African Section of ISES. This is commonly known as the Solar Energy Society of Southern Africa, or SESSA. Recently the words Solar Energy were replaced by Sustainable Energy. Early research in solar energy-related matters in Southern Africa is reviewed as a background to the origin of the Society The first few years, before the birth of SESSA, is described together with the rapid growth of the Section. The most important events include national conferences, meetings, activities, financial matters, and awards that are given. A chronological listing of annual activities of the Section is provided together with solar developments and events in Southern Africa. International Awards that some of the members of our solar community received are also noted. The further development of our Section beyond 1980 is reported in the second volume of this History of ISES.

19.1   The Solar Energy Society of Southern Africa: The Birth—1974

The Southern Africa Section of ISES was born on 2 December 1974 at a meeting of a steering committee at the Sunnyside Hotel in Johannesburg. This was followed by a symposium on 3 December. The Convener of the symposium was Chris Malan assisted by Will Cawood of the CSIR; some 35 people attended. The steering committee comprised Dr. Austin Whillier, Honorary president; Brian Schaller, Chairman; Will Cawood, Secretary; Dr. Richard Turner, Treasurer; Prof. Stefan Smoleniec; Prof. Neville Tully; Prof. Jack Gledhill; Prof. Dick Dutkiewicz; Doyle Liebenberg; Peter Lee; B. Thornton; and Benny du Plooy.

19.1.1   The Origins

The origins of this meeting began in 1957 when Brian Schaller (Fig. 2), a consulting engineer, joined the Association for Applied Solar Energy of Phoenix, Arizona. This became the Solar Energy Society, which shortly after became the International Solar Energy Society. Schaller attended the 1973 ISES/COMPLES/AFEDES Congress in Paris. ISES secretary Frank Hogg asked Schaller to consider starting an ISES Branch in South Africa. The Board of ISES appointed him as International secretary (ex-officio board member), for Southern Africa for the purpose of establishing an ISES Section there. Schaller then found Solar Pioneer Dr. Austin Whillier in Johannesburg.

Fig. 1: Austin Whillier—founder president

Dr. Whillier visited Schaller in Ladysmith, Natal, in August 1974. Austin was in favor of establishing the Society and offered to assist provided he was not asked to be president or chairman. He was already president of two South African learned societies. At the time, Austin was also Director of Research for the world-renowned South African Chamber of Mines.

Fig. 2: Brian Schaller—founder chairman

19.1.2   Early Solar Research in Southern Africa.

As a base to this history of the Society, it seems appropriate to outline the first endeavors in solar energy research in Southern Africa. These appear to have commenced in the 1930s when solar distillation was being investigated.

Dr. Everitt Howe: The late Everitt Howe of San Francisco (later the first editor of *Sunworld*), was well-known for his distinguished work on solar distillation. Everitt was invited to conduct research in solar distillation for the National Chemical Research Laboratory of South Africa in the 1930s. He enjoyed his work and visits to the country immensely.

Dr. Gertrud Riemerschmid: A remarkable young lady for her time, Dr. Riemerschmid (Fig. 3), daughter of a distinguished Munich family, came out from Germany shortly before the Second World War to research solar radiation qualities. Her purpose was also to lay the foundations for research into the benefits of solar radiation on medicine and agriculture. She had worked briefly on similar projects in Central and East Africa. She worked with Dr. Grober, professor Medicine Jenensis, on pyranometers, actinometers, ultra violet dosimeters, and similar devices. In 1937 Riemerschmid went on to establish six solar laboratories around South Africa.

The author met her research assistant, Mr. Van der Westhuizen, some forty years later—quite by chance, by giving him a lift on a country road in South Africa. Dr. Riemerschmid earned fame in many countries in Africa and South America in the few years before she died suddenly in 1942 in Pretoria.

Fig. 3: Gertrude Riemerschmid

Dr. Andrew J. Drummond: The South African Weather Bureau produced another solar scientist, Andrew Drummond, who left South Africa in 1957 to join Eppley Laboratories in the USA. He received his early scientific training at the British Meterologic Office in Kew, near London. He must have come across Gertrud Riemerschmid's work in Pretoria at the Weather Bureau.He was a prime mover in solar radiation measurements, according to his colleague at Eppley Laboratories. Andy, as everyone called him, was the first editor in chief of *Solar Energy*, the world famous ISES Journal first produced by Pergamon Press in 1967. Drummond's good wife later gave a box of his scientific papers to the author.

Dr. Austin Whillier: Whillier received his Ph.D. from MIT in the USA while working with Dr. Hottel. He carried out research in the Barbados, also with Hottel, before returning to South Africa. Here he did much valuable research at the National Mechanical Engineering Research Institute of the Council for Scientific and Research Institute (CSIR) during the 1950s. Whillier was appointed director of the prestigious Chamber of Mines Research Laboratories. It was his research on the cooling of deep mines that won him the President's Gold Medal. It also saved the world-wide mining industry huge amounts of money by switching the accent on mine cooling from air to water. Several presidents of the International Solar Energy Society told Schaller in Paris that probably half the research work in the USA at that time was based on the pioneering research work of Dr. Austin Whillier. His early research has recently been republished by MIT.

S. J. Richards: A researcher at the National Building Research Institute (NBRI), he collaborated with Dr. Whillier on several occasions including on the hugely popular H*ot Water from the Sun*, published in 1958, which was reprinted many times over the next decade. He also published *Solar Charts for the Design of Sunlight and Shade for Buildings in South Africa* in 1952; the charts are still being used today.

D. N. W. Chinnery: He did much solar research while at the NBRI, including on a snow melter for use by the South African Antarctic Team, which worked well. Chinnery took over the previous work at the NBRI from I. Kopke. Chinnery published the fundamental *Solar Water Heating in South Africa* in 1971.

19.1.3   Year 1975

The first meetings of the committee were held at the home of Dr. Austin Whillier and his good wife Mary in Johannesburg. Others who hosted the meetings included Peter Lee, and Doyle Liebenberg. Brian Schaller traveled regularly from Newcastle, Natal (300 km), and Dr. Dutkiewicz and Benny du Plooy from Capetown (1,000 km).

Schaller wrote a series of radio talks for the South African Broadcasting Corporation which was broadcast at almost the same time as the Society was launched. This resulted in a large influx of letters of interest, and membership prospered accordingly, exceeding 100 within six months.

It was decided that this Society should serve the whole of Southern Africa and not just South Africa, as individual country sections would otherwise battle to survive for scarcity of members. Thus it was decided to call the ISES Branch the Solar Energy Society of Southern Africa.

The first conference supported by SESSA was organized by Prof. Dick Dutkiewicz of the Energy Utilization Unit at the University of Capetown and took place in April 1975. It was titled "Energy and its Future in South Africa." Many members attended and some read papers at the conference. We were fortunate indeed to have the great Dr. Hoyt Hottel of MIT in the USA at the conference.

Prof. John Yellott of Phoenix, Arizona, was the first international solar expert invited to Southern Africa under the Norman Hansen Fellowship by

Dr. Webb of the CSIR. Prof. Yellott and his good wife, Barbara, were a delight to all who had the privilege to meet them. He was one of the first international celebrities to be interviewed by the infant South African television system.

The Copper Development Association kicked off with a competition offering the R2 500 award for the best solar water heater design.

The SESSA committee tackled the promotion of local branches in Durban, Capetown, Bloemfontein, Rhodesia/Zimbabwe, Swaziland, Lesotho, and Botswana. By July 1975 branches had been established in Capetown, Durban, and Johannesburg to serve three of the four Provinces of South Africa.

The Engineers Association of South Africa invited chairman Schaller to the Parliament to discuss solar energy with the then-Minister responsible for energy matters, the Honourable Danie Steyn. He was most interested, and on his retirement from politics he joined SESSA.

In April, SESSA members started to receive the *ISES News* from ISES HQ in Melbourne, Australia. The Central Council met regularly and the regional committees were also active, with numerous meetings countrywide. Rhodesia (Zimbabwe), South West Africa (Namibia), Lesotho, Swaziland, and Botswana, were participating.

Workshops were organized where people could, after short lessons, gain hands-on experience, so necessary when installing solar water systems. Selective surfaces were receiving the interest of the University of Capetown, while Pretoria University was investigating wind-driven generators, easy-to-make solar hot water (SHW) systems, and a solar pump. Chairman Schaller attended the ISES board meeting in Los Angeles in July, where he had the pleasure of having SESSA accepted as a full Section of ISES. Also at the conference among 2,000 delegates was our Secretary W. Cawood, A. Johannsen, and Tony Hyde. Dr. Whillier missed the conference but visited the USA later and met with old colleagues Jack Duffie and George Löf.

The membership stood at 150. The little Section was booming.

19.2   The Relationship of SESSA to ISES

We are a Section of ISES and as such our members are encouraged to become full members of ISES. Through the years, three types of Membership were normally offered; ISES (including local), local only, and corporations.

19.3   Our Conferences

Solar (Sustainable/Renewable) Energy Conferences in Southern Africa comprise the well known main types. These include:

1. annual regional solar energy conferences;
2. topical conferences concerning various categories of solar energy, such as solar thermal, architecture, photovoltaic, biomass, solar cooking;
3. ISES Congresses and international conferences;
4. local workshops, symposia, etc., in which contractors, engineers, and other interested people meet.

19.3.1   ISES and Local Publications

ISES publications have always been first-class world-respected journals and magazines. Local publications have fluctuated in quality and regularity with the passing years. Some excellent magazines have been published by SESSA. The ISES literature is extremely helpful in informing all members of worldwide news.

Fig. 4: Will Cawood, first secretary

19.4   Year 1976

Solar hot water workshops were very popular and were held in various cities around South Africa and Namibia.

The Transvaal branch of SESSA held a successful meeting in November at the Copper Pavilion in Johannesburg with Dr. Whillier, Peter Lee, and Mr. Granig of Anglo American attending.

The NBRI established a solar energy and energy conservation committee, appointing as members Dr. Whillier and Brian Schaller. At the inaugural meeting of this committee the Association of Building Societies advised that solar hot water would be included in house loans, even retroactively, an important step forward for solar energy.

Schaller visited Rhodesia, then the breadbasket of Africa (now Zimbabwe) and discussed SESSA with some of the thirty-four solar manufacturers there that were at that time in full production. He then visited Swaziland and Lesotho for the same purpose.

ISES together with the American Section (ASES) and the Canadian Section (SESCI) held a joint conference in August in Canada.

SESSA member Tim Smart proposed the formation of a Solar Energy Industries Association, which idea was soon carried forward to active and beneficial fruition.

The membership had climbed to 183.

19.5   Year 1977

George Löf, the past president of ISES, and another world Pioneer in Solar Energy, was invited to South Africa under the Natal Building Society Fellowship and lectured in various centres in South Africa, Namibia, and Rhodesia (Zimbabwe).

The Solar Water Heating Workshops continued their tremendous popularity and were staged in Windhoek, Capetown, Port Elizabeth, and Durban

Dr. Whillier, our Hon. President asked to step down because of his many other commitments, which request was granted with sadness.

The new SESSA council elected towards the year-end comprised Prof. Smoleniec, President; Peter Lee, Chairman; B. Schaller; R. Turner; B. du Plooy; and P. Kruger as members of the board.

There were now thirty-eight solar manufacturers in South Africa, which had at last overtaken Rhodesia (now Zimbabwe) in this respect.

Prof. Baruch Givoni of Ben Gurion University addressed the solar energy and energy conservation committee of the NBRI. Schaller was the SESSA member on this committee.

The NBRI reported on their work in energy consumption of buildings. NMERI was working on energy requirements for solar air conditioning systems.

The Energy Research Institute at the University of Capetown was investigating selective surfaces, solar ponds, concentrators, and energy in commercial buildings.

19.6   Year 1978

The NBRI arranged lectures in outlying areas to where the popular solar workshops had not been able to reach.

The Natal Branch held a successful symposium in November, featuring speakers Peter Lee, Martin van Schoor, Will Cawood, Ken Long, and Brian Schaller

The ISES Congress was held in New Delhi, India, in January. It was actually scheduled by ISES to be held in November 1977. However local difficulties prevented this.

Brian Schaller, being a South African, was the only person who attended this Congress, as South Africans were not welcome in India at that time. However, with patience and help from many people he was allowed in to deliver his invited paper and to attend the ISES board meetings and ISES committee meetings. ISES has a proud record of being a scientific and non-political organization.

In July Grahamstown hosted The Road Ahead Conference.

In September the Solar Energy Conference in Capetown opened organized by the Energy Research Institute, University of Capetown.

19.7   Years 1979 and 1980

The 1979 ISES Silver Jubilee Congress was held in Atlanta, Georgia. Schaller introduced the Solar Energy Society of Rhodesia to the ISES board of directors, who welcomed them.

This new Society held a symposium in August in Harare.

Schaller was requested to stand as ISES Vice President, but declined as South Africa was then problematic.

The membership grew to a scorching 230 in 1979.

This year saw the South African Bureau of Standards (SABS) issue specifications for solar hot water heaters and apply them across the industry. Manufacturing volumes increased dramatically. In 1992 SABS revised and complicated the specifications. Production then declined in the SHW industry. The SABS later issued new specifications and hopefully this would lead to another boost to the industry. Israel made SHW compulsory this year, and the NBRI of South Africa launched a successful SHW promotion campaign.

The 1980 membership hit a record of 250.

19.8   Years 1981 to 1985

Fig. 5: Dieter Holm, Secretary ISES—2003 and President of SESSA since 1981

At the Annual General Meeting of June 4, 1981, Prof. S. Smoleniec handed over the presidency of the Society to Prof. Dieter Holm (Fig. 5). Prof. Holm has held this position to November 2003 and may well hold it for many years to come.

Peter Lee handed over the chairmanship to Will Cawood, and Irene Field took over the treasury from Dr. Turner. Ms. Stander was the secretary and the other committee members were G. James, Bill Birrer, Prof. N. Tully, and Sir Patrick Walker. Brian Schaller was Chairman of the Natal Branch; Dr. Bernard Scheffler, Chairman of the newly formed Northern Transvaal Branch; Prof. J. van Wyk, Chairman of Southern Transvaal; J. Kok, Chairman of Eastern Cape; and Benny du Plooy, Chairman of Western Cape.

Wayne Beb was re-elected Chairman of the Solar Energy Industries Association.

The 1981 revised constitution provided for the Council to hold office for two years.

The Society had an eventful year, with the laying of several cornerstones for future growth. One of these involved publication of the Section's official magazine called Energy and the Environment. Economics dictated that SESSA combine efforts with three other related organisations, namely the Institute of Energy, the Energy Society, and the Solar Energy Industries Association.

In 1981 these societies organized an overseas tour encompassing solar installations in southern France and Israel, which was timed to wind up at the ISES Solar World Forum at Brighton, UK. The tour was a resounding success and some 30 SESSA members attended the Brighton Conference.

The membership in February 1981 declined to 183 total.

An international conference was held in Pretoria in November 1982. Speakers included Prof. Harry Tabor, then president of ISES; Prof. Tom Lawand, head of the Brace Research Institute in Canada, and Dr. Rodger Farrer of the Mexican Solar Energy Institute. The Society took maximum advantage of the visit of these eminent authorities, and lectures were delivered at eleven centers throughout South Africa. The Solar Water Heating Industry reached an all-time high, installing some 27,000 sq. m. during 1983. This is more than double the 2003 production. Several installations exceeded 1,000 sq. m.

The membership further declined to a total of 91 in July 1982.

An enormous loss to the Society at this time was the death of Dr. Austin Whillier shortly after being awarded Honorary Membership of the Society.

The Austin Whillier Award: This award is presented to a member of SESSA for the best paper or publication. The awards are donated by Mary Whillier and Brian Schaller in memory of our founder president and are generally presented by Mary Whillier.

The ISES board meetings took place in Copenhagen in 1982 at a regional conference. Director Brian Schaller attended and arranged to submit an invitation to the ISES board to hold a Congress in Southern Africa. The ISES board paid homage to the memory of Austin Whillier with a period of silence. The 1983 ISES World Congress took place in Perth, Western Australia. Several SESSA members attended Brian Schaller was elected Chairman of the long range planning committee for ISES-a committee that was dissolved recently, probably to our loss. He was re-elected to continue serving on three other ISES committees; membership, publications and programs.

The 1985 ISES World Congress took place in Montreal, Canada. Schaller missed the Congress but submitted his chairman's Report on Long Range Planning to the Board. Schaller was nominated for election as Vice President of ISES.

19.9   Years 1986 and 1987

A successful symposium and exhibition was held at the Kelvin House, Johannesburg, in February 1986.

The ISES World Congress took place in Hamburg, Germany, and was attended by a large SESSA contingent. Brian Schaller again missed the conference and resigned his ISES posts. The resignation again was not accepted by the ISES board of directors.

A seminar was held in May at Constantia Park, Johannesburg, in cooperation with the Engineers Association of South Africa.

Due to a distressing period for the SESSA Council, Schaller was called upon to accept the chair of SESSA again. Schaller wrote to all members of SESSA, "It is a pleasant surprise to be chairman again after 14 years. The secretary, who has good intentions, can no longer provide a service. If we do not have a secretary the Society will roll over and die. The same goes for the newsletter editor. Are there any willing members...?"

He wrote directly to Dr. Simon Brand, head of the Development Bank of South Africa to sponsor a substantial Conference. This came to pass, in a big way, the following year.

19.10 Years 1988 to 1990

Deon Stassen was chairman for the period 1988-1990. SESSA's HQ was located at the Development Bank of South Africa (DBSA) at this time. In that period we held one of the local SESSA conferences and exhibitions at the Indaba Conference Centre in Johannesburg. Major government institutions such as the SABS, Dept. of Minerals and Energy, Eskom, DBSA, and Agricultural Research actively participated in the event. SESSA paid some funds to ISES to ameliorate the substantial debt accumulated over the last few years.

The 1989 ISES Congress was held in Kobe, Japan. At this time Deon Stassen facilitated the establishment of the Photovoltaic Industries Association (PVIA). One of the main aims of this organization was to adopt a common goal of supporting solar energy development instead of each organization doing its own thing that in many instances was contrary to the common goal.

19.11 Years 1991 to 1992

The ISES World Congress was held in Denver, Colorado.

SESSA produced the *AFRICAN SUN*, a forty-page magazine of quite some caliber. The editorial committee included of Chair, D. Holm; Editor, Bernard Scheffler; Secretary, Mrs. D. Johnston; Water heating, Jim Hickey; PV, T. Cooper; Buildings, D. Holm; Energy policy, D. Stassen; Alternative energy, G. Morris. This excellent magazine ran until 1994.

The membership stood at sixty-one according to the March 1991 AGM Minutes.

19.12   Years 1993 to 1996

19.12.1   ISES AFRICA: by Dieter Holm

When ISES headquarters was moved to Freiburg, Germany in 1994/95 the ISES board decided to create ISES regional offices as part of the ISES 2000 initiative. These should be hosted by existing ISES national sections. On 14 August 1995 the following (hosted by ISES) regional offices were formally established:

> ISES AFRICA (hosted by SESSA, Pretoria, South Africa)
> ISES PACIFIC (hosted by ANZES, Sydney, Australia)
> ISES SOUTH AMERICA (hosted by SALTA, Argentina)
> ISES EUROPE ROMA (hosted by Italy)

The functions of the regional offices were to:

- build global and regional information networks
- assist with technology transfer
- organize workshops/demonstration projects
- liaise with government
- liaise with industry and facilitate solar energies
- advance the growth of other national solar energy societies.

African ISES members who did not have national sections would register under ISES AFRICA.

Individual regional offices would operate as local conditions demanded and were only requested to submit an annual work plan for how they envisaged spending the amount of $5,500 per year they received from ISES headquarters and to report back. The following headings were suggested:

1. Core group of able people
2. Communications
3. Accessibility of centre
4. Solar awareness in area
5. Funding potential
6. Conferences
7. Location of other key organisations
8. Strength of solar industry

9. Economic considerations
10. Unique attributes
11. Envisaged structure and business plan

The wording *solar* in those days is equivalent to *renewable energy* today. In 1995 a designated regional office committee of the ISES board coordinated the work. Under the following presidency this committee was not appointed and funding had to be reduced, which influenced regional office activities.

Under the chairmanship of Marius Willemse, the SESSA council then decided to fold ISES AFRICA and SESSA activities into one. ISES interests were actively fostered such as our previous contribution to the 1992 UNDP World Summit, the Harare ISES conference, ISES membership drives, the African Utilities conferences in Johannesburg and Kenya, the SEPCO workshop, the Summer Academy, and the ISES president and headquarters' visit to WSSD. Dieter Holm was Director of ISES AFRICA.

Next to ISES EUROPE, the ISES AFRICA regional office was probably the most active one. There had never been any doubt that SESSA host the ISES AFRICA regional office, which should not be confused with other national sections in Africa. ISES AFRICA welcomed and supported the creation of new African sections. There was talk of other regional offices in America, Pacific and Africa, which to the best of my knowledge never materialised.

The ISES board of directors presented a Certificate of Appreciation to Brian Schaller for his long and dedicated service as a director of ISES and representative of Southern Africa.

19.12.2   This Section is prepared by Charles Eduard Barnard, better known as Duard Barnard

In April 1993 the chairperson of SESSA was Hazel Hall, the regional chairperson of the Western Cape. She therefore replaced Iain Johnston as chairperson in effect in April 1993. Duard Barnard was elected an ordinary member to the council.

At this stage SESSA did not have the benefit of a permanent secretariat; a sub committee consisting of Barnard, Prof. Holm, and Mr. Danie Steyn investigated, among others, the Renewable Energies Demonstration (RED) Centre for this purpose. In November 1993 Barnard reported to the council that the DMEA (Department of Minerals and Energy Affairs) would fund a secretary at the RED Centre if SESSA provided consultancy services to DMEA. Ms. Louise Luttig was appointed and she reported to Dieter Holm, Anton-Louis Olivier, and Petrus Brits of the Dept. of Agriculture. Several initiatives, including a communication strategy, were being considered, as well as an NGO summit. Training courses were offered in the renewable energy field. Some of the other initiatives dealt with ethics in practice, contact with other organizations in the energy field, and contact with ISES.

On 1 February 1994 Duard Barnard was elected chairperson following Hazel Hall's resignation. Hazel found it difficult to keep up with the changes in SESSA with her being stationed in Cape Town. During Barnard's term of office several African Sun magazines were published, thanks mainly to the work of Bernard Scheffler supported by Dieter Holm.

Ms. Louise Luttig had contact with people in the media and a variety of articles appeared in newspapers, and several interviews were broadcast over national radio and television programs.

An important occurrence was the series of actions developed for the benefit of ISES for submission to the UN Council for Sustainable Development (UNCSD). It was started by an NGO summit conference in April 1994. This was followed by a New York summit, held in the Waldorf Astoria Hotel a month later in May 1995. Five delegates invited to read papers included Dieter Holm, Duard Barnard, Deon Stassen, Saliem Fakir (then from The Land and Agricultural Policy Centre—not a SESSA member), and Prof. Dan Archer (not a SESSA member either). As a result, a major conference was held by SESSA during October 1994. The conference Proceedings were submitted to ISES. Jointly with three other conference Proceedings, it formed the basis of the ISES submission to the UNCSD.

In February 1994 membership totalled 106. It typically comprised sixty ISES members; twenty-five SESSA (local); seventeen corporate and three associate members. In October the total was only seventy-five.

The ISES Congress took place in Harare, Zimbabwe, in 1995.

SESSA played a major role in providing policy input into the drafting of the White Paper on Energy Policy for South Africa and the development of a renewable energy strategy for South Africa.

The 1996 membership stood close to 100.

The training courses offered included a solar energy general module, a biomass course, and an energy-efficiency course in the passive solar energy design of buildings. Further courses in the process of development dealt with solar water heating and photovoltaic design and installation.

Several high-profile meetings with, among others, the ministers of Environmental Affairs and Tourism; Department of Arts, Culture, Science and Technology; the DMEA; the Atomic Energy Council; and ESKOM were held. At this stage we were also involved in establishing the office for ISES Africa.

Louise Luttig and her assistant Sandra Bird resigned simultaneously during mid-1995. This had a negative effect on SESSA operations. Among other matters, the courses did not continue. Janet Wolhuter took over the office for three months and was then replaced by Ms. Erica du Preez.

By 31 January 1996, at the annual general meeting of SESSA, Barnard could report:

1. SESSA membership stood again at about 100 members,
2. The visitors to the RED Center had increased substantially,
3. Prof. Holm was appointed secretary of ISES and Barnard was made a SESSA representative on the ISES board.
4. Healthy cooperation was established with DANCED, the Danish Association for Cooperation for Environment and Development.
5. The SESSA secretariat had been successfully established at the RED Centre.
6. Much had been done to raise the profile of solar energy though a variety of initiatives that include media coverage, training courses, open days, many visitors to the RED Centre, etc.
7. Several editions of the *African Sun* were published.

The term of office of Duard Barnard ended on 31 January 1996. Prof. Holm proposed Deon Stassen as chairman. Deon Stassen indicated that he would agree to take on the chairmanship on a six-month contract basis in view of the limited time available to him.

19.13   Years 1997 to 2001

From September 1997 to February 2001 Marius Willemse was chairman. Dieter Holm was president; Anton-Louis Olivier was secretary and F. Mohr treasurer. Committee members included Sandra Bezuidenhout, Mike Rycroft, Derrick Botha, Lyon van der Merwe, Petrus Britz, Deon Stassen, Leon Drotsche (Western Cape), Deon Raubenheimer (Eastern Cape), Willem van der Merwe (North West Province), Duard Barnard, Marlett Wentzel, Trevor van der Vyfer, Uwe Klingenberg, and Noel Smith.

During Willemses' tenure a new constitution and by-laws were adopted and the Solar Energy Society became known as the Sustainable Energy Society of Southern Africa. Numerous other small but equally important events during this period helped put SESSA back in the playing field and put its finances on an even keel.

The renewable energy sector was still very small during this period, but as always there was a promise of a much grander and more important future on the horizon. During this period the Society set objectives such as "to increase the use of renewable energy and energy efficiency to such an extent that 20% of South Africa's electricity demand and that of neighboring countries are supplied from renewable energy sources." "Those were the days when the only sure way of making a million in the RE sector was to put in 10 million and when the number of Ph.D.s outstripped kW-hours installed," said Willemse.

The photovoltaics industry was bleeding as a result of the highly successful national grid electrification program and the very erratic rural schools and clinic off-grid electrification program by the South African government. "As a result, industry leaders had time on their hands and SESSA helped them establish the Photovoltaic Suppliers and Manufacturers Association (PVSM)," laughs Willemse.

The membership "peaked" at close to ninety members. The SESSA *Friend Newsletter* appeared monthly, and annually the *Who's Who in RE* was published. In addition, numerous articles appeared in the press on SESSA and RE. Two ISES initiatives for Africa conferences where held at the Development Bank of South Africa, and SESSA provided its support and manpower to arrange a similar follow on and very successful conference in Nairobi, Kenya.

"I enjoyed my period in office immensely. We were a great team, all very professional, but that did not stop us from having a whole lot of fun during, but especially after, our monthly meetings" Willemse enthused. "Trevor van der Vyfer, who became chairman in 2003, is the social type"

The very capable and for a long time a pillar of support, Marlett Wentzel, took office as chairperson at the February 2001 A.G.M. that was attended by the Deputy Minister of Minerals and Energy, Ms. Susan Shabangu.

19.14   Years 2001 and 2002

The most important aspect to report regarding membership was the fact that the Department of Minerals and Energy joined SESSA for a period of three years in 2001. The membership numbers are illustrated below:

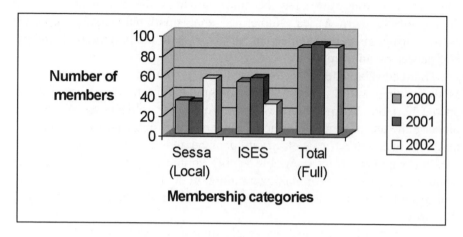

Fig. 6: SESSA membership

Specific steps were undertaken to increase membership during 2001:

- A regional meeting was held in Cape Town in June 2001 and in Durban in August 2001. Both meetings combined a SESSA council meeting with an information event, guest speaker, or a tour of important facilities in the region. Eleven people attended the regional meeting in Cape Town, and the guest speaker was Mr. Gordon Munro, deputy-director of the Cape Metro Electricity Services. Nine people attended the meeting in Durban and Elize Gothard (Eskom/Shell Joint Venture) was the guest speaker and the visit included a trip to Maphephete and the Myeka School. The aims of the regional meetings were to enable SESSA members in the region to attend a council meeting, to increase SESSA activities at the regional level, and to market SESSA to potential new members. Regional meetings were received with great enthusiasm and it was recommended that these meetings be continued.
- During October 2001 letters were sent to twenty-seven individuals and organizations, that were past members of SESSA, encouraging them to join the organization again.

19.14.1   Activities and Projects

During 2001, SESSA continued to publish the monthly newsletter that was distributed to approximately 600 recipients on the SESSA database. A hard copy directory of the 2001 SESSA database containing the names of organizations and individuals was published and was circulated to all members. Additional copies were for sale to nonmembers. Marlett Wentzel was interviewed on Thursday 10 May on SAFM, Woman Today. Good publicity was therefore generated for the organization. Prof. Holm published an article in the *ESI Africa* journal (Issue 3, 2001) titled "Renewable Energy in Africa," and Glynn Morris published an article in *ESI Africa* (issue 4, 2001) titled "Green Electricity: A differentiated product for enhancing global competitiveness"

During 2002 the following articles were published:

- *Engineering News*—Marlett Wentzel and Prof. Holm
- "Sustainable Energy: A SESSA perspective." Marlett Wentzel, 3 July 2003.
- "Wind Energy. A SESSA perspective," Marlett Wentzel, 20 May 2002.
- Solar Water Heating inquiries, *Plumbing Africa*. 17 February 2003.
- "Passive thermal—the only way", *Walls and Roofs*, 2002. Prof. Dieter Holm
- "Shacking up low-cost housing," *Walls and Roofs*, 2002. Prof. Dieter Holm

19.14.2   Projects:

- WSSD: DME requested SESSA to act as the industry representative and organize industry participation at WSSD.
- ISES President Prof. Anne Grete Hestnes and Executive Director Rian van Staden visited South Africa during the WSSD, and SESSA facilitated a fruitful meeting with the Minister of Minerals and Energy, The Honorable Phumzile Mlambo Ncuka.
- Solar Academy: In co-operation with ISES, a solar academy was held in Johannesburg during August 2002
- Robben Island: SESSA, on behalf of ISES participated actively in the formulation and negotiations regarding a sustainable energy project on Robben Island.

19.14.3   Co-operation

SESSA is an Associate Member of the South African National Energy Association.

SANEA. Both Prof. Dieter Holm and Marius Willemse served on the executive committee of SANEA, which is affiliated with the World Energy Council.

19.14.4   Steering Committee Representation

SESSA had a seat on the steering committee of the DME-led Integrated Energy Planning project and had actively been participating. SESSA also had a seat on the steering committee of the South African National Energy Database. SESSA was represented on the GEF project committee for solar water heating and also on the mass production and distribution of solar cookers.

19.14.5   Presentation to the Parliamentary Portfolio committee

Glynn Morris presented an overview of the renewable energy industry and the challenges facing the industry to the PPC on Energy.

Dieter Holm made a presentation to the committee on behalf of SESSA about the Draft White Paper on the Promotion of Renewable Energies and Energy Efficiency.

19.14.6   Council Meetings

Eleven SESSA/ISES Africa Council meetings were held in 2001, one for every month of the year excluding December 2001. An Annual General Meeting was held in March 2000.

19.14.7   Information Service

SESSA was being firmly established as a valuable information source and inquiries were received via the web site and telephonically. A record of enquiries was kept. The majority of enquiries were received via the web site, confirming the importance of an updated web site as an operating tool. Most were concerning PV and solar water heating. Other enquiries, not illustrated in the graph below, concerned solar water pumping, solar charged cell phone batteries, biogas, solar garden lighting, and technical measuring of solar radiation.

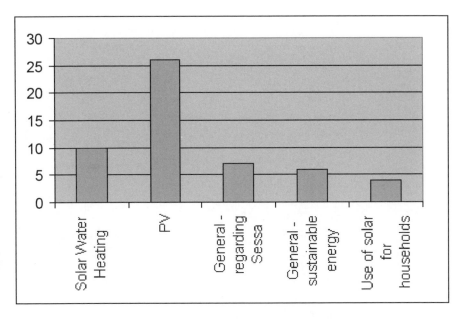

Fig. 7: Analysis of inquiries received by SESSA

19.15   Year 2003

A great honor for SESSA: SESSA President Dieter Holm was appointed ISES secretary in 2003. The SESSA chairman was Trevor van der Vyfer.

The road ahead for SESSA is clear and bright and is set on firm foundations.

Chapter 20

Solar Energy Association of Sweden – SEAS (ISES Sweden)

by
Jan-Olof Dalenbäck
Building Services Engineering
Department of Building Technology
Chalmers University of Technology, Sweden
SE – 412 96 Göteborg, Sweden
e-mail: Jan-Olof.Dalenback@bt.chalmers.se

Abstract

In this part we report about the Swedish section of ISES, which was formally recognized as an ISES section in 1995. The Solar Energy Association of Scandinavia—i.e., a Scandinavian section—was formed earlier in 1978, but the Scandinavian Society faded and a new Swedish organization—the Solar Energy Association of Sweden, SEAS—was not formed until 1987. Swedish solar energy development was, as in many other countries, initiated in the mid-1970s and was rather strong during the 1980s, mainly as a result of an extensive governmental R&D program. The Swedish solar industry and researchers pioneered large-module collectors based on an early Swedish invention, the Sunstrip absorber, and demonstrated large-scale solar heating in the largest plants in Europe. Sunstrip AB is a leading European absorber manufacturer, and there are ongoing efforts to start manufacturing photovoltaic cells in Sweden. The Solar Energy Association of Sweden—SEAS was the proud host for the Solar World Congress 2003, held in Göteborg. Political interest in solar energy is, however, rather limited in a country with well-established renewable energy sources such as biomass and hydro, and SEAS has so far had only limited resources with which to try to increase the interest.

20.1   History of the Swedish Section

Interest in renewable energy was very high in Sweden in the middle of the 1970s and some researchers working for the Swedish Council for Building Research (BFR) proposed the formation of a solar society and contacted the newly formed ISES Section for England to find out their experience. These contacts evolved into the formation of a Scandinavian section in 1978. The Swedish section was formally recognized first in 1995.

20.1.1   Solar Energy Association of Scandinavia— SEAS

In 1978 the Solar Energy Association of Scandinavia—SEAS, was formed, with national branches in Sweden, Norway, and Denmark. The chairman of SEAS was Prof. Vagn Korsgaard, Denmark, and the Swedish representatives on the board of SEAS were Prof. Bengt Hidemark, Arch. M.Sc. Lars Engström, Prof. Ingemar Höglund, Prof. Eric Ingelstam and Chief Engineer Peter Margen. The secretariat of the Swedish Society of Heating and Ventilating Engineers (VVS-tekniska föreningen or Swedevac in English) accepted to act as the secretariat for SEAS and Manager Ph.D. Ulf Rengholt was the first secretary.

In parallel, a number of Swedish industry representatives formed Svenska Solenergiföreningen—SISOL to act as an industrial trade organisation with Mr. Rolf Mårtensson, technical manager at Philips, as chairman.

However, after only a few years the interest was not sufficient to pay for and maintain the combined secretariat of SEAS or to keep SISOL on track, and the activities of both Swedish organizations faded. In Denmark and Norway, however, the activities continued in national organizations.

20.1.2   Solar Energy Association of Sweden— SEAS

In 1986 representatives for the emerging solar energy industry reactivated Svenska Solenergiföreningen—SISOL with M.Sc. Lars Åstrand, managing director of Uppsala Energi, as chairman and Dr. Heimo Zinko, Studsvik Energy, as secretary. In 1987 a new organization Solar Energy Association of Sweden - SEAS was formed by a number of university researchers and consulting engineers, using the same abbreviation as the Scandinavian organisation formed in 1978. M.Sc. Arne Boysen, formerly with the Swedish Council for Building Research, was elected as the first chairman.

The two boards, as well as the memberships, of the two organizations of

SISOL and SEAS were partly overlapping, and after two years it was suggested that the organizations should be merged. In June 1989 new by-laws were adopted assuring that the new merged organization should include representatives of industry, as well as of research, and that decisions of the new board should represent both these categories. The two organizations merged into Svenska solenergiföreningen—SEAS, combining the names of the two organizations. In the following report the abbreviation SEAS relates to this Swedish organization formed in 1987.

Fig. 1: MSc Arne Boysen, Chairman of SEAS board 1987–88 and 1992–94, Editor for SEAS newsletter and six yearbooks 1991–96. President ISES Europe 1995–97. Member of the Organizing committee for ISES SWC 2003

The new SEAS organization gradually took over all activities from the previous two organizations, which then were legally closed in 1990. Mr. Lars Jäderberg, managing director of Falkenberg Energi, served as chairman 1989 – 91. MSc. Arne Boysen served again as chairman 1992–94 and retired from the board in 2001. Mr. Lars Andrén has served as chairman since 1995.

The officers for the Solar Energy Association of Sweden—SEAS and later Svenska solenergiföreningen—SEAS are given in the table below.

Year	Chairman	Vice chairman
1987 – 88	Arne Boysen	Björn Karlsson
1989 – 91	Lars-Erik Jäderberg	Arne Boysen
1992	Arne Boysen	Jan Högberg
1993 – 94	Arne Boysen	Jan-Olof Dalenbäck
1995 –	Lars Andrén	Jan-Olof Dalenbäck

Dr. Jan-Olof Dalenbäck, Chalmers University of Technology, served on the board of SISOL during 1986–88, was one of the initiators of the merger with SEAS in 1989, and has served on the board of SEAS since 1989 and as vice chairman and international secretary since 1993.

20.1.3   SEAS Management

SEAS had its secretariat placed at the Solar Energy Research Center (SERC), Dalarna University in Borlänge from 1987 to 2002. The SEAS secretariat was moved to Teknikförlaget AB in Halmstad in 2003.

SEAS originally published a newsletter, *SEAS-Nytt*, edited by Arne Boysen and distributed to all members four times a year. In about 2002 SEAS initiated co-operation with the national journal *Energimagasinet*, issued by Teknikförlaget AB. The journal has two standing pages for SEAS, one or more articles about solar energy in each issue, and is distributed to all SEAS members about every second month.

In an effort to strengthen the image of solar energy as a viable energy source for Sweden, SEAS published six yearbooks during the period 1991–1996. Arne Boysen and Lars Broman edited the first book, *Solsverige 1991*, while Arne Boysen edited the remaining five books. The six books in hard cover contain more than 880 pages of information and documentation from a period of time when solar energy was demonstrated to the public as a viable alternative for Sweden.

For a couple of years now SEAS has also been present on the Internet and has recently got its own domain and address: www.solenergiforeningen.se

SEAS is working in close cooperation with the Swedish National Testing and Research Institute (SP) regarding testing and international standards for testing of solar heating systems. For the time being, SEAS is also represented in an evaluation group for the present investment subsidy for solar heating systems together with representatives for the Swedish Energy Agency and the National Board of Housing, Building and Planning.

SEAS organizes an annual industry meeting where common problems and activities are addressed. SEAS used to organize an annual research seminar, but as R&D funding has changed, SEAS is instead represented in national seminars organized by the Swedish Energy Agency, FORMAS, etc.

SEAS has about twenty-five industry and 175 individual members and with an annual turnover of the order of 300,000 SEK, SEAS is mainly trying to keep its nose above water.

20.2   International Relations

20.2.1   ISES

Professor Vagn Korsgaard, Denmark, represented the Scandinavian Section on the ISES Board in 1976–1990. M.Sc. Torben Esbensen, Denmark, succeeded him in 1990–1996. In 1995, the new national organizations established in Sweden, Norway, and Denmark were formally approved as ISES Sections and the Scandinavian Section of ISES was abolished. The new national Sections continued, however, to act as an Associated Section for Scandinavia. The number of Swedish ISES members increased, and Sweden got its own ISES Board representative, Dr. Jan-Olof Dalenbäck, in 2003.

Fig. 2: Dr. Jan-Olof Dalenbäck, associate professor at Chalmers University of Technology, SEAS Vice chairman and international contact person since 1993 and ISES BOD representative since 2000. General secretary for SWC 2003

In time for SWC 1987 in Hamburg the Scandinavian organizations started to discuss making a bid for a future SWC. An internal competition was arranged and during North Sun 1992 in Trondheim it was decided that Svenska solenergiföreningen—SEAS should go on to prepare a bid for a future SWC in Göteborg. The first bid was presented by SEAS Chairman Arne Boysen at SWC 1993 in Budapest, which resulted in a close run with Jerusalem for SWC 1999. The second bid was presented at SWC 1997 in Taejon, South Korea, where SWC 2003 was awarded to SEAS.

Fig. 3: Logo for Solar World Congress 2003

ISES 2003

SWC 2003 was held at Göteborg Convention Center and was hosted by the Swedish Energy Agency, FORMAS, Sida, Chalmers University of Technology, Göteborg Energi AB, Sunstrip AB, and ARCON Solvarme A/S. Seven hundred participants from seventy countries attended the Congress.

20.2.2   ISES Europe

Having served as chairman for SEAS a number of years, M.Sc. Arne Boysen also served as president of ISES Europe in 1995–97. Dr. Jan-Olof Dalenbäck has represented SEAS in ISES Europe since the mid-1990's and is now a board member of ISES Europe.

SEAS offered to host the regional solar energy conference Eurosun in 1998, as well as in 2000, but fell in both competitions. SEAS was however, as previously mentioned, appointed to host the Solar World Congress in 2003.

20.2.3   European Solar Thermal Industry Federation

SEAS became a member of the European Solar Industry Federation, ESIF, in 1994. Dr. Jan-Olof Dalenbäck served as ESIF board member 2000-2002 and had an active role when ESIF merged with the Active Solar Thermal Industry Group, ASTIG, into the European Solar Thermal Industry Federation, ESTIF, in 2002.

The Swedish National Testing and Research Institute (SP) and Sunstrip AB are also members in ESTIF, and Mr. Stefan Gustavsson, managing director of Sunstrip AB, is on the Board, as well as on the Advisory Council of ESTIF.

20.3   Solar Energy Development in Sweden

20.3.1   Introduction

John Ericsson (1803–89) was the first Swedish solar engineer and spent his last years developing his early invention, the hot-air engine, to be driven by solar radiation.

Ångström is probably the most well-known Swedish name related to solar energy since Ångström (1 Å = 10^{-10} m), a unit with which the wavelength of light is measured, is named after Anders Jonas Ångström (1814–84), who investigated the spectral distribution of solar radiation. His son Knut Johan Ångström (1857–1910), later invented the Ångström pyrheliometer, an instrument to measure solar radiation still in use today. Both were active at

Uppsala University, which recently has created the Ångström Solar Center focused on advanced solar-related material research including PV. The first Swedish solar heating system was probably a system by architect Gunnar Pleijel (1908–1963) built on the Swedish Solar Observatory, Capri, Italy. Pleijel and his colleague B. I. Lindström presented the system at the UN Congress on new sources of energy in Rome in 1961. The building had gone up the year before and the solar collectors were built right into its façade; this may also have been the first system of its kind to be installed in Italy. In connection with the inauguration of the main building in 1961 a Swedish TV team visited the observatory to report about the solar energy installation. The publisher Aldus/Bonniers published a book about Solenergi from a manuscript by Gunnar Pleijel in 1966. The book covers more or less all major solar applications until 1960, but solar energy was a topic of interest only to some researchers at that time.

During the international energy crisis in 1973–74 it was recognized that Sweden had to reduce its great dependency on imported oil, so a new energy policy was developed. Energy used in buildings represents roughly 40% of the total national energy use, and when the first Swedish Energy Research Program was adopted in 1975, the Swedish Council for Building Research (BFR) was given the responsibility for RD&D related to the building sector. The possible use of solar energy for buildings was one of the alternatives to be studied.

BFR, represented by M.Sc. Arne Boysen, became a member of a working party in the International Energy Agency (IEA) to develop an Implementing Agreement for Solar Heating and Cooling Systems, which was signed in late 1976. Initiated by Sweden and Germany, the original program was enlarged to include R&D collaboration on central solar heating systems with seasonal storage, a technique that was considered necessary if solar energy was to play a considerable role for northern countries. This collaboration continued for ten years, led by Arne Boysen. IEA has been an important forum for Swedish solar energy researchers, both regarding solar heating and solar electricity.

BFR realized early that the development of new energy technology for buildings required that full-scale testing could be made in buildings in normal use. Financing of such experiments supported by experimental loans was made possible in 1978, with the condition that results had to be scientifically measured and investigated. Special monitoring centers for this purpose were created at the Royal Institute of Technology in Stockholm, Chalmers University of Technology in Göteborg, and Lund University. The 1975 RD&D program resulted in a period of rather extensive research and development regarding solar architecture, solar thermal, and photovoltaics at major universities and institutes. The Swedish Institute for Meteorology and Hydrology, SMHI, was assigned increased resources to create solar radiation statistics. The program encouraged participation in the IEA Solar Heating & Cooling Programme, and a number of experimental projects were carried out until the mid-1990s. The Swedish State Power Board, Vattenfall, also allotted considerable efforts to solar energy research until the end of the 1990s.

RD&D related to solar energy has gradually been reduced from all-time highs with 220 MSEK of governmental support for the period 1981-84, and BFR had been merged into the Swedish Research Council for Environment, Agriculture Sciences and Spatial Planning (FORMAS) by the end of the 1990s. The present RD&D program managed by the Swedish Energy Agency is at about 70 MSEK support for the period 2000–02—a much lower national, as well as international level, only partly compensated by increased involvement in R&D projects managed by the European Commission.

20.3.2   Solar Architecture

Architect Gunnar Pleijel (1908–1963), Royal Institute of Technology, created useful diagrams showing the position of the sun as a function of the time of the day, as well as the season, in the 1950s. Ralph Erskine was one of the first architects who tried to adopt solar architecture in Sweden when he designed the Borgafjäll Hotel in Lapland in 1948.

Interest in solar architecture increased after the energy crises in the early 1970s and a number of experimental, mostly single-family, buildings were erected within the Swedish RD&D program. The first so-called passive solar buildings were designed using direct gain south-facing facades and a large thermal mass, (e.g., the Färjelanda House designed by EFEM architects), or using sunspaces (e.g., The Nature House designed by architect Bengt Warne). Architect professor Bengt Hidemark, Royal Institute of Technology and previously an assistant to Gunnar Pleijel, also made several passive solar designs (e.g., a housing area where all units had an integrated sunspace facing south).

The 1980s saw the development of hybrid systems (i.e., where solar air collectors were used in combination with thermal-mass building parts, e.g., the Järnbrott House, designed by architect Christer Nordström). The use of glazed balconies is common in new multifamily buildings as a sunspace, while it sometimes is used in existing multifamily buildings also to improve the overall U-value and reduce façade and window maintenance in existing buildings.

Fig. 4: "Houses without heating systems" in Lindås, Sweden (Lat 58°)—Terraced houses with a comprehensive building envelope design (low overall U-value), efficient heat recovery on ventilation, and Solar DHW systems. Photo: Hans Eek.

However, in the rather cold climate of Sweden, where rather strict building codes were introduced in the late 1960s, it soon became obvious that reduced heat losses were important to achieve a low heat demand.

A recent demonstration project is the so-called "Houses without heating systems" (i.e., (Fig. 4) well-insulated terraced houses with efficient heat recovery on ventilation and relying on internal gains only, designed by Hans Eek et al, EFEM Architects, together with a group of researchers from Lund University and Chalmers University of Technology).

The use of atriums became more common in the 1980s in order to create more comfortable outside spaces between buildings, (e.g., in connection to shopping centres, office buildings, and hotels). Nowadays the use of glazed facades is a common feature on commercial buildings. While the direct solar gain often is positive in the design of residential buildings it also is often the other way around in commercial buildings with large internal heat gains. Willem Boeke, Svenska Fläktfabriken, and Gösta Brown, Royal Institute of Technology, developed methods to estimate the influence of the heat gain from solar radiation through windows on cooling loads in commercial buildings in the early 1960s. Gösta Brown was later one of those who developed BRIS, a computer-based model of building heat balance used by most Swedish engineering consultants until the late 1990s.

Rather extensive research on window coatings and so-called smart windows at the Ångström Solar Center shows interesting prospects for the future.

20.3.3   Solar Thermal

A couple of industries (e.g., Svenska Fläktfabriken, AGA, and TeknoTerm—at that time owned by the Euroc Group) started to import and develop solar collectors in mid-1970s. In 1978 the government introduced the first market subsidy for solar heating systems together with subsidies for other energy-saving measures. About 20,000 m² of solar collectors were sold in 1980, but the market dropped rapidly when the subsidy ended in 1982.

Valdis Girdo presented the first Swedish Ph.D. thesis, Basic Prerequisites for Solar Heated Buildings in Scandinavia (author's translation), at the Royal Institute of Technology in 1978. Professor Folke Pettersson, Royal Institute of Technology, was one of the pioneers regarding small solar systems. He took active part in the early stages of the R&D program managed by BFR and also published for a number of years a quarterly solar energy journal called The Heliograph.

One important development at this time was the Sunstrip absorber (Fig. 5), a roll-band based on a cupper pipe and aluminium fins introduced by Gränges Aluminium in the late 1970s. A production line was sold to China, and Sunstrip was sold to Canada in the early 1980s due to the lack of a market in Sweden and Europe at that time. Gunnar Wilson, now retired but still an active inventor, was one of those behind the Sunstrip development.

The Swedish RD&D program was early focused on large-scale applications for centralized solar heating plants with and without seasonal storage. This was supported by experimental building loans with favorable conditions granted by BFR. The first experimental solar heating plant with seasonal heat storage, supplying year-round heat for an office building, was constructed in 1980 at the Energy Research Company Studsvik Energy. This was followed by a number of larger systems. One of the most well-known plants is Lyckebo, initiated by M.Sc. Lars Åstrand at Uppsala Energi, with the aim to build a solar heating plant with more than 20,000 m² of solar collectors and 100,000 m² of seasonal storage in a water-filled rock cavern.

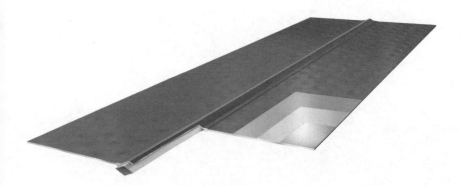

Fig. 5: Sunstrip absorber with a selective sputtered surface

Uppsala Energi tested a number of imported advanced collectors at that time and everyone believed that a foreign collector manufacturer would present the best offer. The result, however, was that a small Swedish company group, Scandinavian Solar, having developed a large-module flat-plate collector based on the Sunstrip absorber and a convection barrier of Teflon, presented the best offer and was appointed to erect the first phase with 4,320 m² of solar collectors in 1983.

The large-module collector, as well as the system design, was further developed in plants like Nykvarn with 4,000 m² in 1985 and another 3,500 m² in 1992 and Falkenberg with 5,500 m² in 1989. The large-module approach was further adopted by German, as well as Austrian, collector manufacturers in the early 1990s.

Several Swedish groups participated in the IEA SHC Programme dealing with large-scale solar systems. Comprehensive R&D work, focused on energy and cost-efficient solutions, was carried through among others at Chalmers University of Technology. A status report, edited by Dr. Jan-Olof Dalenbäck, was presented in 1990. In parallel, a comprehensive study on the feasibility to begin solar collector manufacturing and build a plant with more than 100,000 m² of solar collectors in the city of Kungälv was presented by a group of companies from Göteborg.

However, the Lyckebo plant was never extended to 20,000 m² and the necessary investment support for the Kungälv project was denied. Therewith the development of large-scale plants was more or less abandoned. A major reason was a declining governmental interest in solar energy and the strong development of wood fuels, another renewable energy source with a huge potential in Sweden in block and district heating.

Fig. 6: Solar district heating plant with 10,000 m² in Kungälv, Sweden. The first large-scale application with anti-reflex coated glass. Photo: Kungälv Energi AB

The large-module collector technology was transferred to the Danish company ARCON Solvarme A/S that until recently had delivered turnkey contracts all around Europe (e.g., Kungälv with 10,000 m² in 2001 and Marstal in Denmark with 9,000 m² in 1996 and another 8,000 m² in 2003). All the large-scale plants mentioned from Lyckebo in 1983 to Kungälv in 2000, were the largest solar heating plants ever built in Europe at that time.

Scandinavian Solar developed into TeknoTerm, got Sunstrip back from Canada, and got a new production line running in Sweden in about 1990. TeknoTerm developed into an expanding industry that produced solar absorbers, ceiling panels for irradiative heating and cooling, as well as cooling beams, based on the Sunstrip technology. Lars Andrén, present chairman of SEAS, was sales manager at TeknoTerm in the early 1990s. TeknoTerm was split and all divisions except Sunstrip were sold out at the end of the 1990s. Sunstrip AB is now one of the leading absorber manufacturers in Europe, with an annual turnover of about 25 MSEK and growing.

The original Sunstrip absorber had a selective surface made in an electrolyte. TeknoTerm developed an improved surface deposited in a vacuum chamber (sputter) in close co-operation with Dr. Ewa Wäckelgård, Ångström

Solar Center, and presented it at the first Eurosun conference in 1996. One of the pioneers in Scandinavian Solar and owner of Sunstrip AB is M.Sc. Göran Hultmark. He started out as a Ph.D. student at Chalmers University of Technology for a short period in the late 1970s and is now development manager at Lindab AB, a large HVAC equipment industry group. Another pioneer is Prof. Claes-Göran Granqvist, Ångström Solar Center, Uppsala University, and formerly at Chalmers University of Technology, who was involved in the development of the selective surfaces for Sunstrip.

Another unique development was initiated by Ivar Franzén, chairman of a municipal housing association, EKSTA, in Kungsbacka, south of Göteborg. EKSTA built their first solar-heated residential area in 1979 using air collectors from AGA and initiated a local development of roof-integrated solar collectors based on the Sunstrip absorber and solar systems combined with wood briquette and pellet boilers. A roof module collector developed in cooperation between Chalmers University of Technology, TeknoTerm, and Derome AB, a local building components manufacturer, was introduced in 1995. Today EKSTA has over 6,000 m^2 of roof-integrated solar collectors in operation, the first ones from 1982, and continues to apply solar systems in its new building establishments.

The early development of concentrating collectors and, for example, PVT-collectors, was mainly carried out at Studsvik Energy by Dr. Heimo Zinko and M.Sc. Bengt Perers in the early 1980s. Perers, whose father had connections to the Swedish Solar Observatory, Capri, presented a Ph.D. thesis on collector modeling and is one of those who introduced dynamic collector testing. The present R&D on solar collectors is mainly managed by Prof. Björn Karlsson, active both at Vattenfall Laboratory in Älvkarleby, and Uppsala and Lund Universities. The research is mainly devoted to stationary focusing collectors (e.g., the so-called MaReCo,and also involves concentrating PV, as well as PVT collectors, and is partly carried out within the IEA SHC Programme).

The Swedish National Testing and Research Institute (SP) started to test solar collectors and systems in the late '70s. Dr. Hans E. B. Andersson was the first manager and introduced R&D on solar collectors and durability of collector materials. Dr. Per Bergqvist followed on and carried out a number of research projects with international collaboration regarding collector and system testing, among others, together with Bengt Perers. An important step was the implementation of the P-mark, a performance and durability test combined with production control for solar collectors, in cooperation with

SEAS in the early 1990s. SP is now active in the implementation of Solar Keymark, a European quality label for solar collectors and systems supported by ESTIF and CEN.

The Solar Energy Research Center (SERC) was formed by Lars Broman at Dalarna University in 1984 and was host for the third Northsun conference in 1988. SERC focused on R&D on small solar systems together with solar energy education and has managed a masters program in solar energy engineering since 1999.

The use of F-Chart and TRNSYS (computer software developed at the University of Wisconsin, USA), as well as MINSUN (developed at Studsvik) was introduced in R&D projects in the early 1980s. The use of TRNSYS was significantly enhanced by the introduction of PC computers and later the development of a front-end PRESIM at SERC in the early 1990s.

So-called self-builder groups were a common European development in the 1980s. In Sweden this took a slightly different development as more or less all self-builders were organized in Svenska solgruppen and used the same collector called LESOL, based on the Sunstrip absorber, tested and approved by SP. This solar collector, developed by Björn Stensson, a schoolteacher, is probably the most common collector installed on Swedish single-family buildings even today.

Today there are about 200,000 m² of glazed solar collectors in Sweden (i.e., about 20 m² per 1,000 inhabitants), and a number of small companies selling solar systems. In 2003 the sales amounted to about 20,000 m² (i.e., the same as twenty years ago), mainly as a result of a governmental investment subsidy introduced in 2000. The majority of solar systems sold are so-called combisystems combined with wood boilers, but the market for solar DHW systems has increased in the latest years.

20.3.4   Solar Photovoltaic (PV)

PV systems were introduced on the Swedish market in the late '70s. Use as the power supply for lighthouses and emergency telephones are typical applications for stand-alone systems. The early visions talked about large PV plants but the present visions are related to building- integration. Building-integrated PV has been introduced in several new building establishments during recent years, and there is interest among architects and building owners to take part in future developments.

Professor Peter Weissglas, Institute for Microwave Technology (Institute för Mikrovågsteknik—IM) at the Royal Institute of Technology started the interest in Swedish PV development in 1977. He initiated the first feasibility study on PV cell production in Sweden and developed a test station at Sandkullen north of Stockholm. A number of others later formed a program called Solcell 80, tasked to find applications for a PV cell to be developed by Volvo. The development was not judged to be successful and Volvo dropped out, but it led to (e.g., Riksbyggen [housing association]) creating the first building-integrated and grid-connected PV system in 1984, and it created the prerequisites for cell technology development at IM.

Early development was focused on a new thin-film material, $CuInSe_2$ (within the CIGS group), and IM made several important developments in the early' 90s that contributed to increase the efficiency of CIGS cells above 18%. Esko Niemi, solid state physics, Royal Institute of Technology, presented the first Swedish Ph.D. thesis on PV, titled *CuInSe₂ and Related Materials for Thin Film Solar Cells*, in 1991. The R&D activities were transferred to Ångström Solar Center in Uppsala and the development of a cell production line is now carried out in a new company called Solibro. The aim is to be able to produce cells with a total of 5 MWp per year by 2008.

Nämnden för energiproduktionsforskning (NE) conducted during 1978-1983 a solar energy project based on photo electrochemical solar cells. This project was initiated by results Professor K. Honda published in 1975. In this project, two groups were formed, one at Physical Chemistry at Uppsala University and the other at Physical Chemistry at Göteborg University. The Uppsala group today is associated with Ångström Solar Center, and the Göteborg group today is working at the Industrial Research and Development Corporation (IVF). The two groups have, during the last 6-10 years, focused on development of dye PV cells or Grätzel cells, and IVF has developed extensive knowledge regarding industrial production of dye PV modules.

Chalmers University of Technology and Linköping University since 1997 have an ongoing cooperation regarding the development of materials and devices for polymer solar cells.

It should also be mentioned that a couple of foreign PV module producers for several years have had their production units located at Gällivare in north Sweden due to favorable conditions for industry establishment.

20.4   Future Prospects

SEAS is approaching governmental bodies to set long term goals for the development of solar heating in Sweden and to adopt similar promoting strategies as those used in other European countries.

The public and governmental interest in solar heating is, however, rather limited and, besides Sunstrip, the solar thermal industry is dominated by small players that have a hard time to make a difference. More or less abundant resources of wood fuels and rather favorable opportunities for the use of heat pumps does not increase the opportunities for solar heating.

Large-scale solar systems are well developed but interest among facility managers and thermal utilities is lacking, partly because existing alternatives show rather low energy prices and partly due to the lack of incentives. Small solar systems are becoming more adapted to standard heating equipment in single-family buildings, and there is an increased interest to develop combined solar and wood pellet systems to offer more complete alternatives for single-family houses.

The interest in PV is rather large as in most countries, but the market is negligible due to the high investment costs, and feed-in laws as in Germany are not foreseen in the near future.

Acknowledgements

I would like to acknowledge the professional efforts of the late Ivar Franzén, former chairman of EKSTA Bostads AB, to make solar heating a common practice in housing association. Ivar Franzén was a great source of inspiration for many, myself in particular.

I would like to thank M.Sc. Arne Boysen, former chairman of SEAS; Professor Emeritus Enno Abel, Chalmers University of Technology; Professor Lars Broman, Dalarna University; and Jonas Hedström, IM, Ångström Solar Center and Energibanken, who made special contributions to the content.

I would also like to thank all mentioned and not mentioned persons and organizations that have contributed to the development of solar energy in Sweden. It is not easy to make a completely fair and objective picture of solar development in Sweden, but it is my sincere intention that this review is close enough given the present constraints regarding time and money.

Chapter 21
History of Solar Energy in Turkey

by
Necdet Altuntop, Ph.D.
Department of Mechanical Engineering
Erciyes University, Kayseri 38039, Turkey
altuntop@erciyes.edu.tr

Abstract

The first scientific activities about solar energy were initiated by Dr. M. Kudret Selçuk at the Middle East Technical University (METU) in Turkey. Subsequently studies and scientific research was continued at major universities and institutions. Research was carried out at METU, Aegean, Istanbul Technical (ITU), Ankara, Cukurova, Yildiz Technical, Erciyes, Bogazici, Black Sea Technical, Gazi, and Hacettepe universities and also at the Turkish Scientific and Technical Research Center (TUBITAK) and General Directorate of Electrical Power Research and Development Administration (EİEİ). Among the scientists who were involved are Dr. G. Atagunduz, Dr. D. Inan, Dr. A. Ecevit, Dr. A. Ozturk, Dr. S. Oktik, Dr. O. Ultanir, Dr. M. Akyurt. As an outcome, several scientific papers, symposium proceedings, and books were published for Turkish scientific journals. Findings of this scientific research were transferred to the industry, whereby solar water heating systems became widely used after the 1973 energy crisis. Solar collector exports started after 1995. The Turkish branch of ISES was founded in 1992.

21.1   Introduction

Interest in solar energy research and development in Turkey was initiated after the NATO Advanced Study Institute on Solar and Aeolian
Energy meeting, which was held at Sounion, Greece, during the summer of
1961. Mr. Kudret Selçuk, who was an instructor at the Middle East Technical
University (METU) in Ankara, Turkey, attended the seminar.

Selçuk built the first solar collector, made out of corrugated galvanized
sheet metal, at METU and gave lectures to emphasize the importance of solar
energy. He received a NATO grant to undertake research under John Yellott,
one of the pioneers of solar energy, starting in February 1962.

He attended the graduate diploma course on arid land development during 1962 and 1963 at the Brace Experiment Station of McGill University in
Montreal, Canada. He carried out research at the Solar Energy Laboratory of
the University of Wisconsin before returning to METU in September 1963. In
1963 a course on Solar Energy Utilization was offered by Selçuk at the
Mechanical Engineering Department of METU.

In 1964 the local Solar Energy Society COMPLES (Cooperation
Mediterranean pour l'Energie Solaire), headquartered at the University of
Marseille, France, was founded, and Turkey became one of the founding
members.

Between 1963 and 1967 Dr. Selçuk continued doing research as well as
teaching at METU. With a grant from the Turkish National Research Council
(TUBITAK), experiments were carried out on solar fruit drying. Independent
R&D was conducted on silicon cell performance under concentrated sunlight.
Solar water and air heaters performance and analysis results were presented
at COMPLES conferences, which were held in Istanbul in 1965; Marseille,
France, 1966; and Madrid, Spain, 1967.

From 1967 until 1969 Dr. Selçuk completed his Ph.D. studies at McGill
University and undertook a one-year postdoctoral study at the Environmental
Research Laboratory of the University of Arizona in Tucson, Arizona.

Upon returning to METU in 1970 he continued his studies on solar drying under the support of TUBITAK and on a combination of a solar still and
a greenhouse under a grant from NATO Scientific Council. A scientific collaboration between the Brace Research Institute of McGill University and
METU was arranged. Dr. Mehmet Akyurt at METU contributed significantly
to these R&D activities at METU. Findings were presented at COMPLES
conferences held in Nice-San Remo in 1970, in Athens in 1971 and in
Istanbul in 1972

Dr. Selçuk left Turkey in late 1972 and continued his studies at the Institute of Energy Conversion of the University of Delaware, Newark, Delaware during 1972–73, and he designed and tested the first solar electric house.

During 1973–74 he worked at Honeywell Systems and Research Center in Minneapolis, Minnesota, where his research area was on the Transportable Solar Laboratory and Osseo High School Solar Heating System.

Dr. Selçuk served as a director of the board of ISES and attended several ISES and ASME Solar Energy Division conferences. He served as the vice president of the ASME Solar Energy Division and organized several sessions at ASME conferences on solar thermal conversions. After returning to Turkey from the United States in 1988 he briefly worked at TUBITAK, as the head of Mechanical and Energy Systems.

The scientific research initiated by Dr. Selçuk in the 1960s in Turkey was continued at METU with the university's self resources. Oil prices increased excessively in 1974, with the petroleum crises which resulted in solar energy system production becoming widespread. Production was started in small workshops and continued in factories. After 1974, Turkish universities started to show a great interest in solar energy. Many theses and scientific papers were published about solar energy. The scientific research, which began at METU, spread to some institutions as ITU, Aegean, Yildiz Technical, Ankara, Cukurova, Erciyes, Bogazici, Black Sea Technical, Gazi, Hacettepe, Mersin, and Mugla, universities, and TUBITAK and EİEİ.

Besides Dr. Selçuk, some scientists, including Dr. Gurbuz Atagunduz, Dr. Ahmet Ecevit, Dr. Aksel Ozturk, Dr. I. Demir Inan, Dr. Kemal Altinisik, Dr. Abdurrahman Kilic, Dr. U. Dogay Arinc, Dr. M. Ozcan Ultanir, Dr. Mehmet Akyurt, Dr. Ersoy Tasdemiroglu, Dr. Ali Beba, Dr. Tuncay Yilmaz, Dr. Sener Oktik, and Dr. Nilüfer Egrican, also worked in the solar energy field in the 1970s and 1980s.

Other scientists, who were involved in solar energy research during the 1980s and 1990s include Dr. Ali Güngör, Dr. Necdet Ozbalta, Dr. Cetin Goksu, Dr. O. Ercan Ataer, Dr. Metin Colak, Dr. Kazım Pıhtılı, Dr. I. Engin Ture, Dr. Cetin Goksu, Dr. Turkan Goksal, Dr. F. Nur Demirbilek, Dr. Figen Kadirgan, Dr. Ali Bascetincelik, Dr. Necdet Altuntop, Dr. Galip Oturanc, Dr. Mustafa Tiris, Dr. Orhan Buyukalaca, Dr. Siddik Icli, Dr. Mustafa Gunes, and Dr. Gul Koclar.

21.2   Some Activities Regarding Solar Energy in Turkey

One of the prototype passive solar houses in Turkey (shown in Fig. 1), was built at Aegean University in Izmir, between 1980 and 1984 by Dr. Atagunduz and his collaborators. This building has an area of 3,000 m². Some departments of Aegean University use this building for classrooms. There is a solar thermal electric unit on the top floor of this building. There is also another smaller passive solar house at this university. Dr. Atagunduz and his colleagues have carried out a big large research project about agricultural product drying, such as for grapes, through the use of solar energy.

One of the first centers concentrating on solar energy in Turkey was at METU. Research in this field begun by Dr. K. Selçuk and Dr. M. Akyurt was continued by Dr. Ecevit, Dr. E. Tasdemiroglu, Dr. F. N. Demirbilek, Dr. C. Goksu, and their colleagues. METU scientists planned the TUBITAK passive solar guesthouse at Antalya shown in Fig. 2.

Fig. 1: The large passive solar house at Aegean University

Fig. 2: Solar guesthouse of TUBITAK at Antalya

Hacettepe University also is conducting scientific research on solar energy. The Hacettepe solar house and laboratory built by Dr. Demir Inan and his colleagues is shown in Fig. 3.

Fig. 3: Hacettepe University's solar house

Fig. 4: Erciyes University's first active solar house and solar hot water facilities

Erciyes University in Kayseri was another of the solar energy centers where research has been done. Erciyes active solar house and solar hot water heating system was built by Dr. Necdet Altuntop and his colleagues in the 1990s and is shown in Fig. 4. In Fig. 5, the active solar heating system of a sports complex that is the largest in Turkey is shown. This building uses 330 m^2 of hot air solar collector to heat an enclosed area of 1,650 m^2. The energy storage unit is shown in Fig. 6. In this application, 5120 polyethylene bottles, each containing 1.5 liters of water totaling 8000 liters, is used for energy storage and as a heat exchanger.

Fig. 5: Erciyes University sports complex solar space heating system application

Fig. 6: One of the thermal energy storage units of the Erciyes University sports complex

21.3   The Turkish Section of ISES

The Turkish branch of the International Solar Energy Society (ISES–Turkey) was formed in 1992 by people involved in solar energy in Turkey. The first chairman of ISES Turkey was Mr. Suheyl Elbir. The board of directors consisted of Dr. D. Inan, Dr. A. Ecevit, Dr. G. Atagunduz, Mr. I. Ezinc, Mr. K. Koman, Mr. R. Durdu, and Mr. Suheyl Elbir.

Some universities and institutions were involved in the solar energy field in Turkey before ISES–Turkey was established. Some of them are Turkish Solar Hot Water Heater Association, the Clean Energy Foundation, the Chamber of Turkish Mechanical Engineers, and the Turkish National Committee of World Energy Council. The universities mentioned above and the institutions have arranged symposia and a solar day on 21 June every year. After the establishment of ISES–Turkey in 1992, solar energy-related activities were organized by ISES–Turkey. Institutes and research centers have been established in Turkish universities about solar energy and renewable energy sources. Studies related to solar energy are conducted by these centers and institutes. Most of the researchers involved with the renewable energy sources are members of ISES–Turkey. Therefore activities are being coordinated and organized by ISES–Turkey.

21.3.1   The Growth of ISES–Turkey

After ISES-Turkey was founded, the number of members reached ninety-four. (twenty of them were institutions). The members consist of faculty members, engineers and industrialists, bureaucrats in the government departments engaged in energy-related activities, and other individuals interested in solar energy. The number of members of ISES–Turkey (94) does not necessarily reflect the interest in solar energy in Turkey. A meeting was organized to invite those working in solar energy industry to join ISES–Turkey toward the end of 2003.

21.3.2   Board of Directors and the By-Laws of ISES–Turkey

Mr. Suheyl Elbir took on as the founding chairman of ISES–Turkey in 1992.

First executive committee members were; Dr. Demir Inan, Dr. Gurbuz Atagunduz, Mr. İbrahim Ezinc, Mr. Riza Durdu, Mr. Kemal Koman, and Dr. M. Ozcan Ultanir.

Second period President, Dr. I. Demir Inan (1995–1997),
Third period President, Dr. I. Demir Inan (1997–1999),
Fourth period President, Mr. Osman Ilhan (1999–2000) and Dr. M.Ozcan Ultanir (2000–2001),
Fifth period President, Dr. Ahmet Ecevit (2001–2003),
Sixth period President, Dr. Necdet Altuntop (2003–)
Executive committee members are: Mr. Kemal Uzunboy, Mr. Rıza Durdu, Mr. Yusuf Korucu, Mr. İbrahim Ezinc, Mr. Suleyman Eraslan, and Mr. Kemal G. Bayraktar.

ISES–Turkey's administration has a total of twenty-two people. Fourteen persons are on the executive committee (seven permanent and seven reserves), and eight persons are on the audit committee (four permanent and four reserves). The committee members are elected by the general assembly of ISES—Turkey. Any member can be a nominated candidate for a committee at his own will or upon recommendation of a colleague. The elected executive committee selects the chairman, vice-chairman, treasurer, and general secretary. The remaining three serve as members-at-large on the executive committee.

If a member resigns from the executive committee, a reserve executive member replaces him/her as a main member. The elections are normally held every two years. All executive committee members are elected in these elections by the general assembly. Ex-members of the executive committee may take up a duty in the new committee if they are a scientist who work in a university, or an industrialist, or a representative of a government solar energy department.

21.3.3   Conferences Organized by ISES Section

The first conference about solar energy was COMPLES (Cooperation Mediterranean Pour L'Energie Solaire) in 1965 in Istanbul, Turkey. Another COMPLES conference was organized in 1972 in Istanbul.

Several national conferences about solar energy have been organized by ISES–Turkey. Some of them were related only to solar energy but comprised other topics about renewable energy sources. Some of them were as follows:

a) Solar Energy Symposium and Exhibition. This 2–3 day symposium is organized in cooperation with ISES–Turkey and Turkish Chamber of Mechanical Engineers and is held on June 21 every other year. In the past, these symposiums were organized in Mersin, Diyarbakir, Ankara, and Kayseri. Last year (2003) it was decided that following the symposium would be organized in Mersin.

b) New and Renewable Energy Sources Symposium and Exhibition. This symposium is organized every other year in Kayseri with the collaboration of ISES–Turkey and Turkish Chamber of Mechanical Engineers.

c) Renewable Energy Sources Congress. This symposium takes place every two years in Izmir. The symposium is organized by Turkish Chamber of Electrical Engineers and ISES–Turkey

d) Clean Energy Symposium. This symposium is organized every other year in Istanbul by Clean Energy Foundation and ISES–Turkey.

e) International Exergy, Energy and Environment Symposium

(IEEES-1). It is organized by the Aegean University Solar Energy Institute every two years in Izmir.

f) A Forum of Renewable Energy Sources. This forum is arranged by the Turkish National Committee of the World Energy Council.

g) Turkish Energy Congress. This congress, which is organized by the Turkish National Committee of the World Energy Council in every year and held in Ankara.

h) Turkish HVAC Congress. This congress, which is organized by the Turkish Chamber of Mechanical Engineers, is carried out every two years in Izmir.

i) Turkish–German Energy Symposium. This symposium has been organized in Izmir with the collaboration of Aegean University and the German Embassy for many years.

In these symposia and conferences, on the average 40 to 100 reports are presented at these symposia and conference. Some other international activities (congress, symposium and NATO scientific studies) are also occasionally carried out with the participation of ISES–Turkey. Between 150 and 300 reports have been published yearly about solar energy. Fifty to 100 papers have also been published in national and international scientific journals.

On some occasions some foreign scientists have participated as invited speakers at the national congress. There is an exhibition of solar energy products at most of these congresses.

Academicians have joined the solar energy application seminar in Kayseri, in 1998 from Gaziantep and Kirikkale Universities (Fig. 7).

Fig. 7: Seminar speakers at the solar energy system seminar, from right to left, Dr. Mazhar Unsal, Mr. Yusuf Korucu (treasurer of ISES–Turkey), Dr. Necdet Altuntop (president of ISES–Turkey), and Dr. M. Kudret Selçuk

Executive committee of the ISES–Turkey and the representative person of the solar energy equipment manufacturers can be seen together while the discussions about the sector problems of solar energy equipment manufacturers (Fig. 8).

Fig. 8: Sixth period ISES–Turkey executive committee meeting during the discussions about solar energy equipment manufacturer's problems in November 2003, Ankara.

21.3.4   Financing of the Section

ISES–Turkey's revenue consists of membership fees, donations from industrialists, and earnings from activities such as exhibitions and symposia. The government buildings and facilities (utilities, telephone, fax, photocopy, etc.) are being used at no cost to ISES–Turkey. There are no salaried personnel, and managers are not paid for their services. Although the ISES Section does not have large reserves, its expenses are also minimal.

Individual efforts of the chairman and executive committee members of ISES–Turkey gain financial support by solar energy-related foundations and commercial enterprises. Financial support of commercial business covers most of the revenue of ISES–Turkey.

21.3.5   Relations Between ISES–Turkey and ISES

ISES–Turkey has ninety-four members. Some persons related to solar energy activities such as faculty members, industrialists, engineers, workers, and marketing people are not yet members of ISES–Turkey. The reasons are:

- Objectives of ISES–Turkey have not been publicized well.
- ISES–Turkey has not been effective in attracting new members, and the general public is not aware of the activities of ISES.
- Most members of ISES–Turkey are not yet members of ISES International. Therefore, they have no direct access to ISES publications. They have access to the publications of ISES through university libraries or other institutions. The directors of ISES–Turkey are striving to attract more members among persons in solar energy-related industries and faculty members, through conferences and meetings.

21.3.6   The National Solar Energy Society of Turkey

Membership in ISES Turkey and attendance at conferences and symposia declined. Some faculty members attempted to collect funds to support scientific activities and to publish a journal during the early 1990s. ISES–Turkey published a national journal, but it couldn't be continued.

There was a renewed attempt recently, which showed improvements in 2003. A preliminary study of a law to encourage the use of renewable energy sources was initiated in 2003. This law is expected to pass the parliament during early 2004. The proposed law offers some incentives to use solar, wind, geothermal, biomass, small hydraulics energy, and other renewable energy sources.

21.3.7   The Value of ISES Publications to Our Section Members

Although ISES–Turkey has prepared and published several papers in the news bulletin, these weren't published regularly due to lack of funds and skilled personnel. Therefore publications of ISES–International have great scientific importance in Turkey because, at the present time, ISES–Turkey has no regular scientific publications. Most ISES–Turkey members and others interested in solar energy have to refer to journals published by ISES such as the *International Solar Energy Journal* and *Refocus*.

21.4   Most Significant Research Findings

Solar energy related activities in Turkey cover almost every topic of solar energy. These include:

1) The determination of solar radiation gain according to regions in Turkey and the preparation of solar radiation map;
2) Flat-plate solar collectors with gases or liquids; determination and enhancement of radiation, absorption and reflection properties of solar collector absorbents. Different materials and absorber surface configuration analysis;
3) Geometrical investigations and increase of the heat transfer effectiveness of parabolic solar collectors;
4) Thermal and strength test of solar collector related items;
5) Storage of solar energy as sensible and latent heat;
6) Solar cells and its materials and performance enhancement;
7) Distilled pure water production by using solar energy;
8) Drying of agricultural produce, fruits, vegetables, lumber, etc. by solar energy;
9) Low-temperature water heating in large quantities by using solar ponds;
10) Investigations of solar energy-related items such as fluids, insulation materials, glass, plastics and glazing material;
11) Air conditioning applications by solar energy;
12) Applications of solar energy together with wind, geothermal, or waste heat sources. These studies also include heat pumps applications.

Turkish scientists have published many papers in journals such as *International Journal of Solar Energy, I. J. of Energy, Journal of Engineering for Power, Journal of Building and Environment, Energy Conservation Management, Applied Thermal Energy, ASHRAE Transactions, Transactions of ASME,* and *Journal of Solar Energy Engineering.* They have presented many reports at international conferences, symposiums, workshops and seminars.

The first scientific paper was published in 1962 by Dr. K. Selçuk, titled "Measurement of Direct, Diffuse and Total Solar Radiation with Silicon Photovoltaic Cells." It was published in the *Journal of Solar Energy,* vol. 6, no. 4 (1962).

Although several papers have been published in international journals, a compendium does not exist in ISES Turkey. A partial list of these publications at international journals and presentations at conferences are presented below.

21.5   Contributions of ISES–Turkey to Solar Energy Applications in Turkey

ISES–Turkey has been active in the fields of improvement of solar devices through scientific research and development, promoting use of solar energy, and educating the general public on solar energy-related fields. To realize this aim, ISES–Turkey studied methods utilized elsewhere in the world to promote solar energy applications in the world and prepared a report about the subject. Some activities of ISES–Turkey along these lines are as follows:

Table 1   Some important international journal articles and publications prepared by Turkish scientists

	Author name(s)	Article name	Journal name
1	M. K. Selçuk	A Multiple Effect, Tilted Solar Distillation Unit	I. Journal of Solar Energy, 8 (1), (1964), 23-30.
2	M. K. Selçuk	Flat Plate Solar Collector Performance at High Temperature	I. Journal of Solar Energy, 8 (2), (1964), 57-62.
3	M. K. Selçuk and G. T. Ward	Optimization of Solar Power Production	Trans. ASME, Journal of Engineering for Power (April 1970), 173-81,
4	M. K. Selçuk	Thermal and Economic Analysis of the Overlapped-Glass Plate Solar Air Heater	I. Journal of Solar Energy, 13 (1971), 165-91.
5	M. K. Selçuk and M. Akyurt	A Solar Drier Supplemented with Auxiliary Heating Systems for Continuous Operation	I. Journal of Solar Energy, 14, (1973), 313-29,
6	M. K. Selçuk	Analysis, Development and Testing of Fixed Tilt Solar Collector Employing Reversible Vee-Trough Reflector and Vacuum Tube Receivers	I. Journal of Solar Energy, 22, (1979) 413-26.
7	F. N. Demirbilek, U. G. Yalçiner, A. Ecevit, E. Sahmali, M. Inanici,	Analysis of the Thermal Performance of a Building Design Located at 2465m: Antalya-Saklıkent National Observatory Guesthouse	I. J. Building and Environment, 38/1, (2003)177-84.
8	A. Ecevit, B. G. Akınoglu, B. Aksoy	Generation of a Typical Meteorological Year Using Sunshine Duration Data	J. of Energy, 27, (2002)947-54.
9	F. N. Demirbilek, U. G. Yalçiner, M. N. Inanici, A. Ecevit, O. S. Demirbilek	Energy Conscious Dwelling Design for Ankara	I. J. Building and Environment, 35, (2000) 33-40.

10	B. G. Akinoglu, A. M. Shariah, A. Ecevit	Solar Domestic Water Heating in Turkey	J. of Energy, 24, (1999) 363-74.
11	A. M. Shariah and A. Ecevit	Effect of Hot Water Load Temperature on the Performance of a Thermosyphon Solar Water Heater with Auxiliary Electric Heater	I. J. Energy Conversion Mgmt. 36 (5), (1995) 289-96.
12	B. G. Akinoglu and A. Ecevit,	Construction of a Quadratic Model Using Modified Angstrom Coefficients to Estimate Global Solar Radiation	I. J. of Solar Energy, 45 (2), (1990) 85-92.
13	B. G. Akinoglu and A. Ecevit	Further Comparison and Discussion of Sunshine-based Models to Estimate Global Radiation	I. J. of Energy, 15 (10), (1990) 865-72.
14	A. Ecevit, M. A. M. Chaik Wais, and A. M. Al-Shariah	A Comparative Evaluation of the Performance of Three Built-in Storage Type Solar Water Heaters	I. J. of Solar Energy, 44 (1), (1990) 23 -36.
15	A. Ecevit, A. M. Al-Shariah, and E. D.Apaydin	Triangular Built-in-Storage Solar Water Heater	I. J. of Solar Energy, 42 (3), (1989) 253-65.
16	H. Ogelman, A. Ecevit, and E. Tasdemiroglu	A New Method For Estimating Solar Radiation From Bright Sunshine Data	I. J. of Solar Energy, 33 (6), (1984) 619-25.
17	E. Tasdemiroglu and A. Ecevit	Comparison of the Hourly and Daily Global Irradiances of Turkey on non-Horizontal Surfaces	I. J. of Energy Conversion Mgmt, 25 (1), (1985) 119-26.

Table 2   Some important symposium and congress papers prepared by Turkish scientists

	Author name(s)	Paper name	Presentation place
1	M. K. Selçuk and A. Aghan	Analysis and Two Years of Testing of the Vee-Trough Concentrator / Evacuated Tube Solar Collector	Proceedings ISES Conference 1979, (Sun II-Pergamon Press) Atlanta, Georgia, 434-8.
2	M. K. Selçuk	Low Cost Vee-Trough / Evacuated Tube Collector Module	Proceedings ISES Conference 1979, (Sun II-Pergamon Press) Atlanta, Georgia, 496-500.
3	M. K. Selçuk J. M. Bowyer, and S. A. Bluhm	A Graphical Method for the Prediction of Annual Performance of Solar Collectors	Proceedings ISES 1983 Solar World Congress, Perth, Australia, Pergamon Press, 1322-6.
4	M. K. Selçuk and D. L. Ross	Parabolic Dish Test Site of JPL, History and Operating Experience	Proceedings ISES Biennial Conference, Montreal, Canada, 1985 (Intersol '85, Pergamon Press), 1436-40.
5	M. K. Selçuk	A Fixed Collector Employing Reversible Vee-Trough Concentrator and a Vacuum Tube for High Temperature Solar Energy Systems	Proceedings 11th Intersociety Energy Conversion Engineering Conference, 1976, State Line, Nevada, Paper No. 769222.

6	M. K. Selçuk, P. Moynihan, Y. Wu, F. Day	Solar Stirling Power Generation Systems Analysis and Preliminary Tests	ISES 1977 Conference Proceedings, 20-6 to 20-10.
7	M. K. Selçuk	Experimental Evaluation of a Fixed Collector Employing Vee -Trough Concentrator and Vacuum Tube Receiver	ASME Symposium Proceedings, Heat Transfer in Solar Energy Systems, November 1977, 33-37.
8	M. K. Selçuk	The Role of Solar Distillation in the Saline Water Conversion Processes	COMPLES Bulletin No. 10, (May 1965), 70-8.
9	M. K. Selçuk	Silicon Cell Performance Under Concentrated Sunlight	COMPLES Bulletin No. 19, (July 1966), 52-63.
10	M. K. Selçuk	The Heat Transfer Characteristics of the Overlapped-Glass Plate Air Heater	COMPLES Bulletin No. 12, (July 1967), 15-28.
11	M. K. Selçuk	Further Studies on the Overlapped-Glass Plate Air Heater	COMPLES Bulletin No. 15, (1968), 32-49.
12	A. M. Shariah, B. G. Akinoglu, A. Ecevit	Application of TRNSYS to the Mediterranean Climate of Turkey	WREN Congress, Florence, Italy, Elsevier Science Lt. Sept. 1998, 2488-9.
13	B. G. Akinoglu, A. Ecevit	Comparison and Discussion of Quadratic Models to Estimate Global Solar Radiation	9th Miami Intl. Congress on Energy and Environment, Miami, FL, Dec. 11-13, 1989.
14	A. Ecevit	Black Nickel Selective Absorber for Solar Energy Applications	First Latin American School and Third International Symposium on Non Conventional Energy, Bogota, Colombia, Jul. 13-30, 1982.
15	N. Altuntop, Y. Tekin, Y. A. Çengel	A Diagram to Define a Flat Plate Solar Collector Surface in Solar Energy Floor Heating	Proceeding of ISTP-12, Twelfth International Symposium on Transport, PHENOMEA, Istanbul, TURKEY, July 16-20 2000.
16	N. Altuntop, Y. Tekin, D. Demiral	Experimental Analyses of Volume Heating and Energy Storage by Means of Solar Floor Heating	Proceeding of ITEC 2001, 4th International Thermal Energy Congress, Cesme-Izmir, TURKEY, July 8–12, 2001.
17	N. Altuntop, Y. Tekin, D. Demiral	Analytical Investigation of the Use of Water Filled P.E.T. Bottles as Thermal Energy Storage Unit	Proceeding of ITEC 2001, 4th International Thermal Energy Congress, Cesme-Izmir, TURKEY, July 8–12, 2001.
18	N. Altuntop, Y. Tekin	The First Performance Results of the Solar Heating and Thermal Energy Storage by Using P.E.T. Bottles	Eurosun2002, European Solar Congress, Bologna, ITALY, June 23-26, 2002.
19	N. Altuntop, Y. Tekin	The Solar Space Heating Application in Erciyes University Sport Center and First Experimental Results	Eurosun2002, European Solar Congress, Bologna, ITALY, June 23-26, 2002.
20	N. Altuntop, Y. Tekin	The Solar Floor Heating Application and the Investigation of Its Thermal Performance	Eurosun2002, European Solar Congress, Bologna, ITALY, June 23-26, 2002.

12.6 Contributions of ISES–Turkey to Solar Energy Applications in Turkey

- Photograph and slide shows organized yearly on June 21 during Solar Day;
- Middle School student participation in the International Pictures Competition on solar energy, held in Hungary in 1995, with contributions by ISES-Turkey. Turkey received awards in three different age groups;
- ISES–Turkey joined "Habitat 96," Istanbul;
- ISES–Turkey's "Solar Energy Systems Seminar" was held in cooperation with universities and other institutions. The problems of manufacturers of solar devices were discussed in panels;
- Awards were given by qualified manufacturers in cooperation with Turkish Standard Institute;
- Joint international meetings of ISES among in Hungary, Germany, Korea, and Sweden;
- Hot water heating systems by flat-plate collectors and energy storage applications in greenhouses by solar energy are now in widespread use;
- Other solar energy applications like solar cell production and utilization have not yet been transferred to daily use in Turkey.

Although flat-plate solar collector production amount is large, absorbers surfaces were generally ordinary black painted during the past years. Selective surface absorber production started in 1993, although research in this area was initiated much earlier. The first selective-surface application was black chrome coating on an aluminum surface.

There were nearly 10 million m^2 of flat-plate solar collectors in Turkey for heating water on the year of 2002. Currently, hot water systems in Turkey provide earnings of about 350 to 400 million USA dollars per year and 15,000 to 20,000 persons are employed in this field.

Turkey's flat-plate solar collector production capacity per year is 1.4 million m^2, and actual production is nearly 1 million m^2. Eight to 10 percent of the total production is exported to foreign countries, mainly to European countries. There are solar water heating systems in nearly 3 to 4 million households, most of them in southern Turkey. Most of them utilize the natural circulation system. Forced circulated solar energy systems are used in hotels, holiday villages, dormitories, hospitals, and factories.

There are basic research activities about solar cells in Turkey; however commercial production has not started occur yet. The capacity of total installed electric production system was about 350 kW in Turkey by the end of 2002. Most of the applications are in the fields of forest fire alert systems, GSM stations and to power the fixed emergency rural telephone network.

Thanks are extended to Dr. M. Kudret Selçuk, Dr. Ahmet Ecevit, Dr. Gurbuz Atagunduz, Dr. Demir Inan, Mr. Ibrahim Ezinc, and Dr. Siddik Icli for their kind help in preparing this article.

Chapter 22

University of Florida Solar Energy and Energy Conversion Laboratory

by
Barbara J. Graham and D. Yogi Goswami
Department of Mechanical and Aerospace Engineering
PO Box 116300 University of Florida
Gainesville, Florida 32611-6300 USA
e-mail: solar@mae.ufl.edu

Abstract

The Solar Energy and Energy Conversion Laboratory (SEECL), was established in 1954 by Erich A. Farber, who had just moved from the University of Wisconsin, then professor of Mechanical Engineering at the University of Florida. The laboratory pioneered research in many areas of solar energy, energy conversion, energy conservation, and space power systems. The SEECL became one of the largest and most complete solar energy laboratories in the world, at that time. In the 1950s, many ISES-related meetings were held in Florida at the SEECL. It developed techniques and devices to convert solar energy to all forms of energy used in daily life, including water heating, swimming pool heating, distillation, detoxification, cooking, space heating and air conditioning, refrigeration, electricity, and transportation. Hands-on research at the SEECL has included work in solar energy, solar-powered engines, measurement of solar radiation and the characteristics of this resource. Other ground-breaking work has included heat transfer, properties of materials, solar distillation, crop drying and solar ovens, solar furnaces, solar electric generators, and solar Stirling Engines. Because of the work at the Solar Lab and the Solar House, Dr. Farber was inducted into the Solar Hall of Fame in 1976. In 1986 the SEECL received both the State of Florida and the National Awards for "Energy Innovation." In 1992 the University and State of Florida established the Dr. Erich A. Farber Archives in the Old Solar House. In 1999 the "Solar Hall of Fame" was made part of the Archives and the Laboratory. In 2002, the laboratory was awarded the ASME's Mechanical Engineering Heritage Site designation. The SEECL serves as the editorial office for *Advances in Solar Energy* an annual review of the developments in solar energy, and also for *Solar Energy* the international technical journal of ISES.

22.1   Introduction

The Solar Energy and Energy Conversion Laboratory (SEECL) was originally located on a pad at the Gainesville Regional Airport, near the WW II bunker. The sunny Florida weather provided ample solar radiation for the varied experimentation ongoing at the lab (Fig. 1 and 2). In the late 1970s the University moved the SEECL to the newly developed Energy Research and Education Park (EREP) to house a variety of allied engineering laboratories. The EREP is located adjacent to the University's campus in Gainesville.

Fig. 1: Early experimental devices on the pad at the SEECL, then located near the WW II bunker at the regional airport (1950s)

Fig. 2: Another view of the early SEECL's experimental devices near the WW II bunker at the regional airport (early 1950s)

22.2   The "Solar Capital of the World"

In the 1970s research generated by the Solar Energy Laboratory made Gainesville, Florida, the "Solar Capital of the World" and Dr. Farber the "Sunshine Superman" (*Mother Earth News*, 1974; *The Handbook of Homemade Powe,,* 1974).

Gainesville was called the solar capital of the world because of SEECL's research activities and community outreach through public alternative energy fairs and because it had more large-scale solar installations than any other city in the world at that time (Fig. 3). Gainesville's solar features included one of the few solar powered coin laundries, and the world's largest solar heated and cooled building, the Gainesville Regional Airport.

Fig. 3: A father and daughter view a solar still at an alternative and renewable energy fair at the University of Florida's College of Engineering. In the background stands the football stadium (1960)

Other uses of solar energy were being widely implemented at that time, with applications at the University of Florida's credit union and its teaching hospital, campus married student housing, apartment complexes, a photo lab, homes, clinics, swimming pools, and even a Ronald McDonald House. SEECL was also instrumental in implementing installation of solar hot water heaters on low-cost housing for the city of Gainesville, with the water heaters being built by Florida state prisoners. Research at the early SEECL included investigations into PV cells and air conditioning systems (Fig. 4 and 5).

Fig. 4: A SEECL student monitors the energy converted by these early selinium photovoltaic cells (late 1950s)

Fig. 5: Prof. Erich Farber monitoring data generated by a low temperature ammonia-water absorption air conditioning system, at the early SEECL (early 1960s)

22.3   Training in Alternative Energy Technologies (TAET) Program

In the late 1970s, some two million dollars were awarded to the SEECL by the U.S. State Department's Agency for International Development (U.S.-AID) to train professionals and ranking government officials from developing nations in alternative energy sources. The Training in Alternative Energy Technologies (TAET) program educated professionals from fifty Third World nations in a broad range of alternative energy technologies until the project ended in 1984. The World Bank was citing the urgent need for developing countries to begin formulating strategies for renewable energy development – and the TAET program was able to address those concerns. Some of the early SEECL work included innovative cooking techniques (Fig. 6).

Fig. 6: Early SEECL student demonstrates solar cooking on a collapsible umbrella cooker. The concentrated solar radiation heated the teapot water quite effectively—and the collapsing umbrella made storage easy (mid 1950s)

After fifteen weeks of whirlwind study, building, testing, and visits to U.S. alternative energy projects, TAET students returned to their homelands with the expertise to use local materials in new ways to make their own energy resources work better for them. Not only were participants putting their new knowledge to work, but in more than thirty developing countries, TAET-trained students made direct contributions to their national energy planning and policy.

TAET students explored many facets of renewable energy (Fig. 7).

Fig. 7: Prof. Erich Farber (R) and a student discuss a stationary high temperature collector which produced steam to drive an engine at the early SEECL (1950s)

TAET participants hailed from Latin America, Europe, Africa, and the Far East. Participants reported that they were working in a wide variety of alternative energy technologies, such as: solar thermal, biogas, photovoltaics, energy conservation, crop drying, wind pumping, and gasification. Also under investigation at that time were alternative energy cooling systems, solar cookers, improved stoves, fuel alcohol geothermal energy, wind-electric systems, and energy crops.

22.4   The Solar House

The Solar House wasn't always solar. It was during the energy crisis of the early 1970s that the retrofit of the air conditioning research house took on a more pressing perspective. Following the installation of the solar space heating and domestic hot water heating system, a solar air conditioning system was implemented.

Solar heated water was used for more than hot water for bathing and cooking. It was also used for room perimeter baseboard heating (Fig. 8). The hot water was run through the baseboards with its temperature adjustable via a standard thermostat. Solar-powered air conditioning was also installed into the house. An ammonia-water absorption A/C system used the solar heat from the storage tank to generate the necessary energy to cool the house.

Fig. 8: Prof. Erich Farber works on hot water panels at the early SEECL. Hands-on research remains a hallmark of the laboratory (mid 1950s)

Not only the house, but also the appliances were retrofitted to solar. The solar stove used oil heated by a concentrating trough collector which was then circulated through the copper-coiled burner elements for cooking. A clothes dryer also used solar heated water. Ingeniously, the electrical heating element in the dryer was replaced with a heat exchanger that used solar heated water as a source of heat. The hot water was circulated through coils set in the back of the dryer and a small fan blew across the coil, drying the clothes. A clothes washer was also adapted for use with solar systems.

While the solar house's systems were primarily based on solar-thermal heat exchange, some photovoltaics were used to generate electricity to charge batteries to power a TV set and a lamp. About 1/2 kW of electricity was generated for this purpose. Experiments were also conducted on retrofitting an automobile to electric power. Fig. 9 shows the Solar House as it appears today.

Fig. 9: The Solar House and Erich A. Farber Archives at the Solar Energy and Energy Conversion Laboratory, University of Florida, Gainesville (2004)

Other research conducted during this time included a PV powered air circulation pump, selective coatings on solar flat plate collectors, and solar swimming pool heating. The SEECL was selected by ASHRAE to receive their historical Solar Calorimeter which measures solar properties of glazing materials. Data collected by the SEECL using the calorimeter were used to calibrate solar ratings and published in the ASHRAE Guide (Fig. 10).

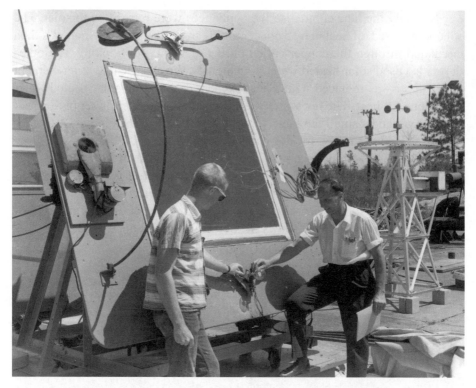

Fig. 10: Prof. Erich Farber (R) and student adjust the ASHRAE/UF calorimeter (mid 1950s)

22.5   Florida State Energy Policy

During the 1970s SEECL research and initiatives provided state lawmakers with data that helped the renewable energy industry identify state licensing code as the principal impediment to the widespread use of solar. The requirement at that time limited installation to a licensed plumber and used conventional building codes.

In 1979 both houses of the Florida Legislature recognized the SEECL's work as "having a profound effect on the public acceptance of solar energy," by presenting an official commendation for continuing "outstanding contributions to the field of solar energy conversion."

The SEECL was also providing data to the State Energy Office for their series *"Save It At Home: Save It, Florida!"* These pamphlets covered solar hot water heaters, passive solar heating/shading, heating/cooling systems, attic ventilation, and heat recovery systems.

22.6   SEECL Awarded Mechanical Engineering Heritage Site of the ASME

In 2002, the American Society of Mechanical Engineers-International (ASME) awarded National Heritage Site status to the SEECL. "This highly diverse facility has pioneered the development of solar energy applications worldwide. The laboratory was unique in developing practical solar energy devices based on established principles of thermodynamics, heat transfer, and fluid mechanics long before solar energy was considered a serious energy alternative. Among its many significant technological accomplishments are advanced solar collector designs, solar-assisted HVAC systems, space power systems, breakthroughs in solar-based housing, and development of advanced materials including glazings and highly selective surfaces. Both the U.S. Department of State and the United Nations have recognized this facility for its global accomplishments in training and innovation," ASME stated (Fig. 11 and 12).

Fig. 11: ASME Mechanical Engineering Heritage Site plaque awarded to SEECL. (2002)

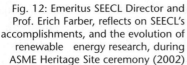

Fig. 12: Emeritus SEECL Director and Prof. Erich Farber, reflects on SEECL's accomplishments, and the evolution of renewable energy research, during ASME Heritage Site ceremony (2002)

22.7   Current Research and Education

Ongoing research at the SEECL continues to provide ground-breaking insights into the refinement of solar energy systems, along with fundamental work into energy conversion, heating, air conditioning and refrigeration, and fenestration properties.

22.7.1   Some of our projects include

- *Renewable Hydrogen Production by Biomass Gasification:* The advantage of using a biomass feedstock is that it is CO_2 neutral and renewable. Resources in Northern Florida and waste products from the citrus industry can be an attractive feedstock for hydrogen production.
- *Passive Vacuum Water Desalinization:* Using a simple yet innovative idea, a column of brine in an evaporator falls under the natural forces of gravity, creating a high vacuum in the vessel. This brine can be vaporized using low grade thermal energy (e.g. non-concentrated solar thermal energy), and then condensed to collect the condensate.
- *Solar Photocatalytic Detoxification and Disinfection of Water:* Treatment

of contaminated water by photocatalytic oxidation using titanium dioxide as a catalyst is an attractive alternative to conventional techniques in use, especially to treat samples with trace quantities of contaminants.

- *Thermodynamic Power and Cooling Cycle:* The cycle is essentially a hybrid of the Rankine power production and absorption refrigeration cycles. It is well suited for low temperature, sensible heat sources such as non-concentrated solar thermal energy, low-grade geothermal, or waste heat recovery (Fig. 13).

Fig. 13: SEECL Ph.D. candidate, Christopher Martin, adjusts the expander on innovative thermodynamic power and cooling cycle (2004)

- *Antenna Solar Energy to Electricity Conversion:* Research conducted in the past at the SEECL and by other University of Florida researchers suggest that solar energy can be captured by the use of suitably sized antennae with a very high efficiency.
- *Solar Chimney:* A solar chimney works as a natural-draft device that uses solar radiation to move air upward, thus converting thermal energy into kinetic energy and finally into electricity using a suitable generator.
- *Hybrid Solar Liquid Desiccant Air Conditioning*: Desiccant cooling systems have the ability to provide efficient humidity and temperature control while reducing the electrical energy requirement for air conditioning as compared to conventional systems.
- *Solar Photocatalytic Disinfection of Indoor Air*: Indoor air environments typically are contaminated with micro organisms and VOC's (Volatile Organic Compounds). Titania catalyzed photocatalysis has been shown to be a novel method to disinfect and detoxify indoor air.
- *Solar Properties of Fenestration Systems*: Solar properties of fenestration

systems include Solar Optical Properties and the Solar Heat Gain Coefficient (SGHC). The UF-ASHRAE Solar Calorimeter is used for measuring the solar-heat gain of the fenestration system.

22.8   Current SEECL Director

Prof. D. Yogi Goswami is the current director of the SEECL, assuming the reins of control in 1990 from Prof. Erich A. Farber who had been the lab's director for thirty-seven years. Dr. Goswami is the University of Florida's Research Foundation Professor of Mechanical Engineering (Fig. 14). He has developed many technologies that are available commercially. Foremost among them is the photocatalytic disinfection and detoxification of indoor air. Systems based on Dr. Goswami's technologies are being investigated as a defense against bioterrorism.

At present, Dr. Goswami is the President of the ISES (2004-2006), and a Governor of ASME-International (2003-2006). He is also a co-author of the textbook *Principles of Solar Engineering*, Editor-in-Chief of ISES' *Solar Energy* international journal, and the ASES' prestigious annual publication in solar energy, *Advances in Solar Energy: Annual Review of Research and Development*.

Fig. 14: Current SEECL Director, Prof. D. Yogi Goswami accepting the ASME's Mechanical Engineering Heritage Site award on behalf of the laboratory and the University of Florida (2002)

22.9   Editorial Activities

The Solar Energy Laboratory is the Editorial Office for the ASES yearly review book, *Advances in Solar Energy: An Annual Review of Research and Development*. *Advances* had been under the sole editorial control of Dr. Karl W. Böer since 1982. Dr. Goswami was brought on-board in 1999 as co-editor-in-chief and then became principle editor-in-chief in 2000. We are also the editorial office for the ISES technical journal, *Solar Energy*.

22.9.1   Advances in Solar Energy (published by the American Solar Energy Society)

Advances in Solar Energy is considered a premier technical resource for solar energy experts, utilities and industry professionals, educators and researchers, and others who need the latest solar technology information, who depend on the in-depth reports written by recognized experts in renewable energy. Whether you are keeping abreast of the latest solar technology discoveries as an integral part of your work, or as a newcomer learning about the field of solar energy, you can rely on each years' collection of reports in *Advances in Solar Energy*.

22.9.1.1   Some topics which have been covered in the past include:

- Optical Principles for Daylighting
- Transparent Insulation Materials
- Fundamentals of Hydrogen Energy Utilization
- Advances in Wind Turbine Technology
- SMUD: Grid-Connected PV
- Desalination
- Country-Specific Solar Energy Developments
- The Nature and Implications of Climate Change

22.9.1.2   Some topics which will be included in upcoming issues include:

- Solar Ponds
- Modeling Solar Hydrogen Fuel Cell Systems
- Comparison of Projections of PV Generation and European and U.S. Domestic Oil Production
- Quantum Well Solar Cells
- Anthropogenic Global Warming: Evidence, Predictions and

Consequences
- Advances in Solar Photovoltaic Technology and its New Roles in Contributing to Environmental Issues
- Renewable Solar Energy for Traveling: Air, Land, and Water
- Photocatalytic Detoxification and Disinfection of Water with Solar Energy
- Recent Advances in Parabolic Trough Solar Power Plant Technology
- Progress of Highly Reliable Crystalline Si Solar Devices and Materials
- Passive Cooling of Buildings
- Solar Heat for Industrial Processes
- Renewable Energy for Russian Economy
- III-V Compound Multi-Junction and Concentrator Solar Cells

22.9.2   Solar Energy journal (published by the International Solar Energy Society)

Solar Energy, the official journal of the International Solar Energy Society® (ISES), is devoted exclusively to the science and technology of solar energy applications. The journal publishes twelve issues per year in two volumes of six issues.

The journal began publication in 1957. With the move of the editorial offices to the University of Florida in 2002, a new approach to invigorating the associate editor team was implemented aiming to revitalize the journal. New initiatives have improved the paper flow and review process of the *Solar Energy* journal. An expanded editorial board has built depth into the topical areas to better serve the journal's stringent review process. At present, there are thirty-four associate editors covering twenty-four areas of direct and indirect solar energy. A new feature is the printed acknowledgement of the associate editors who handle the review process for each paper.

Solar Energy associate editors propose special topical issues across a range of sectors effectively expanding *Solar Energy*'s coverage of renewable energy research, providing a wide spectrum for readers to access. Two special issues published in 2003 included the Solar World Congress 2001, Photocatalysis and Thin Film Desalination. Special issues currently in process include the ASES Solar 2003, CISBAT, Hydrogen, and SEGA. Additional special topical issues on the drawing board include: Organic/TiO_2, ANES Retrospective, ASES Solar 2004, Concentrated Solar, EuroSun 2004, SPEA III, Solar Paces 2004, Polymeric, and URBVENT.

A wide range of regularly appearing topics include: active solar thermal; biomass/bioconversion; chemical processes; collector technology; daylighting; education and information; energy storage; fundamentals and thermodynamics; high concentration and solar thermal power; low concentration system and thermodynamic cycles; materials, thermal applications; optical properties; passive cooling; passive systems; PV systems and cell physics; renewable/solar energy and the environment; solar architecture; solar cooking; solar cooling; solar radiation; solar policy; solar ponds; solar thermal and fundamentals and also wind energy.

Solar Energy is published by Elsevier and is available both in print and online via ScienceDirect. Since its launch in 1997, ScienceDirect has evolved from a web database of Elsevier journals to one of the world's largest providers of scientific, technical and medical literature, full text and bibliographic information. ScienceDirect provides free viewing of abstracts, with complete articles available for a fee.

A new feature of ScienceDirect is the availability of articles which are still "in press"—allowing researchers to see papers in practical real-time instead of waiting months for the printed version. This effectively increases the worldwide visibility of renewable energy research. Elsevier shows that the journal's citation ranking index impact factor has been rising steadily. Currently the journal is ranked 14 of 63 titles in the Institute for Scientific Information's (ISI) energy and fuels journal citation ranking.

22.10   For More Information

22.10.1   The University of Florida
http://www.ufl.edu

22.10.2   Solar Energy and Energy Conversion Laboratory
http://seecl.mae.ufl.edu/solar
Prof. D.Y. Goswami e-mail: goswami@ufl.edu
Solar Energy Laboratory e-mail: solar@mae.ufl.edu

22.11   For More Information About ASES' Advances in Solar Energy

http://www.ases.org
Click on Print Catalogue
Click on *Advances in Solar Energy*
Advances in Solar Energy e-mail: solar@mae.ufl.edu

22.12   For More Information About the ISES Solar Energy journal

http://www.ises.org/shortcut.nsf/to/sej
Solar Energy journal e-mail: solarjrl@mae.ufl.edu

Chapter 23
The Indian Section of ISES

by
Dr. Jayarao Gururaja
Now
Senior Interregional Advisor
Energy and Transport Branch
Division for Sustainable Development
Development of Economic and Social Affairs
United Nations
2 UN Plaza New York, NY 10017
e-mail: gururaja@un.org

(Adapted from ISES Silver Jubilee Presentation)

Abstract

The origin of the Solar Energy Society of India (SESI) goes back to the year 1967, when a Solar Energy Working Group was constituted at the Central Salt and Marine Chemical Research Institute (CSMCRI), Bhavnagar (Gujarat-India). Dr. R. L. Datta, Dr. Gomkale, Dr. Chaman Lal Gupta, Ms. Anna Mani and Mr. J. C. Kapoor were the key players during the formative days of the Society. In the run-up to the formal establishment of SESI as a registered body and as the national section of ISES, several meetings and conferences on solar energy were organized under the auspices of the Working Group, with Dr. R. L. Datta as its first secretary. A conference on solar energy was first held followed by several meetings during 1967–68. In the next year, the Working Group, under the chairmanship of Dr. R. L. Datta and Dr. S. O. Gomkale as secretary, organized a national Conference at CSMCRI, Bhavnagar. In 1970–71, the Working Group was expanded and was renamed as the All India Solar Energy Working Group. The third annual conference was held in the same year at the Indian Institute of Technology, Kanpur. In 1971–72, the Central Building Research Institute at Rourkee was the venue for the Conference of the Working Group. The Conference in 1972–73 was organized at the Indian Institute of Technology, Madras. In 1973–74, the

Conference of the Group was held at the Motilal Nehru Regional Engineering College, Allahabad.

In 1974–75 the All India Solar Energy Working Group formally became affiliated with the International Solar Energy Society and was named Solar Energy Society of India (SESI). The Society's membership increased appreciably, with members joining from all parts of the country. That year, the elected secretary of the Society was Prof. C. L. Gupta, and Dr. R. L. Datta continued as elected president. The annual conference was held at the Panjab Agricultural University, Ludhiana.

The Solar Energy Society of India was formally registered under the Societies' Act with a full governing council and office bearers, and its first national convention was held at Jadavpur University in 1976. In July 1977, Dr. A. Ramachandran and Dr. J. Gururaja were elected President and Secretary of the Solar Energy Society of India, respectively. The outgoing President, D. R. L. Datta, was elected President of the International Solar Energy Society for 1978–79.

Fig. 1: Dr. J. Gururaja

In 1978, SESI undertook to organize the International Solar Energy Congress (ISEC) of ISES under the sponsorship of the Department of Science and Technology, Government of India and co sponsored by the Ministry of Energy, the Indian Council of Agricultural Research, the Council of Scientific and Industrial Research, Bharat Heavy Electricals Ltd. and Tata Energy Research Institute, and was held at New Delhi.

The ISEC was organized under the chairmanship of Dr. A. Ramachandran and Dr. J. Gururaja, who functioned as the general secretary for the conference. On behalf of ISES, the technical program committee was chaired by Francis De Winter. In conjunction with ISEC, a major exhibition of solar energy devices was also organized. The ISEC was the first ISES Congress in a developing country. It was well attended by both international and national delegates and was a resounding success. In many ways ISEC was an important landmark in the history of ISES.

The 1978 convention of the Solar Energy Society of India was held at CSMCRI, Bhavnagar, in December 1978.

Since 1978, annual conventions of SESI are being held regularly at various institutions in the country, and the proceedings of these conventions are disseminated to SESI members and others through its publications. SESI has been led by reputed energy experts under the guidence of successive governing councils headed by Mr. J. C. Kapoor, Dr. R. K. Pachauri, Dr. A. Ramachandran, and Dr. V. Bakthavatsalam.

SESI has been playing a prominent role in India in supporting national efforts to promote the development and applications of solar energy. In 2004, SESI hosted the ISES Board meeting and retreat when new ideas to strengthen ISES' role, not only in the area of R&D, but also in efforts to mainstream renewable energy for sustainable development were explored.

Dr. J. Gururaja is the author of this chapter and has been with the United Nations since 1996 in the Energy and Transport Branch of the Department of Economic and Social Affairs as Senior Interregional Adviser. Prior to this, as Adviser in the Ministry of Nonconventional Energy Sources of the Government of India, he made significant contributions to renewable energy development in India. He has been associated with the Indian section of ISES almost from its inception and currently serves as a member of its Governing Council.